DATA BASE

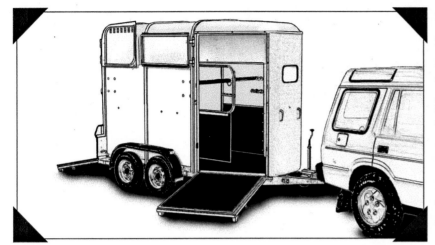

This page enables you to compile a list of useful data on your trailer, so that whether you're ordering spares or just checking the tyre pressures, all the key information - the information that is 'personal' to your trailer - is easily within reach.

Make:...

Model: ....

Year of manufacture (if known): ....

Chassis number: ....

Unladen weight:...

Maximum laden weight (MAM): ....

Maximum load capacity:...

Body length:...

Overall length:...

Overall width:..

Tyre pressure:...

Tyre size and type: ....

Wheel nut torque: ....

Hub type: ....

Hub nut torque:..

Door key number/s: ....

Security lock number/s (if applicable): ....

Coupling make:...

Coupling model no. (on casting):...................................

TOW VEHICLE: Weight: ....

Max. unbraked trailer weight:.......................................

Max. braked trailer weight:..

Trailer manufacturer name address and tel. no.

....

....

....

Trailer dealership name, address and tel. no.

....

....

....

First published in 1996 by

Porter Publishing Ltd
PO Box 701
Clifton-on-Teme
Worcester
WR6 6UQ

www.porterpublishing.com

British Library Cataloguing in Publication Data

A catalogue record for this book is available from the
British Library.

ISBN 1-899238-21-2

Series Editor: Lindsay Porter
Front cover design. Pineapple Publishing, Worcester
and Porter Publishing Ltd.
Back cover design: Porter Publishing Ltd.
Layout and Typesetting. Pineapple Publishing,
Worcester.
Updated: Editorial Services, Martley.

Every care has been taken to ensure that the material
contained in this Service Guide is correct. However, no
liability can be accepted by the authors or publishers
for damage, loss, accidents, or injury resulting from
any omissions or errors in the information given.

GREAT CARS ON VIDEO

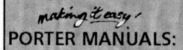
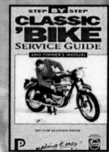

The Complete Trailer Manual

by
Lindsay Porter
& Claire Leavey

Introduction

Thanks are due to the following: Ifor Williams Trailers and Indespension for their kind co-operation and assistance in compiling this book. Peter Brown of Indespension for technical consultancy on Chapters Two, Three, Four and Six. Peter Leslie of Ifor Williams for technical consultancy on Chapter Four. Derek Leavey for technical consultancy on Chapter Three. C.P. Powdrill for use of his photographs and text. Dave Pollard for use of his photographs and text. And to Glynn, Paul, Bob, Alan, Martin and all who kindly gave assistance at Ifor Williams Trailers Ltd and Indespension.

Claire Leavey

Claire Leavey

CONTENTS

CHAPTER 1 - SAFETY FIRST

SAFETY FIRST!

Although a basic load-carrying trailer is mechanically relatively simple when compared with the car, it is still extremely important to bear in mind a number of essential safety considerations before any work is carried out.

By carrying out your own servicing and maintenance work on your trailer, you are taking on the responsibility for both your own safety and the safety of those working with you. It is therefore strongly advisable that any work is carefully planned in advance, with particular care being taken for safety.

It is also advisable to take as much time as is necessary with any work that is carried out. Remember that many accidents are caused by rushing to get work done.

• Never wear loose clothing when undertaking any mechanical task, and never ever carry out any work in sandals or bare feet. If you have a boiler suit, then wear it - even for the most straightforward of jobs. Failing that, good strong old jeans and a close-fitting sweatshirt will ensure that you don't get caught up on power tools or jutting components - and it won't matter too much if they get dirty and end up being thrown away!

• Whether you're working on your trailer in a well-appointed garage or on your own front drive, it is essential to keep the workplace tidy and clean. Don't leave tools scattered on the floor around you, but keep them all together, and take them out as required. You'll find that you work far more quickly and efficiently if everything is readily to hand. It's also important not to allow grease, oil or brake fluid to run over benches or floors. Not only can these liquids make things exceedingly slippery, they can also be poisonous to children and pets.

• There will always be new ways of having accidents, and the following points do not pretend to be a comprehensive list of all dangers. They are intended rather to make you aware of the risks, and to encourage a safety-conscious approach to all the work you carry out on your trailer. When using proprietary materials or equipment, consult the supplier about any special health or safety precautions you may have to take - and always be sure to read the manufacturer's recommendations and instructions carefully.

Essential DOs and DONTs

DON'T rely on a single jack when working underneath the trailer. Always use reliable additional means of support, such as the trailer's own static supports, or axle stands securely placed under a part of the trailer which you know will not give way.

DON'T attempt to loosen or tighten high-torque nuts (e.g. wheel hub nuts) while the trailer is on a jack; the force required may pull it off.

DON'T inhale any brake lining dust - it may be asbestos, which is extremely dangerous to health.

DON'T use ill-fitting spanners or other unsuitable tools which could slip and cause injury.

DON'T attempt to lift a heavy trailer or component if it might be a struggle. Get some help.

DON'T rush to finish a job, or take unorthodox short cuts. Plan ahead, and allow plenty of time.

DON'T allow children or animals to get in or around the trailer while you are working.

DO locate and use the correct jacking points when using a jack to raise the trailer.

DO make sure that the wheels of the trailer are firmly chocked or braked before carrying out any work.

DO clean the area to be worked on thoroughly before starting and wipe up any spilt oil, grease, water or brake fluid straight away.

DO wear eye protection when using power tools such as drills, sanders, bench grinders etc., and when working underneath the trailer.

DO wear a barrier cream on your hands prior to undertaking dirty jobs. It will protect your skin from infection, as well as making your hands easier to clean once you've finished. Even better, wear thin disposable gloves, available from DIY outlets.

DO remove all jewellery from wrists and hands before starting work - especially when working on the electrical system - and always keep long hair tied firmly back.

DO carry out work in a logical sequence, and check that everything is correctly assembled and tightened once you've finished.

DO remember that your trailer's safety affects both your own personal safety and that of others. If in doubt about any aspect of its upkeep, get some specialist advice.

DO have a basic first-aid kit handy in case of any mishap, and IF, in spite of following these precautions, you are unlucky enough to injure yourself, seek medical attention as soon as possible. Even if you have just suffered a minor cut, an anti-tetanus injection may be necessary.

Fumes

Certain fumes are highly toxic. Many adhesives give off toxic or flammable gases, and so do solvents such as thinners. Use them only in a well-ventilated area. When using cleaning fluids and solvents, read the instructions carefully. Never use any materials from unmarked containers.

Mains Electricity

When using an electric power tool, inspection light etc., always ensure that the appliance is correctly connected to its plug and that, where necessary, it is properly earthed (grounded), and that the fuse is the correct rating for the appliance concerned. Do not use mains

appliances in damp conditions, and beware of using mains-powered tools in the vicinity of fuel, fuel vapour, or bottled gas.

Use rechargeable power tools wherever possible, and a DC inspection lamp powered by a remote twelve-volt battery - both are much safer than the mains-powered alternatives.

Brakes and Asbestos

Whenever you work on the braking system mechanical components, or remove brake pads or shoes:

i) Wear an efficient particle mask.

ii) Wipe off all brake dust from the work area using a damp cloth (never blow it off with your own breath or compressed air).

iii) Dispose of brake dust and discarded shoes or pads in a sealed plastic bag.

iv) Wash hands and face thoroughly after you have finished working on the brakes, and certainly before you eat, drink or smoke.
v) Install only asbestos-free replacement brake shoes or pads. Note that asbestos brake dust can cause cancer if inhaled.

If your Trailer is fitted with brakes, do not dismantle them unless you are fully competent to do so. If you have not been trained in this work, but wish to carry out the jobs described in this book, it is strongly recommended that you have a garage or qualified mechanic check your work before using the trailer.

Welding

For safety's sake, you are strongly recommended to seek proper tuition in whichever type of welding you intend to undertake, from your local evening institute or adult education classes. In addition, all of the information and instructional material produced by the suppliers of materials and equipment you will be using must be studied carefully. You may have to ask your stockist for some of this printed material if it is not made available at the time of purchase.

Wear cover-all clothing, preferably in natural or fire-retardant materials. When arc welding, remember that ultra-violet light is given off, and this can be damaging to skin - keep it covered! Also, hot sparks fly out from welded material, and these could find their way down your neck or into the tops of your shoes. And most importantly, wear a proper welding mask. The potential for permanent damage to the eyes both from UV light and from hot sparks is very real!

COMPRESSED GAS CYLINDERS
There are serious hazards associated with the storage and handling of gas cylinders and fittings, and standard precautions should be strictly observed in dealing with them. Ensure that cylinders are stored in safe conditions, properly maintained and always handled with special care. Eliminate the possibilities of leakage, fire and explosion.

SAFETY REQUIREMENTS FOR ACETYLENE:
Cylinders must always be stored and used in the upright position. If a cylinder becomes heated accidentally or becomes hot because of excessive backfiring, immediately shut the valve, detach the regulator, take the cylinder out of doors well away from the building, immerse it in or continually spray it with water, open the valve and allow the gas to escape until the cylinder is empty. If necessary, notify the emergency fire service without delay.

SAFETY REQUIREMENTS FOR OXYGEN:
No oil or grease should be used on valves or fittings. Cylinders with convex bases should be used in a stand or held securely to a wall.

SAFETY REQUIREMENTS FOR LPG:
The store area must be kept free of combustible material, corrosive material and cylinders of oxygen.

Work with Plastics

Work with plastic materials brings additional hazards into the workshop. Many of the materials used (polymers, resins, adhesives and materials acting as catalysts and accelerators) readily produce dangerous situations in the form of poisonous fumes and skin irritants, as well as the risk of fire or explosion. Do not allow resin or two-pack adhesive hardener, or that supplied with filler or two-pack stopper to come into contact with skin or eyes. Read the safety notes on the tin, tube, or pack extremely carefully, and be sure to follow any special safety instructions faithfully.

Jacks and Axle Stands

It is essential that when jacking up your trailer, you use the correct type of jack. It is also very important to locate and use the correct jacking points. If your trailer is not equipped with special jacking points, only jack it up from underneath the axle, and as close to the chassis (or wheels) as possible.

Any jack is made for lifting a vehicle, not for supporting it. *Never* work underneath your trailer with just a jack to support its weight. Once you have used the jack to raise the trailer to the desired level, use axle stands to provide solid support for it while you work. You can get axle stands from many discount stores, and auto. parts stores. Simple triangular stands (fixed or adjustable) will suit almost all potential working situations, but drive-on ramps are not suitable for use with trailers.

When replacing a wheel, always use the correct torque settings and the correct North, South, East, West sequence of tightening.

Never over-tighten the wheelnuts, as this can distort the wheel rim, but always check wheel nut tightness with a torque wrench at regular intervals.

FACT FILE:
SAFETY FIRST! - GAS CYLINDERS

The cylinder gases which are most commonly used are oxygen, acetylene and liquid petroleum gas (LPG). Safety requirements for all three gases are:
i) Cylinders must be stored in a fire resistant, dry and well ventilated space, away from any source of heat or ignition and protected from ice, snow or direct sunlight. Valves of cylinders in store must always be kept uppermost, even when the cylinder is empty. ii) Cylinders should be handled with care and only by personnel who are reliable, adequately informed and fully aware of all associated hazards. Damaged or leaking cylinders should be immediately taken outside into the open air, and the supplier and fire authorities should be notified immediately.
No-one should approach a gas cylinder store with a naked light or a cigarette. iii) Care should be taken to avoid striking or dropping cylinders, or knocking them together. iv) Cylinders should never be used as rollers. v) One cylinder should never be filled from another. vi) Every care must be taken to avoid accidental damage to cylinder valves. vii) Valves must be operated gently and without haste, never fully opened hard against the back stop (so other users know that the valve is open) and never wrenched shut, but turned just securely enough to stop the gas. Before removing or loosening any outlet connections, caps or plugs, a check should be made that the valves are closed. viii) When changing cylinders, close all valves and appliance taps, and extinguish naked flames, including pilot jets, before disconnecting them. ix)When reconnecting, ensure that all connections and washers are clean and in good condition and do not overtighten them. x) Immediately a cylinder becomes empty, close its valve.

Workshop Safety - Summary

1) Always ensure that the trailer is secure before starting work.

2) Never use a naked flame if there is fuel in the vicinity.

3) Always have a fire extinguisher to hand whenever welding or when working on the electrical system. If you do have a fire, *don't panic*! Use the extinguisher effectively by directing it at the base of the fire.

4) Never use petrol (gasoline) to clean parts. Use paraffin (kerosene) or white spirit.

5) NO SMOKING! There's a risk of fire, or transferring dangerous substances to your mouth, and in any case, ash falling into mechanical components is to be avoided!

6) Be methodical in everything you do. Use common sense, and think of safety at all times.

CHAPTER 2 - BUYING A TRAILER

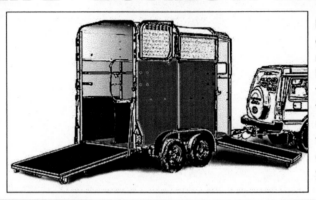

If you are thinking of buying a trailer, then you are bound to have a fair idea of the purposes to which it will be put. It may be that you are thinking in terms of a small, general purpose utility trailer for carrying garden waste, or to carry luggage and equipment on camping trips. You may belong to a canoeing club, or have a dinghy which needs to be carried to the local reservoir; a horse to the gymkhana; livestock to market. Whatever your needs, you can be sure that there is a trailer designed especially for you!

PART I: TRAILER TYPES

The first step towards identifying exactly which trailer you will eventually buy is to narrow down your requirements as closely as you can. Use this simple checklist to work out exactly what you need:

• What is the maximum weight of your planned load - and does this match up to the maximum weight which your vehicle will be able to tow? Look in *Appendix 3, Vehicle Towing Limits* (and *Appendix 4, What Things Weigh* if applicable) to find out.

• If you are looking at a horsebox, or a stock, dinghy or canoe trailer, how many animals or boats will you need to carry at any one time?

• What are the special requirements of your load? Will it need to be tied down, or kept dry, or kept cold?

As soon as you have established these simple facts, you will be able to start looking for the trailer you need. Let's have a look at some of the different trailers on offer:

Camping Trailers

❑ 1. Do you just want a multi-purpose 'something' in which to stow all your surplus equipment, or would you like to camp in a little more comfort? If you are just looking for carrying capacity, then a basic multi-purpose box trailer would suit your needs. There are several makes available and they can usually be purchased as self-assemble kits. A drop-down tailboard is a tremendous asset when lifting or sliding out heavy loads or when shovelling loose materials, while a simple tipper facility, will make unloading easy!

❑ 2. If you need to keep your load dry, but don't want anything too large, then one of these sturdy moulded plastic or glassfibre trailers with their own purpose-made lids would be ideal. - but there is not usually a waterproof seal, so vulnerable things would still be best carried in the car.

3. If your family goes camping regularly, then perhaps a trailer tent would be the ideal purchase. Some trailer tents have removable canvas and frames, and so could be used as a normal trailer when you're at home. Here's a rather more elaborate version, complete with furnishings and fridge and a sun canopy extension. (Illustration, courtesy Conway Trailer Tents)

BUYING SECOND-HAND. Make sure you check every relevant point on the checklist below. For trailer tents, see the relevant section of *Chapter 6, Servicing & Maintenance* for details on potential problem areas.

Vehicle Transporters

4. A sturdy general-purpose trailer like this Ifor Williams model will be perfect for carrying a car or light plant machinery. The rear portion of the flatbed is hinged to drop down for loading. Some have a sloping 'beaver-tail' to assist loading while on others, the entire bed tilts. (Illustration, courtesy Ifor Williams)

5. When choosing your trailer, it's important that you don't 'over-specify' - otherwise you could find yourself towing an illegally large outfit. This Indespension trailer is little more than a chassis and ramp, and so the over-specification trap is easily avoided but it is, of course, less versatile.

6. For breakdown recovery a spectacle-frame transporter is light and manoeuvrable, and has a winch to draw the 'frame' into the towing position. On the other hand, once the car is loaded, it becomes a 'four wheeled trailer' and, since it exceeds 750 kgs, should have brakes on all wheels. Since it doesn't, this type of trailer can only be used, by law, for vehicle breakdown recovery. (Illustration, courtesy Carmovers Ltd.)

BUYING SECOND-HAND. Check the rope hooks and the condition of any winch carefully. If buying a spectacle-frame transporter, examine the swivel point for signs of undue wear. And DO NOT omit to carry all the necessary suspension and chassis checks.

Look especially hard at the condition of drive-up ramps and corner steadies and check that the trailer is not bowed in the horizontal plane. Ill-treated car trailers are prone to bending from the wheels-back.

MOTORBIKE CARRIERS
You can select a specialised trailer with individual bays to carry one, two, or three machines - but you will find in many cases that a 'three-bike' trailer is too narrow to accommodate more than two bikes. Measure up the space between the bays to check that there will be sufficient 'elbow-room' for secure loading and lashing. Some bike trailers have steel loops fixed to the fronts of their bays to locate the front wheel. Pick one of these if you can, since they will help to hold the bike upright.

To carry large numbers of machines or spares at one time, a good sized agricultural trailer, such as the Ifor Williams GD6 with a ramp may be another option.

Box and Van Trailers

Roller shutter doors will speed up loading and unloading times and cause less obstruction to the person using the trailer or to passers-by.

7. A second door at the drawbar end is a feature of the Ifor Williams range and makes access easy - even when the trailer's full. The best enclosed box trailers, like this one, have tracking along the walls to help secure the load - and there are load restraint accessories available. See *Chapter 5, Using a Trailer.* (Illustration, courtesy Ifor Williams.)

For carrying foodstuffs, or certain sorts of chemicals and medical supplies, a refrigerated trailer is the logical choice - but there are strict regulations for their use!

BUYING SECOND-HAND. If roller shutter doors do not work perfectly, reject the trailer unless the price is right - replacing them will be expensive. Check the inside for damp ingress and the seams for cracking and opening-up.

Livestock Trailers

☐ 8. Purpose-designed livestock trailers come in a wide range of shapes and sizes, and it's up to you to decide which one is best for your purposes. Ifor Williams, are featured again because they are Britain's biggest producer of stock trailers. Look out for adjustable ventilation, a heat reflective white roof and sturdy construction. (Illustration courtesy Ifor Williams),

BUYING SECOND-HAND. Check carefully the condition of ramp gates, ramps, partitions, sheepdecks, restraint bars, halter rings and so on. Replacements are all readily available from a large stock trailer specialist - but they will cost money!

ℹ INSIDE INFORMATION: Some experts say that, because they lead such a hard life, second-hand livestock trailers are best avoided! ℹ

Horseboxes

Assess your needs carefully. The country's top-selling range of Hunter horseboxes, - from Ifor Williams, again! - runs from the largest double horsebox, with even more room than normal, through the slightly smaller 505R double-box, down to a single horse/mare-and-foal model as shown in this chapter's heading picture.

ℹ INSIDE INFORMATION: It might seem as if the larger the horsebox the better, but do bear in mind that the narrower it is, the less wind resistance it will present and the easier it will be to tow - and that larger ones could exceed your tow vehicle's towing limit. ℹ

Also check that any horsebox you are interested in buying comes with:

• front loading/unloading door (if required)

• suitable floor and non-slip ramp covering, such as rubber mats

• breast bars and breaching bars

• adequate partitions in double 'boxes

• adequate natural and 12V lighting

Horseboxes are available in every form imaginable, from small moulded GRP-bodied pony-sized trailers, to large-size, top-quality boxes. Check the legal requirements detailed in *Chapter 5, Using a Trailer* if you are looking to buy a larger, double box, and investigate all special equipment carefully, as for livestock trailers, above.

BUYING SECOND-HAND. Make the same checks as for livestock trailers, and also check the propstands (if fitted) for damage. It's wise to disinfect your second-hand horsebox, but not so crucial as with livestock or poultry carriers.

Boat Trailers

There are almost as many different types of boat trailer to choose from as there are boats and Indespension seem to specialise in them all!

☐ 9. You'll find boat trailers for power boats of all sizes...

☐ 10. ...and for canoes. This Indespension trailer can carry up to fourteen canoes!

☐ 11. Or for carrying dinghies. This trailer comes with a launching trolley, so there's no need to get the trailer wet when launching. At the front there's a mast support, which holds the mast at an angle above the towing vehicle.

BUYING SECOND-HAND. Boat trailers suffer badly from exposure to water and salt, so read the relevant section of *Chapter 6, Servicing & Maintenance* for details of the problems they may be prone to. Make sure that the winch is positioned correctly for a straight-line pull without the cable or strap rubbing on the trailer, and that it is in good condition and securely mounted. Examine the rollers particularly carefully - especially if the trailer is old - since they do disintegrate, and replacements can be rather expensive.

12

SAFETY FIRST!

BOAT TRAILERS TO AVOID!

❑ *12. Cheap American boat trailers are imported to this country in large numbers - generally with boats on board - and these are then often given by the importer to the boat's British purchaser as a 'freebie'. Their hitches, dimensions, lights and brakes are invariably illegal - and dangerous - for use in this country, and if offered one of these trailers, the only sensible option is not to buy. Details of those features which, typically, should set your alarms bells ringing are: i) Hydraulic brakes ii) Aluminium wheels iii) Illegal 'all-red' US-style lights iv) Most dangerous of all - a 2 in. hitch, or - worse still! - are fit-all-types (or drop-off-all-types!) hitch.*

⚡ INSIDE INFORMATION: Indespension, one of Britain's leading boat trailer manufacturers, will PAY you to take one of these trailers off the road! Part-exchange it with them for a new (legal!) boat trailer, and they will give you a trade-in price for it - and scrap it! ⚡

General Haulage Trailers

13

❑ 13. There are any number of different general-purpose trailers on the market, and since only you know your needs, only you can make the right decision about which to buy. Note that some have tail board ramps for easier loading. (Illustration, courtesy Ifor Williams)

Again, beware of over-specification, since too large a trailer could mean too small a load, bearing in mind the legal capacity of the tow vehicle.

14

❑ 14. If you are planning to carry heavy, wheeled items, a winch might be of use.

15

❑ 15. Or, if you are going to be carrying large quantities of soil or sand, a hydraulic tipper unit like this one would be an excellent feature to look for. (Illustration, courtesy Ifor Williams)

BUYING SECOND-HAND. Ramps, tail boards and so on may be missing or damaged, so get some sample spares prices before going to look at the trailer, and work out whether the asking price is economical. Check the operation of any tipping or winching equipment, and DO NOT OMIT to make the checks on chassis and suspension detailed below.

Making the Purchase

A number of the big trailer manufacturers deal in ready-made trailers, kits - and even reconditioned second-hand units. If you have an old trailer which you would like to get rid of, making a part-exchange deal with one of these firms will probably represent the most economical and convenient option. An added benefit of dealing with a reputable firm is that they offer a number of customer care benefits such as warranty arrangements, for example, and the guaranteed availability of spare parts.

PART II: SECOND-HAND BUYING CHECKS, STEP-BY-STEP

When you go to look at the trailer, take this book - and a tape measure or a ball of string - with you, and before even beginning to closely examine its condition, you should check the following points:

❏ 1) Does it have a manufacturer's identification and maximum weights recommendation plate fixed to, or near, the nearside of the drawbar? If it doesn't, make your excuses and leave unless the trailer is cheap enough to be worth considering!

FACT FILE: STOLEN TRAILERS

If buying other than through a recognised dealer, insist on seeing proof of ownership before purchase. If the trailer is found to be stolen (whether or not either you or the seller were aware of it!) you will loose your cash *and* the trailer.

❏ 2) If it is a braked trailer dating from 1989 or later, it MUST be equipped with auto-reverse brakes. The old-fashioned type with a manually operated reverse brake lock-out, known as 'standard mechanical' brakes, were banned on trailers built from that date on, and so will be illegal if the trailer was built after that date. Added to which, standard mechanical braking systems are now so old that they are likely to be worn out - and getting hold of spares can be a problem.

❏ 3) If it is an unbraked trailer, does it have a Gross Vehicle Weight ('GVW') of 750 kg or less? If its GVW is more than 750 kg, OR if its GVW is higher than your tow vehicle manufacturer's recommendations, then using it would be illegal.

❏ 4) How are the brakes operated? If you can see hydraulic brake lines of the sort found on cars, then WALK AWAY! There are almost certain to be illegal, and won't be equipped with that essential auto-reverse system.

❏ 5) How is the hitch marked? If it is marked as being a 50 mm hitch, then this is perfectly all right. Any other measurement - especially if it gives a range of different towball sizes to which it can be fixed, then again, DO NOT TOUCH IT WITH A BARGE-POLE! Any ball hitch other than the 50 mm EC standard hitch is illegal - and will probably be dangerous.

❏ 6) What type of suspension does it have? If it has rubber suspension blocks encased in steel housings, or traditional leaf-springs

running along its sides, then these are both acceptable. If, however, it is equipped with car-type coil-over shock absorbers, then think very hard about whether you want this trailer. Coil sprung suspension units are not suitable for use on the majority of trailers. And again, they could even indicate that someone has cannibalised car parts to make the trailer up.

If the trailer has four wheels, check for suspension damage or wear by checking that each pair of wheels is aligned.

❏ 7) What sort of tyres does it have? Look at each tyre individually to make sure that they are all the same size and rating. DON'T mix radials and cross-ply on the trailer! If the tyres are all the same, but the wheels are from a car or van, then chances are that they will not be robust enough to stand up to the weights required. Look at the embossed lettering on the tyres' walls to see what type they are. See *Appendix 6, Wheels & Tyres.* Check that the tyres have not perished, that their treads are up to legal limits, and that they haven't suffered any scuffs or cuts - and check the inboard sides as carefully as the outsides.

❏ 8) Now move on to the towing hitch. Check that the handbrake's operation is satisfactory, and that there is no rust in evidence on the drawtube. Push the coupling in, towards the trailer. If it pushes in and out quickly, the damper will need replacing. It should move smoothly under constant pressure and return slowly and smoothly.

❏ 9) Is the breakaway cable in good order? Are its fixing clips rust-free, and do they spring in and out quite easily?

❏ 10) Get down on your hands and knees and inspect the suspension. If you can get a fingernail into the rubber suspension blocks, check whether they are noticeably hard or soft. If they feel about the same consistency as rubber doorstops, then they should be just right. Leafspring suspension should be free of breaks in leaves or clips and U-bolts should be tights. Look for excessive wear in the shackle pins.

❏ 11) Stay down there for the next check! Look at the brake compensator mechanism, and see whether it is very dirty, or even corroded. A bad encrustation of dirt on the compensator unit means it certainly hasn't been adjusted recently!

❏ 12) If the trailer has an over-centre handbrake (i.e. the sort without a ratchet mechanism), first roll the trailer forward to ensure the auto-reverse is disengaged, then take hold of the brake operating rod, parallel with the drawbar, and give it a good shake back and forth. If you can feel any slack in its operation, then it is badly adjusted, and may have been for some time.

❏ 13) If the adjuster stub on the brake backplate is obviously rusty, or caked in dirt, then the brakes won't have been adjusted in a long while!

❏ 14) You can get up off the ground for the final braking check, which is simply to follow the instructions given in *Chapter 6, Servicing & Maintenance* (Jobs 29 and 30, as applicable) for checking brake adjustment.

❏ 15) Now, check the tow hitch for wear. Try to lift and lower the end of the ball coupling and see if the shaft is worn. The ball cup should be well greased (if it isn't the stabiliser type). Connect to a vehicle, and shake it about to see if it feels loose. IMPORTANT NOTE: See *Job 18* in *Chapter 6* for details of coupling wear indicators.

❏ 16) Check that the jockey wheel and its mechanism are not bent, or damaged. They commonly suffer if they're left down when someone drives away!

❏ 17) If you're quite happy with everything you've looked at so far, then you are now in the closing stages of your examination - and this is where your tape measure or ball of string comes in. First of all, with the trailer on level ground, confirm your examination of the suspension by measuring the distance from the ground to the bottom of the chassis at the same point on either side. If the two measure-ments show much of a discrepancy, then the suspension on one side may be damaged or broken.

❏ 18) Now measure the two diagonals of one body panel. (If you're not sure how to do this, see *diagram 1 on page 22.* Are both diagonals the same? Measure the diagonals on another panel as a second check. If you find any discrepancy on either panel, the body could be distorted.

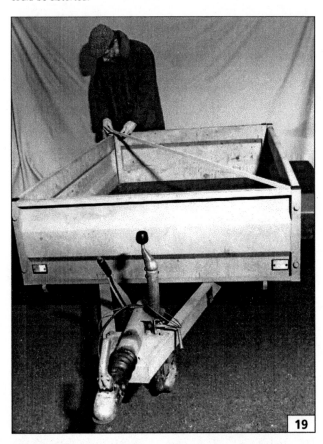

❏ 19) Repeat the exercise on the main trailer body and the chassis - it may be a difficult job, but it's worth it. You could well find that the main trailer body and the chassis is perfectly true, even though the body has distorted. On the other hand, the body's twisting could be due to a seriously twisted chassis - and it's certainly worth the effort to find out!

❏ 20) There are a few final measuring jobs to be done, and they'll need two people - but don't miss them out! If the trailer has twin close-coupled axles, extend your string so that it lies alongside both tyres, at around hub height. Hold it taut so that it makes a perfectly straight line, and see that it touches both edges of both tyres - if it doesn't, then the axles could be out of line. Move the trailer forward so that the wheels rotate by half a turn, and perform this check again. If again you find that there's a significant amount of daylight showing on one edge of one, or both tyres, then the wheels are almost definitely either buckled or out of line.

❏ 21) The second check on axle and undergear alignment should be done whether you have one axle or two. Measure the distance from the 'top dead centre' of each tyre to the bottom of the chassis or frame member directly above it. Rotate the wheel through half a turn and measure again. The two measurements should be the same.

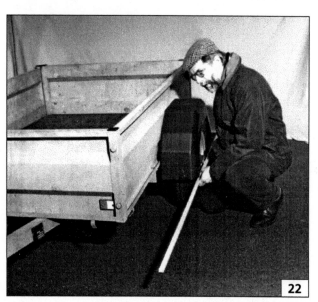

❏ 22) Now extend a long straight-edge forwards (or backwards) from the hub centre, or the edge of the hub cap, to a point exactly level with the end of the chassis. Rotate the wheel again, and re-measure. Again, the two measurements should be the same. If there is a discrepancy of more than a fraction (which you can put down to error with such a rough-and-ready check), then there could be a problem with the running gear, and you should either reject the trailer, or call in an expert for a second opinion.

SAFETY FIRST!

Once you have bought your second-hand trailer - or even as a final check BEFORE buying - it is always a good policy to take it along to a specialist for a profes-sional once-over. There are plenty of trailer specialists who would be happy to do this - but Indespension main depots are set up to carry out a FREE routine safety inspection on any used trailer, whether it's a new purchase, or whether you have owned it for years. We would always recommend that you obtain a professional second opinion on any second-hand purchase you might make and replace any safety-related items before using the trailer.

CHAPTER 3
BUILDING A TRAILER

There was a time when building your own trailer pretty much guaranteed that you would make a bumper saving over the bought alternative. Sadly, these days the retail prices of materials, and the legal requirements which must be borne in mind, generally conspire to make home-building no cheaper - and an awful lot more troublesome - than simply choosing and buying a ready-made trailer.

However, if you have access to a cheap source of materials, or if you just enjoy making things yourself, there can be some benefit to be gained from building your trailer yourself. And if you want a sort of halfway-house, there are DIY kits available for your to self-assemble your own trailer. (Illustration, courtesy Indespension)

PART I: PLANNING THE TRAILER

The first job which you will have to tackle is deciding exactly what sort of trailer you are going to build.

Read *Chapter 2, Buying a Trailer*, if you are unsure of your precise requirements. Decide what you want the trailer to carry, and check *Appendix 4, What Things Weigh* for a guide as to what certain items might weigh. Tot up a theoretical load weight; you will have to add this to your projected trailer's own weight, and this total figure will be the one you use when looking in *Appendix 3, Vehicle Towing Limits,* refer to *Chapter 4, Rules & Regulations,* giving details of the legal requirements which you will have to bear in mind.

If you are building from scratch, or according to a DIY plan, the ultimate Gross Vehicle Weight will help to decide many of these points for you. Either of the biggest manufacturers, Ifor Williams Trailers or Indespension, will be able to supply the components you'll need and they will also be able to tell you which components, - such as

coupling, brakes, axle(s) and suspension - will be suited to the weights which it will be expected to tow. There are many variations on basic themes: pressed or cast coupling heads, for example; unbraked wheels, or those with braking systems - and the legal requirements for dealing with your target weight will in many instances make an automatic decision about these items for you.

Basic Rules To Bear In Mind:

• Light, pressed-steel couplings will only be safe for use with the lightest trailers.

• You will have to fit auto-reverse brakes if your trailer is to be heavier than 750 kg laden. It's the law!

• Bought-in axles or hubs of the right specification will guarantee safety. We would not recommend that you make up your own.

• Buying the axle or hub complete with brake drums is the best way to avoid any fitting problems.

• Coil-spring suspension is not a good choice for trailer applications. Pick either rubber or leaf-spring units from a recognised source, and design your chassis around them.

• Car or van wheels are unlikely to be strong enough. Buy proper trailer wheels, whether new or second-hand.

• DON'T use old car brake or suspension parts since they will almost certainly be illegal, even on a DIY trailer.

SAFETY FIRST!

You will be drilling and cutting metal, so wear good quality goggles and industrial leather gloves. You may be welding, in which case make sure that you have a proper BSI approved welding mask.

Even if you have done this sort of work before, take the time to re-read Chapter 1, Safety First! of this book, before beginning.

Choosing the Materials

If you are building a kit, all this is taken care of. If you follow one of the plans reproduced in *Appendix 5, The Plans* you will at least have a list of precisely what materials you need - and what size each piece should be - to make life as simple as possible.

ALUMINIUM

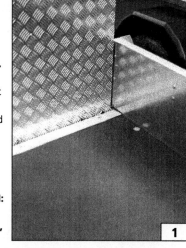

INSIDE INFORMATION: **Sectional aluminium is good for building strong, lightweight chassis, but is extremely difficult to join sections together satisfactorily. Do not choose aluminium tube for your chassis unless you are an accomplished aluminium welder.**

making it easy! ☐ *1. Aluminium sheet, on the other hand, is the easiest material to use for constructing body panels. It can be easily cut or drilled, and also offers a certain amount of scope for moulding, since it is quite easy to bend. You can get aluminium sheet in various different gauges with a smooth finish, or as 'checker plate', which has patterns pressed into its surface to give grip and added strength. Checker plate used over marine ply is the ideal choice for trailer floors.*

PLASTICS

It takes skill - and lots of time - to make your own plastic glass reinforced (GRP) panels successfully, and DIY production of GRP panels from scratch is not really an option.

However, points to consider if you were to construct a body from ready-made GRP panels are:

• **Stress points**. Identify where the chassis mounting points, door hinges and so on will be, and make sure you reinforce these areas properly, as well as all corners.

• **Sealing**. Consider the relative merits of ready-made rubber strip type seals and liquid silicone sealant and adapt your body design accordingly.

WOOD

Marine ply is the commonest choice for body construction. Do not use ordinary cheap plywood for your trailer, since the bonding compounds used to make it will not stand up to the weather. Make sure the plywood you use for the floor is about 25 mm (1 in.) thick. The walls of the box can be thinner, bearing in mind the kind of load you are likely to be carrying.

Softwood tongue-and-groove boarding (T&G) is really the only other practical option if you want to use wood - but do not buy the thin boarding available in most DIY centres, since this is only meant as a

decorative cladding for walls. 20 mm (3/4 in.) or 25 mm (1 in.) board should be suitable for your trailer's floor and sides.

making it easy! *Remember to add 25 mm (1 in.) to the finished length of each board when working out how much wood you need. Cutting the boards a little over-length, then clamping them together, and making the final cut to all the boards from one panel at once, is by far the best way to ensure a neat edge.*

Bolting the boards individually to an angle-steel box frame is the simplest way of making your panels into a trailer! You can buy these frames ready-made, from leading trailer suppliers.

Whichever type of wood you use, weather protection will be essential. After soaking the timber with a suitable clear preservative, several lavish coats of a good quality yacht varnish should ensure that your ply or softwood trailer keeps on looking good for many years to come.

STEEL

Steel is just about the most versatile material for use on your trailer. Its advantages are adaptability, price, and strength. Its disadvantages are weight, difficulty of cutting and bending, the necessity for welding, and its vulnerability to corrosion.

Sheet steel is a good option for body panels, and will work out considerably cheaper than aluminium. You can buy it ready galvanised, in which case DO NOT attempt to weld it, and DO take steps to protect cut edges against corrosion. Ungalvanised, it will be even cheaper - but you will have to paint it to protect against rust.

☐ 2A. Sectional steel comes in a wide variety of forms. As a box-section...

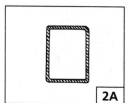

☐ 2B. ...as 'angle'...

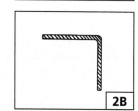

☐ 2C. ...as 'joist'...

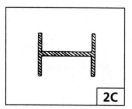

☐ 2D. ...or as 'channel'.

Box section and angle are the two types you're most likely to come across when making your trailer. Box-section is ideal for making up a strong chassis, while angle or a slender box-section would be best for making up a body frame. If you're making a motorcycle transporter, you'll also need channel for the bays.

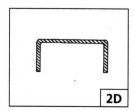

Once you have cut and drilled all your steel panels, or welded up your chassis or frame, you could deliver your finished work to a local galvanising plant. Remember though that any cutting or drilling done after a piece has been galvanised will allow rust into the steel beneath the zinc coating unless the edges are protected.

FASTENERS

In assembling the trailer's body, the number of different fasteners you have to choose from can be confusing! Here are the alternatives:

❏ 3A. **Heads**. If a smooth inner surface on the trailer body is important, you have two options: either countersunk, or raised (low-profile) heads. Using countersunk heads will only be practical if the panel material you are using is thick enough to allow you to sink the head and strong enough not to need a flat washer - which rules out timber. Ordinary hexagon-headed bolts would do the job, but would not be so neat looking, or so kind to the body as 'mushroom' headed bolts, unless flat washers are used. The following fasteners would be suitable for securing thick panels to the body frame:

i) **Countersunk machine screws and nuts**. When measuring the length of a countersunk bolt or screw, remember to include the head.

ii) **Coachbolts**. These have a square section beneath the head itself, which is usually forced into the material surrounding a drilled hole in a timber panel, and prevents the bolt from turning as the nut is done up, hence the word 'coach' - that's what they were originally used on!

Force-fitting into a round hole is adequate if fixing wood; if fixing metal, you will need to cut a square hole. Drill a hole of sufficient size, and then mark it up and use a file to cut the corners.

The following fasteners would be suitable for securing thin panels to the frame:

iii) **Round or domed head machine screws and nuts**. These often have the large bearing surface mentioned above - if not, use large flat washers with each one.

iv) The sort of bolt you are most likely to use in building the trailer's body. **Mushroom-headed roofing bolt**. These are readily available, cheap, galvanised, have a good crossed-slot drive, and come complete with a square or hexagonal nut. Use a flat washer, once again.

For securing non-welded chassis joints, conventional hexagon-headed nuts and bolts of an appropriate size and thread will do perfectly well. These must be high-tensile when connections are made to the suspension, braking or tow frame (grade 8.8 or better), but mild steel are OK for 'bodywork'.

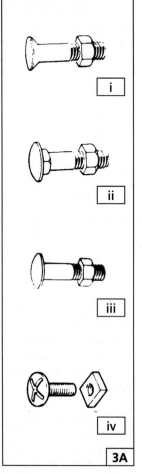

3A

❏ 3B. **Threads**. You will need relatively coarse threads for your trailer if you intend tapping your own threaded holes, especially if you are working with aluminium, since its softness means that fine threads can easily pull out. You can get fasteners with threads which go all the way up to the head (i, 'setscrews'), or others whose threads stop partway up the shank (ii, 'bolts').

Materials. Use high-tensile steel bolts - U-bolts should also be high-tensile (grade 8.8 or better) - for all structural work. Cheaper alternatives will easily shear in normal use. A protective coating such as zinc or cadmium plating is definitely worth the extra cost.

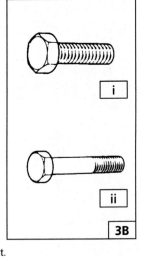

3B

If your trailer is to be used in a marine environment, seek out 'full passivated cadmium' coated fasteners. This more than doubles the life of a bolt when exposed to sea-spray and salt water. These bolts are golden-brown in colour.

making it easy! Size is important! Do not make the mistake of using bolts or screws which are too slender for the items which you intend to fasten. The hole diameters in the plans shown in **Appendix 5, The Plans** dictate the sizes of the fasteners to go through them. If in doubt, your local engineering firm or workshop may be able to identify the size of fastener you need if you tell him the type and dimensions of the materials you are using.

IMPORTANT NOTE: When using steel fixings on aluminium, always use a copper-rich grease to protect against electrolytic corrosion.

❏ 3C. **Special fasteners**. There are a couple of fastener types which you may find useful, but do not fall into any of the above categories. They are:

i) **Blind, or 'pop' rivets**. You need a special gun to use these, but they are an excellent way of fixing sheet metal to a drilled frame in double-quick time.

ii) **U-bolts**. These are essential for attaching leaf-spring suspension to an axle. Always pick a U-bolt of the right size for the job!

iii & iv) **Self-tapping screws**. These are hardened, and have the advantage of creating their own thread as they are driven into the workpiece. This means that, properly fitted, they will stay tightened despite vibration. You drill a pilot hole of the correct size, and then simply screw the self-tapping screw into place. You can use them for attaching hinges and catches, and for joining sheets together.

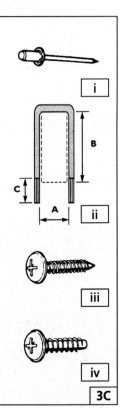

3C

Tools

You will need a good bench with a vice (a Black and Decker Workmate may be ideal), and a number of G-clamps with jaws large enough to hold things together while drilling, cutting or glueing.

For cutting metal, a full-size hacksaw will be needed. To speed things up, you might like to use an electric jigsaw to cut thinner sheets. Specific blades are available for cutting aluminium, steel or wood due to their different softnesses.

When working with wood remember that marine-quality ply is one of the hardest woods to cut, and select your drills and saws accordingly: Cut slowly; resharpen or replace edges regularly.

If you are planning to make your own chassis, it would be best if you are able to weld. Electric MIG welding machines are available in most DIY stores, and are relatively simple and safe to use, though the smallest should be avoided because they won't have to power to weld chassis steel. We strongly recommend that you take some specialist instruction, and practice until you are completely proficient before attempting to make up your own trailer chassis. We give basic instructions on how to weld further on in this chapter.

making it easy! If you want to use a welded-steel structure but you're not sure of your welding skills, try constructing and 'tack' welding the frame together using small but strong dabs of weld. Then have a professional make all the final welds for you.

Using the Plans

Indespension pioneered DIY trailer building in the 1960s, and have built up quite a library of useful trailer plans. You'll find a good selection of these in *Appendix 5, The Plans* - and you may well find one which suits the type of trailer you are planning to build. We would recommend using these plans wherever possible, unless you are an experienced design engineer who can be confident that their own creation will be road legal - and safe. One particular bonus with using the plans is that you will know from the outset that the trailer is of a weight suitable the intended purpose.

PART II: TEACH YOURSELF TO WELD

1

☐ 1. Unless you choose the less satisfactory option of bolting the frame together, there is no way that you'll be able to make a road-legal trailer chassis from scratch without being able to weld. If you have never done it before, buy a number of off-cuts of a similar thickness to the trailer frame to use as practice pieces.

To understand how welding works, all you really need to understand is that heat melts metal, and when metal is melted, it all flows into one. As you can imagine, it takes a lot of heat to melt a piece of steel; and that's why you need special equipment to do it - equipment which must be treated with a great deal of respect.

Types of Welding

There are several types of welding which you might consider when choosing your equipment, and we'll run through them very quickly here.

IMPORTANT NOTE: Brazing is not legal in this country for structural work on vehicles, and if you choose to braze your trailer's chassis, it may not pass the predicted trailer MoT. However, it should be fine for non-structural 'bodywork' above the chassis.

ARC WELDING

Electric arc welding is the cheapest and simplest method with which to get started, although if you plan to weld thin sheets of steel it won't

be suitable. The equipment consists of a welding set, or transformer, which converts ordinary mains electricity into a 'low voltage, high amperage' current, suitable for welding steel. Leading from the machine you'll find two heavy-duty cables. One of these is the earth, with a clamp on the end which you clip onto the workpiece. The other cable has a special handgrip and welding rod holder on the end.

SAFETY FIRST!

The greatest danger when arc welding comes from the extremely bright light given off during the process. The light contains a good deal of ultra-violet light which can cause direct and permanent damage to the eyes. Always use the full face shield provided when arc welding and resist the temptation to peek round the edge 'just to start off with'. Since UV light can cause skin damage too, always wear gloves and button-down sleeves. Red hot sparks are thrown off as arc welding takes place, so wear shoes and overalls that prevent a red-hot droplet of metal going down inside your shoe, and for the same reason, keep the overalls buttoned at the neck. When welding overhead, keep the sleeves closed at the wrists. Don't weld in enclosed spaces without ventilation because the fumes can be harmful. Wear cotton overalls - nylon can quite easily catch fire! Take very great care when handling hot metal.

Keep children and pets right out of the work area so that they can be neither burned, nor affected by the UV rays. Make sure that there is nothing flammable near the area where you are working. Always have a fire extinguisher of the correct type available, and have a washing-up liquid bottle full of water to douse local outbreaks. Don't whatever you do, allow water to come into contact with mains electricity equipment because of the high risk of electric shocks.

When cleaning the weld, clear goggles should be worn because the brittle slag can 'fly' as it is chipped off the weld.

One of the special steel welding rods is gripped by the holder/handgrip, and when the power is on, the end of the rod is touched onto the workpiece at the place you want to weld. The circuit is thus completed, and the current coming from the transformer causes a bright electric arc to jump out from the welding rod to the workpiece. This melts the end of the rod, and the steel beneath the rod's end; the molten metal of the rod is thrown in liquid droplets into the 'weld pool'. When working with thin steel, it's almost impossible to stop the heat burning right the way through but arc welding is great for making an angle-bracket type of trailer chassis!

❑ 2. Here's how arc-welding works:

a) The circuit is completed, the arc is created, and the end of the rod and the workpiece begin to heat up.

b) Melting point is reached in the two edges, and a puddle of molten metal flows between them.

c) The end of the rod reaches melting point, and steel from its tip drips into the welding pool.

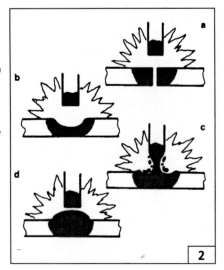

d) The extra metal which the rod has added completes the bridge between the two members, and the weld is complete.

• Main 'pros': it's the cheapest to buy and requires least in the way of consumables.

• Main 'cons': the arc can damage eyes or skin if unguarded; too fierce for thin metal; leaves unsightly 'slag' which has to be chipped away.

OXY-ACETYLENE WELDING

Oxy-acetylene welding uses a special torch, which is plumbed into cylinders of oxygen and acetylene gases, and mixes the two together to make an extremely hot flame when lit. This pointed flame is then played onto the workpiece, and once a molten puddle has begun to form, a thin steel welding rod is used to feed extra molten metal into the weld pool.

Since you have to move the rod and the flame along the workpiece at the same time, it can take a little while to master the technique of oxy-acetylene welding. Added to which, the gases you'd be using are extremely dangerous unless handled with great care. DIY set-ups are available and both BOC and Air Products the UK's leading gas suppliers stock oxygen and acetylene in small bottles for home use. However, unless you have a lot of welding to carry out, the equipment will be prohibitively expensive.

Another significant disadvantage of gas welding is that it heats the metal up to melting point quite a lot more slowly than the electric option, which makes for a far greater chance of the workpiece distorting.

• Main 'pros': One big advantage of using gas is that you can use the equipment to cut metal or loosen seized threads, as well as to weld.

• Main 'cons': Most potentially dangerous; requires most skill to use.

MIG WELDING

MIG welding is a convenient and efficient system based on the principles arc welding, but better in many ways. There is a continuous roll of welding wire rather than individual rods, which means you won't have to fiddle about fitting a fresh rod in the middle of a weld. The wire is pushed through a tube to the handgrip by an electric motor controlled by the welder. As the wire is fed through the pipe to the handset, the MIG machine pumps an inert gas (i.e., one which does not react with the weld, such as Argon or Argon/Carbon Dioxide mix in most cases), which flows over the weld as you work allowing a 'clean' weld to take place. As a useful side-effect, the gas cools the metal, with the result that distortion is minimised. The only slight disadvantage of using MIG equipment is that you must get the workpiece absolutely clean before starting work.

• Main 'pros': Easiest to use; cleaner weld than arc; less distortion.

• Main 'cons': Least versatile; needs expensive cylinder of gas; dangers of any electric are (see 'ARC WELDING'). Small Mig welders lack the power to weld chassis steel - check before you buy.

TIG WELDING

TIG welding is closely related to the MIG process described above, but demands rather more knowledge and skill and is highly specialised and expensive. Its one big advantage is that it is good for working with aluminium, so if you have any commercial ambitions in that direction, you may want to find out more about using TIG.

PRINCIPLES OF WELDING

The four points you must bear in mind when trying to weld anything are:

COMPATIBILITY
You can only weld certain things to certain things - and with certain things. Welding steel to steel, for example, is quite straightforward - but there is no way you could weld a piece of steel to a piece of aluminium, however hard you tried! Welding rods and wire come in all different compositions to suit different applications, so when you're out shopping for welding supplies, make sure that the supplier knows what you will be using them for.

PROTECTION
Welding - of whatever variety - is dangerous. It gives off an enormous amount of heat, and blindingly bright light. Wear the protective clothing described in *Chapter 1, Safety First!* - and never be tempted to leave off your mask, however irritating it might be, for even a second.

DISTORTION
When pieces of metal are cut or shaped, and then welded, all sorts of forces affect them as they go through each process. Distortion is most likely to happen if a great deal of heat is put into the metal before it attains melting point - as with gas welding - or if the piece being welded is a large, fairly flat panel. If you're only planning to weld up an 'angle-iron' trailer chassis, distortion shouldn't bother you too much; but you should still take every precaution to guard against it:

i) Always clamp pieces together and tack-weld at regular intervals before carrying out the final weld and, ii) Avoid welding from one end of a long seam to the other all in one go. Instead, weld from one end for a little way, stop, weld from the other end a little way, and then weld from the original end to join the two in the middle. This helps to equalise the stresses in the workpiece, and stops too much heat building up in one place.

IMPURITIES

If you allow impurities into a weld, it will lose a lot of its strength.

i) Make sure that the metal you are using is free from paint, rust, grease or other impurities before you start work.

ii) Any welding using an electric arc creates its own impurities unless the air is excluded for the duration of the weld.
Even with oxy-acetylene welding, the only sort which doesn't create its own impurities, it's essential to start off with clean metal.

TYPES OF WELDED JOINT

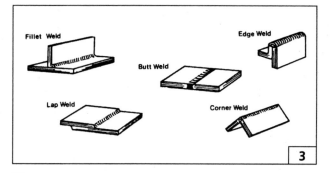

3

3. Here are the most common types of welded joint. In making your chassis, you will have to be proficient at the 'butt weld' and 'corner weld' for making the frame mitres; the 'lap weld' and 'fillet weld' for attaching the box uprights; and the 'fillet weld' and 'lap weld' for attaching mounting brackets to the frame.

When making butt welds on long seams, it's best to use the 'multiple-pass' method. This is where you weld first from one side of the joint, then, with the torch or transformer on a slightly hotter setting, weld from the other side of the joint.

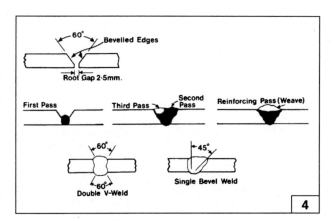

4

4. In this example, before beginning to weld, the edges of the pieces have been bevelled, and several runs will be made before the weld is complete.

SAFETY FIRST!

*Read the section in **Chapter 1, Safety First!** relating to welding safety, and follow the instructions shown there.*

FACT FILE: ARC WELDER SETTINGS

The thickness of the material to be welded determines how high you should set the machine. The rod or wire selected should also be matched to the thickness of the work. The following table gives a basic idea of how to set the machine, but once you become more practised you should be able to use your experience to get the most accurate setting for the job.

Electrode Diameter	* swg *	Current Required (amps)
1.60mm (1/16 in)	* 16 *	25 - 50
2.00mm (5/64 in)	* 14 *	50 - 80
2.50mm (3/32 in)	* 12 *	80 - 110
3.25mm (1/8 in)	* 10 *	110 - 150
4.00mm (5/32 in)	* 8 *	140 - 200
5.00mm (3/16 in)	* 6 *	200 - 260
6.00mm (1/4 in)	* 4 *	220 - 340

MAKING YOUR FIRST ELECTRIC WELD

Clean an area of the workpiece where the earth clamp will make good contact, and attach the earth clamp. Arrange the electrode cable so that it is safely draped out of the way of your work.

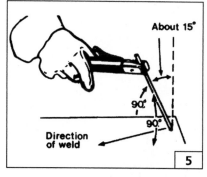

5

5. Present the electrode to the workpiece at an angle of about 15 degrees off the vertical, leaning in the direction of the weld you are about to make. Practise the motion of moving the electrode along the weld with the machine switched off. Once you're happy that you can do it smoothly, try it a couple of times with your eyes shut - because that's pretty much what you'll be doing when you begin to weld for real!

6

6. When you're ready, switch on the machine. Pull down your mask, or hold your face shield over your face with your free hand - and from this moment on, do not let it move away!

Hold the electrode a couple of inches away from the workpiece, and strike an arc. Getting the arc to start working can be difficult. The main problem is starting up a flow of current without letting the electrode stick to the workpiece. To stop it sticking, there are two methods of striking up the arc. The first is to bounce it off the workpiece in the place where you want to start work, which should allow the arc to spring up, but shouldn't give it time to 'catch' the electrode before the weld begins to flow. The alternative method is to scratch the electrode across the workpiece, and again, it should be moving fast enough to escape the magnet-like effect of the completed circuit. If the electrode does stick fast to your work, try twisting it off. If this fails, take the earth clamp off the workpiece to break the circuit, or turn off the machine. If you are using an ordinary arc welder, a simpler solution would just be to press the lever on the holder and loose the rod.

making it easy! If the electrode sticks to the workpiece and can't be flicked off, wait until it is completely cool and then pull it off. There is a big chance that the flux coating will now have degenerated through overheating - replace it!

If you have very much trouble getting an arc to spring up at all, check that the earth connection is a good one, and then try turning the power up, just one notch at a time, until you can get started. If the electrode then burns right through the steel - which it might well do - turn the machine down again!

⚡ INSIDE INFORMATION: Flux-covered rods may become damp, in which case you'll find it difficult to weld. For this reason, you should keep them somewhere dry. If they do get slightly damp, you can dry them out in a cool oven; but if the flux coating starts to get flaky as they dry, they will have to be thrown away. ⚡

Once your weld is successfully in progress, you'll have to master the further technique of feeding the rod into the weld, as it erodes and simultaneously moving the point of it along the seam.

❑ 7. Once you are proficient at welding in a straight line, try swirling the rod or wire in a spiral as you move it along. This technique is called 'weaving'; it helps the weld to penetrate better, and to make the seam extra strong.

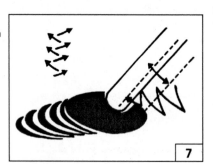

❑ 8A. Welding with the current too low makes for a feeble weld sitting high on top of the work.

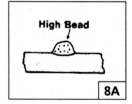

❑ 8B. Welding with the current too high makes for a wide, thick bead of weld sitting in a sunken channel - and a wasted rod.

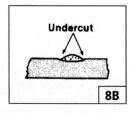

❑ 8C. Travelling too slowly means that metal builds up too much; 'slag' (impurities) is trapped; and the bead of weld hangs over the edges of the seam.

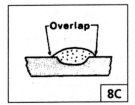

❑ 8D. If you hold the electrode too far away, the arc will be too long. The weld's surface will be rough, the arc will hiss, and the rod will melt off in messy lumps rather than a steady stream.

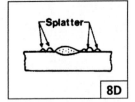

❑ 8E. If you weld too fast, the weld will be feeble; a small bead sitting in a wide channel, with a rough surface and little penetration into the seam. This weld would be unsafe.

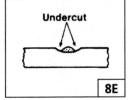

❑ 8F. A good weld! The arc makes a steady crackling sound as it moves along, and uniform ripples are seen on the weld's surface.

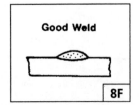

❑ 9. Once you are happy with your technique, try a simple lap joint. Angle the rod towards the bottom piece when working on thick material.

Tack welding. Start off by 'tack welding' the two pieces to be joined. This is simply the application of blobs of weld at intervals along the seam's length to hold it together while you work. The tacks will disappear into the final weld.

10. Chip off or wire-brush any slag from the tacks before you make the weld proper. It must be clean before you start.

11. If you've been practising hard, the finished weld should be as good as this one, which we prepared earlier!

PERFECT YOUR TECHNIQUE

Now you have got the basic technique, experiment with the different sorts of joints you'll need.

12A. The hardest bit of making a fillet joint can be getting the upright piece to stay put while you tack it!

INSIDE INFORMATION: Mole grips are handy for quickly clamping parts together.

12B. One good thing about a fillet joint, however, is that you can adjust the angle of the two pieces after it has been tacked.

12C. Hold the rod or wire at 45 degrees to each, and use a seam weld to join the two together.

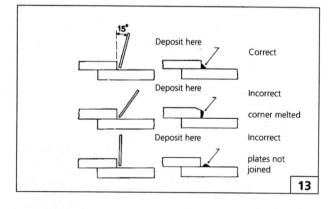

13. Making a lap weld is more involved than it might first seem.

☐ 14. Welding the outside of a corner is pretty easy to do; but tack and clean it all the same. Butt the two pieces together, rather than overlapping them; which makes the corner joint even easier to weld.

☐ 15. Fitting the box uprights into the frame corners will be a fiddle, so rearrange the frame to provide the easiest of work angles.

PART III: BUILDING YOUR OWN

Building from Scratch

MAKE A SIMPLE CHASSIS

The simplest chassis is one of angle-section steel, with four mitred corners and a single strengthening member running across and to the rear of the mid-way point (to give a good balance) such as in *Appendix 5's Plan A*. If working from scratch, use the length of your axle to work out how wide the trailer will be - you must allow good clearance from the inside of the tyres to the edge of the frame. Cut the steel to length for the basic frame, make the mitres, and then lay the strips out on the floor and make any necessary refinements to the mitres using a grinder or file.

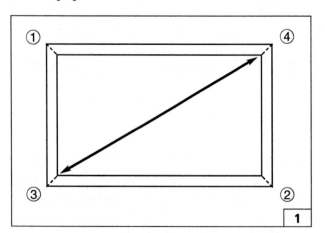

☐ 1. Clamp and tack-weld the corners, and then, to establish whether the chassis is square or not, measure the diagonals,which must be exactly equal. Now weld the corners in the order 1-2-3-4 as shown. Check the cross-member's fit, adjust as necessary with the grinder or file, clamp it into position and weld. Check the frame's squareness once more, then turn the whole thing upside-down and add the box-section drawbar (the size of bar you'll need will be determined by your choice of coupling). Check that the structure is perfectly square and not twisting at every stage of construction, and correct any faults you find straight away, since small problems early on in a build have a nasty habit of resulting in a 'Leaning Tower of Pisa' effect further down the line!

TURN IT INTO A TRAILER

Assemble the axle and suspension units if necessary, and fit the wheels. Measure the distance from the inside of one tyre to the edge of the baseplate, and make sure that you will have adequate wheel clearance before cutting out and attaching the mounting plates to the junction of cross-member and frame. Again, check their equal spacing and correct alignment before making your final welds. Fit the suspension, axle and wheels, to make a rolling chassis. Once you've got to the rolling chassis stage, life becomes much easier. Not only can you wheel the trailer about; you'll now be working at a far more convenient height!

IMPORTANT NOTE: Never weld rubber suspension units to the chassis - you'll melt or burn the rubber! Bolt to carefully welded mounting plates.

Now you are on the home straight, and it's time to add the uprights to turn the rolling chassis into a box. Weld in the uprights (turn the trailer on its side if you're not too good at welding vertically!) and - if you're not going to use a tailgate - the body just needs its panels, and it's finished. If you do want a tailgate, the next thing to do is decide how you are going to arrange the lights. You could fit them in a panel beneath the floor, in pods on the two rear uprights, or for super convenience, use a lighting board.

Make up the tailgate, and offer it up to the trailer to mark up positions for hinge and catch fittings. See FITTING A TAILGATE towards the end of this chapter for details. Mark the hinges first, and fit these loosely before marking up the catches. You may want to weld the catch brackets to the frame for added security, and special weld-on hinges and catches are available from any worthwhile trailer manufacturer or parts supplier. Now's also the time to make up your mudguard stays. Cut and bend the stays, and clamp them to their final welded positions before offering up the mudguards, so that you can check that your stays will hold them firmly in the right position. Make sure you position the mudguards high enough above the tyres to prevent the wheel fouling problems mentioned above. The 'right' amount depends on the amount of available suspension movement, of course.

Complete all the metal-working jobs: make up mounting brackets for jockey wheel and prop stands in steel angle, and weld these on.

DON'T bolt direct to the chassis! Again, careful measuring, and being prepared to grind away your tacks and start again are the keys to getting these positioned just right!

Fit the prop stands and jockey wheel, and lower them ready for fitting the coupling. Put the coupling in its eventual position, and measure the height from the floor to the centre of the head. It should be comparable with the average height of a car's towball, usually 420 mm high when unladen. If it's not high enough, you'll have to use a piece of the same section material as the draw bar as a spacer and weld it onto the drawbar to get the height just right. Drill the coupling mounting holes and put the coupling on one side until the frame is painted. Now weld on any rope hooks, lighting brackets, cable guides and so on, and drill any further holes you plan to use.

Make up the body panels, clamp them onto the frame, and drill the holes you'll use to mount them. Use a wood bit to cut through wooden panels, and then, using the hole through the wood as a guide, fit a steel bit and drill through the frame. The next thing you'll have to do is probably the most depressing bit of the whole project: unbolt and remove every item from the trailer except the basic welded framework. You have to take everything off in order to ensure that whatever protective coating you plan to use can get into every nook and cranny - any little chinks in the anti-rust armour will swiftly be found and penetrated once the trailer's in use. If you're taking the frame to be galvanised, any degreasing will be done at the plant. Otherwise you must thoroughly degrease before applying a suitably tough paint to the whole structure. Work the primer, then paint well into all drilled holes, and into the very bottom of every corner. While you're at it, varnish or paint your individual tongue-and-groove boards or wooden panels at the same time. Now retire for a well-earned cup of tea!

If you have used paint to coat the frame, you must give it plenty of time - preferably up to a week or so - to cure completely before reassembling the trailer. If you don't give it long enough, the paint could pull off as the bolts are tightened, and rust will be able to get in.

> *making it easy!* When affixing the panels, whatever their material, run around each one with a bead of silicone sealant before bolting it in - don't wait until they're assembled! This won't just stop water leaking through; it will also provide a cushioning surface for the panels, which will eliminate rattles and help keep the fasteners from undoing themselves.

The final job is to wire the whole thing up. We would recommend that you use a ready-made all-in-one lighting board and cable assembly, These are easy to install, but see 'Wiring a Trailer' (below) for tips on fitting. If using individual components and assembling your own custom-made wiring harness, you will still have to cut the main seven-core cable and individual wires to length, and make the connections - but even so, bought-in specialist electrical components are by far the best route to safe wiring.

Congratulations! You have just made a trailer!

Build a Kit

One of the simplest and most economical ways to own a trailer is to build one from a kit. If you can put together a set of flat-pack kitchen units, you can enter the self-build trailer business - and save money! We put together one of the Caddy range of self-build trailers, typical of the simple kits supplied by many manufacturers and sold in car and DIY superstores throughout the country. Available in a variety of sizes, the Caddy comprises galvanised steel sheet panels and chassis and rubber suspension and all the owner has to sort out is a suitable rear number plate. Even the tools are provided with this kit, the box spanner doubling as a 'wheel brace', especially useful if you order the optional spare wheel.

K1. The whole trailer comes in just one cardboard box, which includes absolutely everything - even the wheels and tyres. Always read the instructions thoroughly, and check the number and type of fasteners supplied against the contents list. The Caddy kit is fine, but with some makes you should use thick gloves when handling the larger pieces to prevent cuts. We also specified the high-side kit, available in a separate box.

K2. Whichever type of self-assembly trailer you buy, spend some time studying the instructions and exploded diagram and comparing it all to the set of parts laid out on the floor. (Illustration, courtesy Caddy Trailers Ltd)

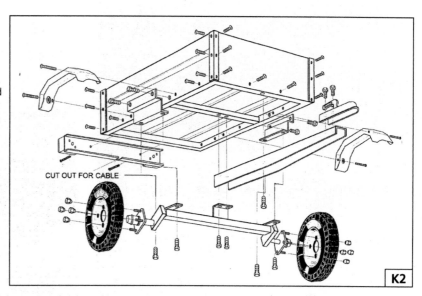

CUT OUT FOR CABLE

K3. First job with the Caddy kit was to screw first the trailer sides then the ends to the trailer base, screwing through the two outer holes in each case.

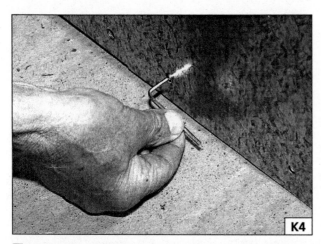

K4. The Allen-key head screws were screwed in but not tightened, using the Allen-key provided with the kit.

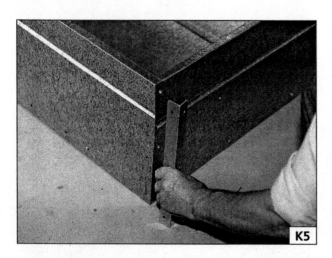

K5. Once the sides are in place, all four corner brackets can be fitted - more screw twirling required!

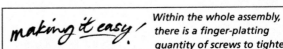

making it easy! Within the whole assembly, there is a finger-platting quantity of screws to tighten up! The job will be a lot quicker to carry out if you have an electric screwdriver or drill with a low-speed setting into which you can insert the relevant size of Allen-key drive.

ℹ INSIDE INFORMATION: The Caddy instructions don't tell you this, but if you are fitting the high-side extensions, you'll be wasting your time if you fit the corner brackets at this stage - they'll only have to come off again later! ℹ

K6. The trailer tub can now be turned over so that it becomes bottom-up.

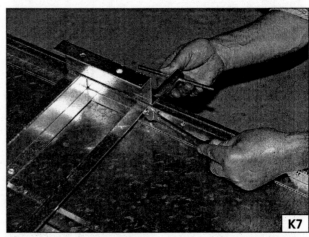

K7. The spanners supplied with the kit are used to bolt the axle brackets to the bottom of the trailer tub.

K8. The drawbar is now bolted to the trailer tub using the relevant bolt and locknut, but only at the front...

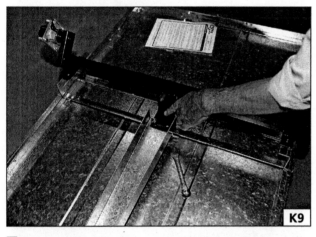

K9. ...because at the back, it shares its fixings holes with the suspension beam. All of the nuts and bolts are loosely fitted, holding the suspension beam to the trailer, and only tightened when all are in place.

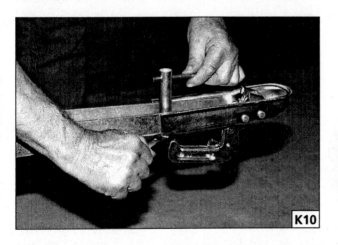

K10. The 50 mm tow hitch is simply bolted to the front of the drawbar.

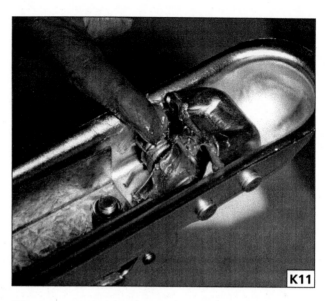

K11. While the trailer was upside down, we took this opportunity to liberally grease the catch and spring mechanism inside the hitch.

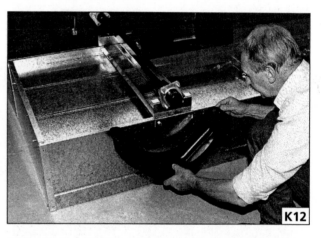

K12. When we came to offer up the mudguards, we found the only glitch in the whole proceedings. The holes in the soft plastic mudguards were about 10 mm out.

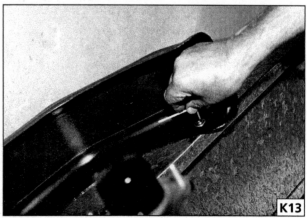

K13. It was a simple matter to drill a fresh hole in each mudguard but note the large washers that Caddy supply to spread the load of the fixing screw over the soft plastic. They also recommend that you don't overtighten.

K14. The wheels must be fitted with the air valve on the outside - for obvious reasons! - and it is also MOST IMPORTANT that the wheel nuts are fitted with the domed side going on to the wheel first.

making it easy! Looking ahead, you will undoubtedly have to remove the wheels again at some time in the future. To reduce the risk of the nuts rusting on solid, smear a little copper-grease on to each thread before you fit the nut.

K15. The trailer wiring is already connected up for you, so work out where the trailer board will go on the back of the trailer and leave yourself with enough slack at the front end so that the wiring won't become taught as the car goes around a corner but neither will it drag on the ground.

K16. We carefully wrapped the surplus cable around the suspension beam bracket, securing it with the plastic tie provided in the kit.

K17. To prevent the cable dragging on the ground where it passed from axle beam to the front of the trailer, a simple DIY bracket was added to the front mounting bolt on the drawbar and the cable was connected to it with the other plastic tie provided in the kit.

K18

K20

☐ K20. The little trailer is extremely easy to manoeuvre and has a worthwhile capacity of 200 kg. This is the smallest of the several kit sizes available from Caddy and there are also many different options available, including jockey wheels, covers and much more besides.

☐ K18. The trailer was now turned right over and the lighting board screwed to the mounting points provided. We added silicone sealer to the backs of the light units to help prevent moisture from getting in. At the bottom of the lighting board, Caddy provide a rubber grommet which must be clipped into place as the board is screwed on to the back of the trailer.

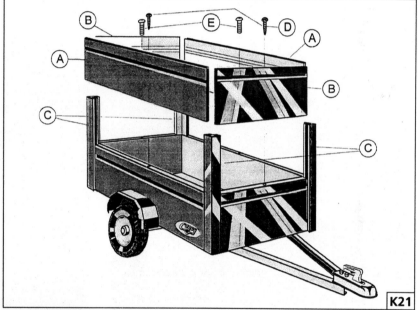

K21

☐ K19. Things will be slightly different if you build your own trailer or purchase another make with a drop-down tailboard. This type of catch is easily and simply screwed into place.

☐ K21. As was said earlier, we opted for the high-side kit. (Illustration, courtesy Caddy Trailers Ltd)

K19

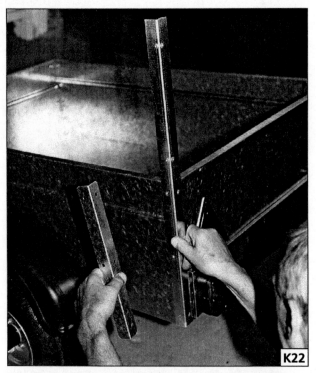

K22. Having finished the job off, it was mildly frustrating - though no more than that - to have to take off each of the corner brackets and fit the new ones supplied with the high-side kit.

K23. The beauty of the kit is that the high-sides simply slot into place and can be removed, leaving the corner posts in place if you wish to carry, say, lengths of timber which are longer than the length of the trailer.

K24. When the job is complete it's absolutely essential that you go over the whole trailer checking the tightness of every fixing. Of particular importance, of course, are those holding the suspension and the wheels in place. After the first 100 miles, some of them may well have shaken loose and it is essential that you then check them once more. Also, before you use the trailer on the road, check the tyre pressures in accordance with the manufacturer's recommendations.

K25. The finished trailer, complete with homemade extensions to the elasticated cover hold-downs.

FITTING A TAILGATE

Getting the tailgate to open and close properly - and getting the catches positioned and fixed just right - could be a nerve-wracking job if you're not an experienced cabinet maker. Follow these simple steps to make sure that the tailgate will work properly:

Fit the hinges first. Measure carefully to make sure that the tailgate is positioned with an equal gap on either side, and that both (or all) hinges are squarely in line with one another before final fixing - otherwise the tailgate will be stiff and difficult to open. Once you are happy with the operation of the tailgate on its hinges, mark up the positions for the catches which you plan to use.

CHAPTER 4
RULES & REGULATIONS

The law relating to trailers and their use is not the minefield that some make it out to be. Admittedly, it has become a little more complex than it used to be, but don't despair - things are nowhere near as bad as they may seem!

IMPORTANT NOTE: The following information is intended as a guide to the law and is based on information available at the time of going to press. In order to establish the current requirements of the law relating to any aspect of a trailer's construction or its use, you can purchase a copy of the relevant legislation from any HMSO stockist. (If they don't have it, they'll be able to order it for you.)

PART I: THE TRAILER & THE TOW VEHICLE

Weight Limits

The information here applies in the main to trailers up to 3,500 kg (3.5 tonnes) MAM. It is important to note that there are certain weight limits applying to some categories of driving licence other than to the vehicles themselves - see *PART III: THE DRIVER* later in this chapter.

UNBRAKED TRAILERS

A tow-vehicle up to 3.5 tonnes can tow a trailer with a MAM of 750 kg, provided that the kerb weight of the tow-vehicle is at least twice the maximum gross weight of the trailer. However, note that the tow-vehicle manufacturers maximum recommended figure must never be exceeded - and this is usually less than 750 kg! According to the regulations, trailers in this category should be permanently marked on the near side with the trailer's MAM.

BRAKED TRAILERS

For everyone who passed their driving test before 1 January 1997, there is one simple rule to follow with regard to towing a braked trailer: it must not exceed the maximum weight recommended by the tow-vehicle's manufacturer.

There are all sorts of rules and regulations which relate to the MAM of braked trailers, but in practice, all you have to do is ensure that you follow the manufacturers figures.

INSIDE INFORMATION: Manufacturers can and do amend their maximum recommended towing weights retrospectively. You are strongly advised to call into your local main dealer (especially if the tow-vehicle you drive is still current) and find out the latest specification.

MOTORCYCLES

❏ 1. Motorcyclists are entitled to tow trailers too, and the following rules apply to you: (Illustration courtesy Watsonian-Squire.)

i) If your 'bike's engine capacity is less than 125cc, you will not be allowed to tow a trailer at all.

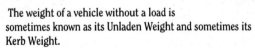

> **FACT FILE: WEIGHT JARGON**
>
> You will need to become familiar with a little bit of technical jargon relating to trailer and vehicle weights:
>
> The weight of a vehicle without a load is sometimes known as its Unladen Weight and sometimes its Kerb Weight.
>
> A trailer's weight without its load is its Unladen Weight.
>
> The weight of either a vehicle or a trailer carrying a load which is the maximum approved by the manufacturer is said to be its Maximum Gross Weight (or Gross Trailer Weight), or in the latest jargon, its Maximum Approved Mass. The abbreviations GVW or MAM are also commonly used.
>
> The term Gross Train Weight is sometimes used to mean the MAM of both the tow vehicle and the trailer combined.

This Chapter has been produced in association with two companies. One is Ifor Williams Trailers Ltd who, as the largest manufacturer of trailers in Britain are in regular consultation with the Society of Motor Manufacturers and Traders and the relevant government departments on trailer legislation. The other is Indespension who have for many years made key information readily available to trailer users.

ii) If you are riding a solo of more than 125cc, you are entitled to tow a trailer as long as its overall width is not greater than one metre, and its overall length - measured from the rear wheel spindle of the motorcycle to the back of the trailer - is not greater than 2.5 m. The gross weight of the laden trailer must not be greater than 150 kg (330 lb), or two-thirds of the bike's all-up weight, whichever figure is the least. Bear in mind that most middleweight machines weigh no more than about 450 lb, so do confirm your own bike's weight before using it to tow.

COMBINATIONS AND THREE-WHEELERS

If your bike is fitted with a sidecar, or if you drive a three-wheel car or van, the maximum trailer width increases to 1.5 metres and the weight of trailer that you are permitted to tow increases to 254 kg, or 560 lb.

MILITARY TRAILERS

☐ 2. It is illegal to use many military (including Sankey) trailers on the road in the UK because their over-run brakes do not have automatic (or indeed any) reversing lock-out mechanisms. Before buying an ex-militiary trailer, readers are strongly advised to check whether they comply with regulations for the country concerned.

Size Limits

LENGTH AND WIDTH

In establishing the maximum length of a trailer for legal purposes, the drawbar is not included. The maximum length your trailer is allowed to be is seven metres, unless:

i) The trailer has four wheels, and is towed by a commercial vehicle whose Gross Vehicle Weight is greater than 3500 kg. In this case, the maximum permitted length for the trailer itself is 12 metres (not counting the drawbar), and the maximum permitted length for the 'train' - the whole outfit - is 18.35 metres.

ii) Agricultural trailers can be up to 12 metres long.

☐ 3. The maximum permitted width of the trailer is 2.3 metres, unless:

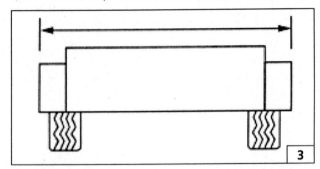

i) The trailer is towed by a vehicle with a maximum plated weight of more than 3500 kg. In this case, the maximum width can be 2.5 metres.

ii) Agricultural trailers can be up to 2.5 metres wide. (Illustration, courtesy Indespension)

MAXIMUM HEIGHT

There is no legal requirement for the maximum height of a trailer but the SMMT recommend that the overall height should not exceed 3.0 metres or 1.7 times the wheel track of the trailer. (The wheel track is the distance between the centre lines of the trailer's near side and off side wheels.)

Lights and Brakes

LIGHTS

☐ 4. The laws regarding lighting on trailers are similar to those for other vehicles. The chart opposite, reproduced with the kind permission of Indespension, specify the type of lights and other markings required on trailers.

All lighting units must carry an "E" marking to show they comply with the required performance standards.

1. If, in the case of the direction indicators, it is not possible to meet the maximum height requirements, this dimension can be increased to 2,300 mm.

2. If, in the case of the rear position (tail) lights and stop lights, it is not possible to meet the maximum height requirement, this dimension can be increased to 2,100 mm.

3. On trailers first manufactured after 1 October, 1985, the maximum height of the red triangular reflectors can be increased to 1,200 mm if necessary.

4. Trailers manufactured after 1 October, 1985 require number plates illuminated by an 'E' or 'e' marked light. If a clear window in the rear position light section is approved, this can be used instead of a separate number plate light but as with all number plate lights must be fitted to the manufacturer's instructions with regard to distance from the number plate.

5. At least one rear fog light is mandatory on trailers over 1.3 metres wide. Two lights are preferred but, if only one is fitted, it must be to the offside or on the centreline of the trailer.

6. No maximum distance from the outer edge of the trailer is stated for a fog light(s) but there must be a minimum distance of 100 mm from the stop light and the height from the ground to the lens must be more than 250mm

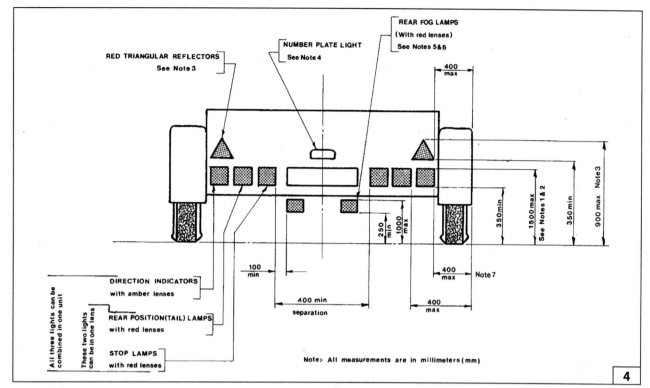

RED TRIANGULAR REFLECTORS
See Note 3

NUMBER PLATE LIGHT
See Note 4

REAR FOG LAMPS
(With red lenses)
See Notes 5 & 6

400 max

1500 max See Notes 1 & 2

900 max Note 3

350 min

350 min

1000 max

250 min

100 min

DIRECTION INDICATORS
with amber lenses

REAR POSITION (TAIL) LAMPS
with red lenses

STOP LAMPS
with red lenses

All three lights can be combined in one unit

These two lights can be in one lens

400 min
separation

400 max Note 7

400 max

Note: All measurements are in millimeters (mm)

4

7. The distance of the direction indicator from the side of the vehicle may not exceed the actual distance of the rear position light by more than 50 mm. (Illustration, courtesy The Society of Motor Manufacturers and Traders Limited)

BRAKES

All trailers fitted with brakes, no matter when they were built must have brakes which work efficiently, and must be fitted with a parking brake which is capable of holding the trailer at its maximum gross weight. The parking brake must operate on at least two road wheels on the same axle of the trailer and it must be operated by rod or cable action - ruling out the use of hydraulic brake systems. All trailers, including DIY built braked trailers, must be fitted with type-approved brakes - and therefore newly built DIY trailers cannot be fitted with reclaimed car brakes. Braked trailers built after 1 April 1989 have to be fitted with auto-reverse brakes.

BREAKAWAY CABLE

An emergency breakaway cable must be fitted to the parking brake linkage so that if the trailer becomes detached from the towing vehicle, the cable applies the parking brake automatically.

UNBRAKED TRAILERS

It is recommended (and it may by the time you read this, be a legal requirement) that a safety chain or other restraining device is used on an unbraked trailer. This must be short enough to prevent the front end of the trailer from striking the road surface should the trailer become detached, but it is obviously important that the trailer is also allowed full articulation which is not restricted by the safety chain.

THE TOW BRACKET

Legislation has been introduced to ensure that all tow brackets for new vehicles are Type Approved. It certainly pays NOT to buy the cheapest around, but to go for a reputable brand. That way, you'll be certain to buy a properly tested and built tow bracket - some of the cheap 'n nasty ones can be dangerous!

Tax, Insurance and the MoT

ROAD TAX

As long as: i) You are driving a private or light goods vehicle (weighing less than 3500 kg), or... ii) You are driving a heavy goods vehicle, towing a trailer whose weight is not greater than 4000 kg... You will not have to pay any extra vehicle excise duty before you can tow.

INSURANCE

Most normal car or van policies will provide for third-party cover while towing your trailer. However, once it is un-hitched, the vehicle policy will normally no longer cover it, and we would strongly advise that you arrange special insurance cover for your trailer and its load.

INSIDE INFORMATION: If you hire a trailer or caravan, the hire company will probably expect you to provide your own insurance. Check this point with them before hiring the trailer!

Motorcycle insurance policies are unlikely to cover when towing or for your trailer. Check the situation with your insurers.

THE MoT TEST

Obviously, the vehicle which is used to tow must have a valid MoT certificate if it is over three years old. As the law currently stands however, there is no requirement for a trailer to be tested by a Ministry of Transport examiner, as long as its unladen weight is less than 1,020 kgs. At the time of writing, the trailer industry are lobbying the government to introduce a safety test for trailers similar to the car MoT - *Chapter 8, Perform Your Own 'MoT'* looks at the checks which we think will probably be made in the new test when it comes in.

IMPORTANT NOTE: While there is currently no requirement for trailers to undergo an MoT test, using your vehicle to tow a trailer which is subsequently judged to be unroadworthy will invalidate your vehicle's insurance and you will be liable to prosecution.

PART II: ON THE ROAD

UK Laws

There are specific rules and regulations that you must bear in mind when towing in the UK.

SPEED LIMITS

When towing a trailer whose gross combined weight does not exceed 7.5 tonnes you are restricted to a maximum speed of 60 mph on motorways and unrestricted dual carriageways, and 50 mph on other roads where no other limit is in force.

MOTORWAYS

Trailers should not be towed in the outside lane of a three or four lane motorway, unless you're instructed to do so as the result of roadworks or an accident on the inside lanes.

NUMBER PLATE

A trailer must carry a number plate bearing the number of the towing vehicle and be illuminated at night. It must be of the same reflective type as a car's rear number plate. Hand-written number plates are not allowed.

REAR VIEW MIRRORS

You must be able to see the road behind the trailer through two rear-view mirrors. If the rear view through the tow vehicle's rear window is inadequate, the law states that you must fit an additional mirror to the nearside of the towing vehicle. However, it may also be necessary that extension mirror is also fitted when the trailer or its load obscure the view through the 'outside' mirror/s. Any extension mirror must not project more that 200 mm outside the width of the trailer when being towed or the width of the towing vehicle when driven solo.

PASSENGERS

Passengers may not travel in a trailer under any circumstances, unless they are authorised test personnel working on behalf of a dealer or manufacturer.

Legal Loads

Restrictions also apply to the loads which you are allowed to carry, and the majority of these laws apply to live loads. You should, however, remember at all times that over-loading and insecure loads are illegal!

• Carrying passengers in any trailer or caravan while travelling on the road is strictly forbidden.

• There are strict rules regarding the carrying of petroleum spirit on the road but in general, we recommend that you don't carry it in a trailer.

OVERHANGING LOADS

❏ 5. Overhanging loads are subject to regulations too. If you should load your trailer with items which project to the extent detailed below, then you should follow the given guidelines for marking to ensure that you are carrying the goods legally:

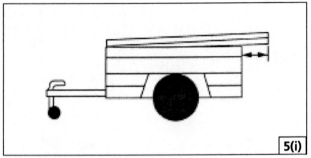

5(i)

i) If the load overhangs the back of the trailer by one to two metres, ensure that the end of the load is clearly visible to following traffic by tying a brightly-coloured rag to it, or using a marker board. Hard or sharp projecting items MUST be padded. (Illustration, courtesy Indespension.)

ii) If the load overhangs the back of the trailer by 2 to 3.05 metres, you will have to fit a proper reflective end marker board, which must be illuminated if you are towing at night.

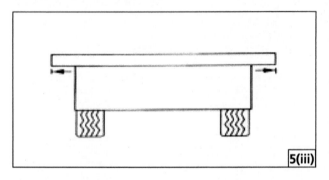

5(iii)

iii) The load MUST NOT overhang the sides of the trailer by more than 305 mm (about a foot) on either side. (Illustration, courtesy Indespension.)

iv) If you absolutely have to carry anything which does not fall within the above limits, then consult the police about whether you can carry it - and whether or not you will need an escort.

v) If the towing vehicle has a Gross Weight exceeding 7500 kg, a particularly long trailer should be marked with a 'Long Vehicle' sign. If the towing vehicle is smaller than this, the trailer does not need to be marked - however long it might actually be!

TRANSPORTING ANIMALS

❏ 6. Carrying livestock is permitted, but there are quite complex regulations covering the construction and use of trailers for the purpose some of which are as follows. If you arre intending to build a trailer for carrying livestock you should study the Transit of Animals Regulations: a) The trailer must be cleaned and disinfected after every journey. b) No animal should be transported if it is not in good health. c) You must use a properly constructed ramp when loading the animals on board. d) If you are carrying several sheep or horses, the trailer must have partitions fitted to form pens. These must be no more than 3.1 metres long for sheep, and no more than 3.7 metres long for horses. e) When carrying a horse, it must be tied or tethered with a rope which is strong enough not to break, and long enough to allow the horse to lie down.

f) If you are carrying more than one horse in a box, partitions must be fitted to keep the animals apart.

g) You must provide animals in transit with food and water at least every eight hours.

TOWING ABROAD

If you are travelling abroad, whether in the EC or beyond, there are many different speed limits in force on the different grades of road in each individual country. You should check with your
ferry operator, or with the Embassy or High Commission of the country you plan to visit, to find out about licensing and size requirements for towing in that country, and the speed limits you will have to observe.

As far as the legal status of your trailer and vehicle combination is concerned, if the outfit is legal for use in the UK, it should be accepted for temporary business or pleasure use on the roads of any other EC country. You should take note of the following requirements for towing abroad: i) Ensure that you have a full driving licence, and take it with you. ii) Carry your vehicle's registration document, or a letter from the vehicle's owner authorising you to have it. iii) Ensure that you have arranged insurance cover which is valid in the country or countries you'll be visiting and carry evidence of it. iv) Arrange continental breakdown assistance cover with the AA or RAC before leaving Britain. v) Make sure you have a country identification plate or sticker fixed to the rear of the trailer. vi) The only countries which

require you to have a 'green card' insurance certificate are Andorra, Greece and the countries of the former Yugoslavia. However, you are 'strongly recommended' to carry one if you plan to visit either Italy, Portugal or Spain. In fact, the AA recommend that you arrange one for all foreign travel, wherever you may be going. vii) If the trailer is large enough to warrant it, fix towing mirrors to both sides of the tow-vehicle. viii) Service the trailer and tow vehicle before leaving the UK, and ensure that both are perfectly roadworthy. It's a good idea to pack the following emergency trailer equipment: • Spare wheel • Jack and wheelbrace • Two sets of wheel bearings • A red warning triangle • Spare bulbs for both indicator and stop/tail lights • Spare trailer light lenses.

TACHOGRAPHS

There has been a great deal of confusion regarding the requirements for tachographs when towing.

The EEC drivers' hours and Tachograph Regulations apply to vehicles with a permissible maximum weight of more than 3.5 tonnes. If the weight exceeds 3.5 tonnes, a tachograph should be used and the driver must comply with EEC rules.

There are many exceptions, however, including:

The weight of trailers which include fixed equipment, such as compressors, need not be taken into account. For example, a 3.5 tonnes GVW truck towing a 1.0 tonne GVW portable compressor does not require a tachograph.

The Regulations do not apply to private driving, that is, driving which is not done for a living or as part of a trade or business.

Cars and dual purpose vehicles with rear seats do not need tachographs unless they have more than 17 seats or more than nine seats on an international journey, and are being used commercially and are intended for that purpose.

PART III: THE DRIVER

On 1 January 1997, new driving licence regulations came into force. These have caused some unnecessary concern and Ifor Williams Trailers have gone to some trouble to create the following FACT FILE: to help clarify matters. Before getting into the detail, however, it is important to bear in mind the following points:

1) Drivers who passed their test before 1 January 1997 are not affected in any way and can carry on as before. (The one exception is HGV drivers who obtained their licence after 1 April 1991. From 1 January 1997, they will be restricted to towing trailers with a MAM of 750 kg until they pass an additional trailer test.)

2) Holders of the new licence can still tow unbraked trailers with a MAM of up to 750 kg (subject to the regulations described earlier in this chapter).

3) Holders of the new licence can also tow braked trailers provided that a) the maximum gross weight of the trailer is less than the UNLADEN weight of the car, and b) the total train weight is less than 3.5 tonnes.

But for a more detailed explanation, it's over to Peter Leslie of Ifor Williams who has conscientiously put together the following:

FACT FILE: DRIVER LICENSING FROM 1 JANUARY 1997

Existing holders of car driving licences and those who pass their test before 31 December 1996 will retain their existing entitlement to tow trailers. They will have entitlement to categories B + E, C1, D1, C1 + E and D1 + E. This includes entitlement to tow vehicle and trailer combinations up to 7.5 tonnes or, where the trailer is limited to 750 kg, up to a combined weight of 8.25 tonnes, subject to any limits set by the vehicle manufacturer.

Licences for C category (goods vehicles over 3.5 tonnes) and D category (passenger carrying vehicles with more than eight seats) issued following a C or D test taken after 1 April 1991 have further restric-

tions on towing. During the period from the date of issue until and 31 December 1992 a concession existed allowing single axle (and close coupled twin axle) trailers of any weight to be towed. From 1 January 1993 a limit of 5 tonnes was introduced, and from 1 January 1997 this was further reduced to 750 kg. In order to be freed from these restrictions, drivers will have to pass an additional test for C & E and D & E respectively. Drivers passing the car driving test from 1 January 1997 will gain the entitlement for category B only.

(continued on page 34)

FACT FILE: DRIVER LICENSING FROM 1 JANUARY 1997

(continued from page 34)

Category B - Vehicles up to 3.5 tonnes and with up to 8 passenger seats

The new car driving licence allows the holder to drive a 3.5 tonnes MAM vehicle. Trailers can be towed under this licence but with the following restrictions: Vehicles and trailers with a combined MAM up to 4.25 tonnes may be driven provided that the towing vehicle does not exceed 3.5 tonnes and the trailer does not exceed 750 kg.

Larger trailers may be towed provided the maximum gross weight of the trailer is less than the unladen weight of the car and total MAM of the combination is less than 3.5 tonnes. Note that the maximum gross weight of the trailer for the purposes of this regulation is the figure stated on the manufacturer's plate rather than the weight actually being carried. It may, therefore, be necessary to down-rate trailers to enable category B licence holders to tow them.

Category B + E - Vehicles up to 3.5 tonnes MAM with a trailer over 750 kg MAM

Holders of category B licences who wish to tow trailers and combinations which do not fall into category B will have to pass an additional test to upgrade to category B + E.

The upper limit for the trailer is not defined. Therefore, the existing Construction and Use regulations apply. For unbraked trailers up to 750 kg MAM, this limits the gross weight of the trailer to half the unladen weight of the towing vehicle. No specific limit is set for braked trailers but this will be either by the towing limit/train weight given on the manufacturer's plate or the manufacturer's recommendations.

Category C1 - Medium sized goods vehicles 3.5 - 7.5 tonnes

Maximum trailer weight 750 kg (max. combined weight 8.25 tonnes): Category B licence holders will have to meet higher medical standards and pass an additional test in order to gain this entitlement.

Category C1 + E - Medium sized goods vehicles 3.5 - 7.5 tonnes plus trailer over 750 kg

Maximum combined weight 12 tonnes provided the MAM of the trailer does not exceed the unladen weight of the towing vehicle. Category B drivers will have to pass two further tests: C1 followed by C1 + E. It will not be possible to go directly from B to C1 + E. Category B drivers will be upgraded to B + E entitlement on passing the C1 + E test.

Note that drivers under 21 years of age will be restricted to vehicles or combinations up to 7.5 tonnes. 18 year old drivers will be allowed to take the C1 + E test to allow towing of trailers over 750 kg with the tonnes entitlement becoming effective automatically when the driver reaches 21 years.

Category C - Large goods vehicles over 7.5 tonnes

Maximum trailer weight 750 kg MAM. For driving licence purposes, no maximum weight is set for the towing vehicle. Therefore, existing regulations will apply. Category B drivers will have to pass a further test for category C. (It will not be necessary to gain sub-category C1 entitlement first.)

Category C & E - Large goods vehicles over 7.5 tonnes with trailer over 750 kg

For driving licence purposes, no maximum weights are set. Therefore, existing limits apply. Category B drivers will have to pass two further tests: C followed by C + E. It will no longer be possible to take a test for C + E immediately after taking a car test. (It will not be necessary to gain C1 or C1 an E first). Category B drivers will be upgraded to B + E and C1 and C1 + E entitlement will be included on passing the C + E test. Categories D, D + E, D1 and D1 + E cover passenger carrying vehicles.

PART IV: THE TRAILER TEST

If you first passed your driving test after 1 January 1997, you will have to take a trailer test in order to drive certain categories of heavier trailer. See *Part III: The Driver* for further information on how those categories are determined.

Practising

1) You must display L-plates front and rear (or D-plates may be used in Wales). 2) Have with you someone who has either passed their driving test before 1 January 1997 or who has passed the new Trailer Test and has held their licence for three years. 3) You will need to practice the skills described under *The Test,* below.

Preparation

1) You will have to have passed the 'ordinary' Category B driving test and you will have to take it with you to the test. 2) You will have to display your L-plates. 3) Both the car and the trailer will have to comply with all the normal legal requirements - see elsewhere in this Chapter.

4) The trailer will have to be fitted with a plate showing its maximum authorised Maximum Authorised Mass (MAM) - which is the same as its Maximum Gross Weight. 5) The trailer will have to have an MAM of at least one tonne.

ℹ INSIDE INFORMATION: Your trailer will have to be fitted with a plate showing its MAM. If yours is not fitted with such a plate, the vehicle inspectorate will do it for you for an agreed fee. Ask at your local Heavy Goods Vehicle testing centre which will be listed in your 'phone book. ℹ

The Test

THE THEORY TEST

There will be a theory test relating to the principles of the law relating to Trailers - see the remainder of this Chapter.

The Reversing Exercise

☐ 1. You will have to reverse the tow-vehicle and trailer from the starting point, past cone B and into the bay shown in the bottom left-hand of the illustration.

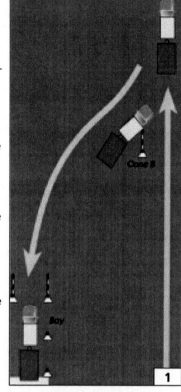

So that you can practise in your own time, it is important to note the following dimensions: 1) The bay is 1.5 times the width of the widest part of the unit apart and will be one metre in from the boundary line of the test area. 2) The distance between the bay and cone B will be twice the length of the tow-vehicle and trailer. 3) The overall length of the test area will be five times the length of the tow-vehicle and trailer. 4) The width of the bay will be 1.5 times the widest part of the unit. 5) The length of the bay will be approximately the overall length of the tow-vehicle and trailer but it can be varied at the discretion of the examiner within the range of plus one metre or minus two metres. (For some reason, the Driving Standards Agency state that the precise length of the bay won't be disclosed before the start of the exercise.

You will have to demonstrate that you can:

1) Reverse in a reasonable time and under control with good observation and reasonable accuracy. 2) Show that you have accurate judgement of the size of your vehicle and trailer. 3) Show that you can keep within all of the prescribed boundaries. 4) Demonstrate that you know how to turn the steering wheel correctly when starting to reverse.

IMPORTANT NOTE: If you have an older-type trailer with non-auto-reverse brakes, there will be a manual catch to prevent the brakes locking when you reverse. The examiner will no doubt be looking for evidence that you know how to apply this catch and that you remember to release it after the reversing part of the test has been carried out unless it is of the later auto-release type.

⚡ INSIDE INFORMATION: If you own a tall trailer which you find difficult to reverse because of the lack of rearward visibility, there is nothing to stop you hiring a suitable trailer, such as a car trailer, for the duration of the test. You will then be able to see the obstacles by looking over your shoulder as well as through your mirrors. ⚡

The Braking Exercise

This will take place on a special area and not on the public road and the examiner will be with you.

There will be two marker cones approximately 61 metres (200 feet) ahead. You will have to drive up to a speed of about 20 mph then, as the front of the vehicle passes between the two markers, apply the brakes.

You will have to demonstrate that you can: 1) Stop as quickly as possible and under full control. 2) Brake safely, in a straight line and without skidding. 3) Come to a halt without stalling the engine.

You won't be allowed to drive too slowly or to brake before the marker points.

The Drive

This test will take approximately one hour and the standard will be to at least that of the 'ordinary' category B driving test. You will have to drive on ordinary two-way roads, dual carriageways and, where possible, a one-way system. You will also be expected to demonstrate that you can move off smoothly and safely going both uphill and downhill and you will have to show that you can move off normally from the side of the road and at an angle.

The examiner will be looking for evidence that you can safely: 1) Meet other vehicles. 2) Overtake. 3) Cross the path of other vehicles. 4) Keep a safe distance when following other vehicles. 5) Negotiate various types of round-about and corners with the trailer in the appropriate position. 6) Display courtesy and consideration to other road users, especially pedestrians, riders on horseback, cyclists and motor cyclists. 7) In essence, the remainder of the test will be based on the same criteria as those for the Category B test but bearing in mind the extra length, width, weight and manoeverbility of the trailer. 8) The examiner will especially be looking for good all-round observation and use of mirrors, plus the ability to negotiate hazards and junctions safely.

YOU WON'T HAVE TO ...

...carry out any of the following exercises: 1) An emergency stop. 2) Reverse around a corner. 3) Reverse park. 4) Turn around in the road.

Isn't that all a relief!

Coupling and Uncoupling

You will be asked normally to uncouple and recouple your vehicle and trailer at the test centre at the end of the test. You will have to: 1) Stop where there is safe and level ground. 2) Uncouple the tow-vehicle and trailer and pull forward approximately one vehicle length. 3) Reverse the vehicle up to the trailer and recouple.

The examiner will be looking for evidence that you: 1) Correctly apply the brakes on both the vehicle and the trailer. 2) Lower the jockey wheel correctly. 3) Remove any stabiliser which is fitted and the safety cable/chain. 4) Release the coupling and move the trailer clear of the towing hitch.

When you recouple you will have to demonstrate that you can: 1) Position the tow-vehicle so that the trailer can safely and easily be coupled to it, and apply the parking brake on the tow-vehicle. 2) Attach the trailer to the tow-vehicle and check that the coupling is secure, including the safety chain and stabiliser (if fitted). 3) Ensure that the jockey wheel, corner steadies or any other supporting devices are raised and secured correctly. 4) Release the trailer brake and (DON'T FORGET TO DO THIS) check the operation of the lights and indicators. 5) When you uncouple and recouple the trailer, the examiner will be looking for evidence that you can do so confidently, in good time and in the correct order of operations.

*Our thanks our due to HMSO and the Driving Standards Agency for their assistance with this section. We recommend that you purchase **The Driving Test**, an HMSO publication available from most bookshops for further information on all types of driving test. Crown copyright is reproduced with the permission of the Controller of HMSO.*

CHAPTER 5 - USING A TRAILER

Towing is not as difficult as you may think. All it needs is some time, patience, a bit of thought and some practice. The first thing that you will notice is that the outfit needs more time for accelerating and braking. As a result, you should take care to leave far more time for overtaking and stay a greater distance from

the vehicle in front than you would with a solo vehicle. It is also necessary to take a wider arc on corners and at roundabouts to stop the nearside wheel of larger trailers catching the kerb, although the extra width is not usually as big a problem as beginners first imagine and you soon get used to it.

PART I: ON THE ROAD

Snaking

'Snaking' refers to the excessive side to side swaying motion caused by a badly loaded outfit, excessive side winds or the change in air pressure caused by an overtaking high sided vehicle. If this 'snaking' motion is allowed to continue it can result in the outfit getting out of control. Curing a snaking outfit is a matter of keeping a cool head and knowing what to do. It's also a matter of keeping out of snaking situations, by not driving too fast for the outfit and keeping your eye on large vehicles that are approaching or are about to overtake you. If snaking recurs during the course of your journey, slow down! (But also stop somewhere safe to see if you have a puncture or some other physical reason for the snaking to be taking place.)

INSIDE INFORMATION: There's an old chestnut that has been around since the beginning of trailer time and if followed, it can be EXTREMELY DANGEROUS. You may well hear it said that the best way to get out of a 'snake' is to accelerate out of it. In fact, the faster you go, the more difficult it will be to regain control. In general, the best thing to do is sit it out, make the minimum amount of steering wheel movement (consistent with following the road and avoiding other traffic!) and take your foot off the accelerator pedal, or decelerate slowly if going up hill. HOWEVER, some combinations are not able to be driven at the legal maximum - establish what the safe limit for *your* trailer is.

making it easy! If snaking with your large or high-sided trailer becomes a persistent problem, and you have checked that the load, wheel bearings and so on are all as they should be, then you might consider fitting a stabiliser. See **Chapter 7, Repairing and Upgrading Your Trailer**, for more information.

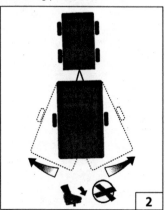

☐ 1. If your outfit starts to snake, simply take your foot off the towcar's accelerator allowing the car to gently slow down, which will dampen out the snake.

If you are going down hill, it might be necessary to VERY GENTLY apply the car's brakes.

☐ 2. Whatever you do, don't brake suddenly or try to accelerate out of the snake. These actions will NEVER succeed in curing a snake.

Hill Starts

In general, you will have to resign yourself to slipping the clutch rather more than you would normally do when starting away on a hill. Your car's first gear is, technically speaking, too high for the extra load imposed on it for a hill start with a trailer, so you must compensate with extra clutch slipping until the combination is under way. But don't overdo it by slipping the clutch for prolonged periods, otherwise you'll end up with clouds of smoke and a burned-out clutch. NEVER hold the car and trailer on the clutch, to stop it slipping back; always use the parking brake.

With an automatic car, you won't have this problem: just give it a little extra gas and away you go!

☐ INSIDE INFORMATION: If you tow heavy loads regularly with a car fitted with an auto-gearbox, consult your vehicle main dealer about having an oil cooler fitted. ☐

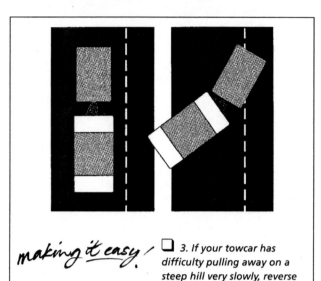

making it easy! ☐ 3. If your towcar has difficulty pulling away on a steep hill very slowly, reverse the trailer back at an angle so that the outfit is facing slightly across the angle of the hill. This will allow the outfit to pull away across the hill, making it less steep than straight up the hill.

Cornering

When approaching a corner with your outfit, you must remember two things:

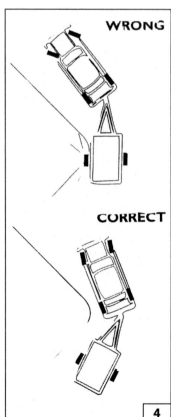

☐ 4. You will need to compensate for the greater length of your vehicle by widening the turning circle slightly to avoid hitting the kerb.

☐ 5. You must remember that there is a danger that the rear end of a large trailer might swing out and hit another vehicle. (Illustrations, courtesy Indespension)

Using the handbrake

☐ 6. For using the handbrake see *Chapter 5, Part IV, picture 2.*

Reversing the Car and Trailer

For many owners, the idea of reversing the unit brings them out in a cold sweat! However, while it is certainly not an impossibly difficult skill, it does require a bit more thought and practice, and should always be conducted at walking pace. You should also have an assistant keep an eye open behind the trailer, to ensure that small children, animals and obstructions aren't going to be at risk.

Remember that reversing with a trailer cannot usually be done in the smooth sweep that you can achieve with car alone. It takes place as a series of corrections, as the trailer tends to go too far in one direction or another. Start by going *very* slowly, making *very small* corrections as you go along and remember that over-corrections and vigorous movements will be your downfall as the trailer locks into a rapidly tightening curve. Smaller trailers 'jack-knife' faster than longer ones!

When reversing in a straight line you should keep your eyes on the towing vehicle's wing mirrors. If the side of the trailer begins to appear in the left hand mirror, turn the steering wheel SLIGHTLY to the left until the trailer straightens up again.

Similarly, if the side of the trailer begins to appear in the right hand mirror, turn the steering wheel SLIGHTLY to the right until the trailer straightens up.

❑ 9. As the trailer progresses around the corner, steer slightly back to the right so as not to turn the trailer too much.

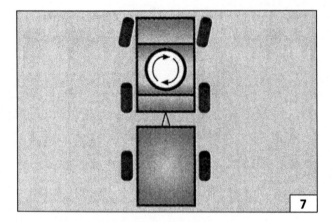

❑ 7. For reversing around a left-hand corner, start by turning the towcar's steering wheel to the right, until the trailer starts to turn to the left.

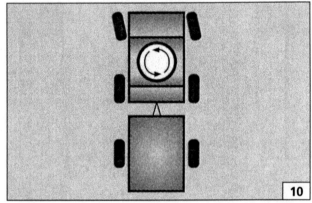

❑ 10. For reversing around a right-hand corner, start by turning the steering wheel to the left, until the trailer starts to turn to the right.

❑ 8. Then change the steering direction to the left to maintain the trailer's smooth progression round the corner.

❑ 11. Then change the steering direction to the right to maintain the trailer's smooth progression around the corner.

12. Finally, steer slightly back to the left so as not to turn the trailer too much.

If you find that the trailer has turned too much, then simply stop, drive forward just a couple of feet and start again. Don't try to over-compensate by making a large steering wheel correction in the opposite direction, because it will probably only make matters worse! Remember, it's not a race and don't be embarrassed if you don't get it right first time. Just go back to where you started and have another go. And in the end, if you become too flustered to know which is left and which right (and it has happened to us all some time or other!), don't be afraid to unhitch the trailer and move it by hand, if the ground is level enough for you to do so.

INSIDE INFORMATION: There is no doubt that reversing a trailer is a skill quite separate from any other driving skill. If you are wise, you will try it out somewhere safe and with room to make mistakes, such as in a supermarket car park, after the supermarket has closed, or some other suitable space.

Towing Courses

Both of the major caravanning organisations in Britain, The Caravan Club and The Camping and Caravanning Club, run their own towing courses although for members only. These offer those new to the pastime the chance to learn the basic skills of towing (specifically a caravan) in a safe environment before going out on to the open road. Similarly the Institute of Advanced Motorists have their own 'Caravan and Towing Test' that is available only to IAM members.

For further information on these courses, telephone The Caravan Club on 01342 326944, The Camping and Caravanning Club on 01203 694995 or the Institute of Advanced Motorists on 0181 994 4403.

PART II: LOADING YOUR TRAILER

It's only too tempting to just pile things into the trailer and try to remember to drive smoothly as you go along. However, an insecure load will make the trailer unstable and hard to drive, as well as damaging the load as it gets thrown from side to side. Also remember that the fine for losing a load can be considerable! Follow these simple rules for loading your trailer!

Loading Up

In fact, there are only really two things to consider. What goes where in your trailer and towcar, and noseweight. Remember that, if you want to ensure a stable and enjoyable 'tow', getting the load properly packed is paramount, once the basics such as tyre pressures are in place. You are trying, above all, to avoid the 'pendulum effect' of a lot of weight swinging from side to side as your car picks up speed, known as 'snaking'.

SAFETY FIRST!

i) Familiarise yourself with the recommended loading for your trailer and tow vehicle before loading up. If you do experience snaking caused by poor loading, don't try to overcome it in future by fitting an anti-snake device. All that will happen is that the snaking will take place at an even more dangerous higher speed than before. Instead, work out how to load-up properly!

1. You should position as much weight as possible over the axle of your trailer, with a fairly equal loading on each side of the trailer. If there isn't enough space, place the heavier items in the centre and put lighter items towards the ends of the trailer, but do remember that under heavy braking, items may slide forwards. Locate them as securely as possible. You should never put any heavy weights either towards the rear or high up in a boat trailer or horse trailer because either will make the trailer unstable. (Illustration, courtesy The Caravan Club.)

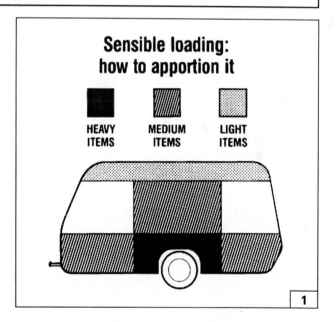

Sensible loading: how to apportion it

HEAVY ITEMS   MEDIUM ITEMS   LIGHT ITEMS

The next thing to consider is the trailer's noseweight. This refers to the maximum weight limit that should be exerted vertically downwards on a towing vehicles towball. This is dictated by the noseweight limit on the towcar's towing bracket and can vary from vehicle to vehicle. To find out the noseweight limit of a towing vehicle you can check the owners' manual, refer to the maker's plate on the bracket or consult your local car dealer. It is often between 25 kg and 50 kg.

When loading your trailer, you should aim to get the noseweight as close to the limit as possible without exceeding it. To measure a trailer's noseweight you can either buy specialist noseweight gauges from your local trailer dealership, or use a DIY version, such as bathroom scales. See next page.

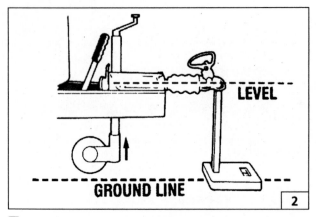

2

☐ 2. A DIY noseweight gauge means using a short length of broom handle and some bathroom scales. Put the bathroom scales beneath the tow hitch and put one end of the broom handle up into the hitch with the other end on the scales. DON'T place the scales beneath the jockey wheel, otherwise a false reading will be given. The trailer must be level and on level ground.

Alternatively, a specialist noseweight gauge can be placed under the trailer's hitch, taking the weight in the same way as the DIY version.

3

☐ 3. Once your trailer is loaded and hitched up to your car, take a couple of minutes to stand back and admire your work. Ideally the outfit should be level, with, if anything, a very SLIGHT dip at the front of the trailer. If the trailer is either nose-up...

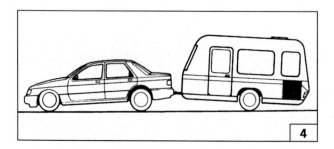

4

☐ 4. ...or the back of the towcar is sagging badly, then you've got the loading wrong or your car's towball is too high. Recheck the noseweight and if that is correct, it might be, that your car's rear suspension is just being asked to do too much, in which case the amount loaded into the car and even the nose weight could be reduced a touch from the recommended figure, in the short-term, while long-term, you may wish to consider having your car dealer fit uprated rear suspension (if available) or one of the proprietary brands of suspension assisters. (Illustration, courtesy The Caravan Club.)

Securing the load

TIE DOWNS

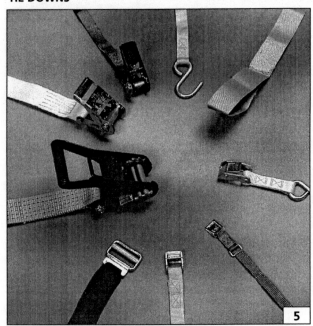

5

☐ 5. Whatever sort of load you plan to carry, a handful of good quality tie-downs is an essential purchase. They might seem expensive, but they will last you a lifetime if cared for properly - and the beauty of using tie-downs as opposed to ropes is that they are far less likely to come loose than ropes and they can easily be tightened up in seconds! They come with a variety of different hooks or latches, as shown, and you should select the most appropriate fixing for the hooks, buttons or tracking slots on your trailer. The most commonly used type is the simple steel hook. (Illustration, courtesy Indespension)

Some of the cheaper varieties have a sliding catch, through which the strap is threaded, and once you have the hooks in place and the strap laid in position across the load, you simply pull the strap tight through the catch, and it will hold a given weight of load perfectly firm. To undo these, you pull on a lip on the edge of the catch to tilt it up, and the strap is automatically released. The only problem with these occurs when you use a load which is too heavy for the strap. The catch relies on friction to operate, and will only withstand a certain pull before it starts to let go.

6. A much more upmarket alternative is the ratchet strap. If you are planning to carry large, heavy objects, always go for these, since not only do they hold the strap more firmly than the other type, they can also be pulled far tighter in the first place. The four diagrams show how a ratchet strap should be used. Again, lay the strap over or around the load in its intended final position, locate the hooks or latches on their anchor points, and then follow the simple steps shown here for tightening the strap with the ratchet. Always pull the strap as tightly as you possibly can, whether using a ratchet or simple friction catch. As the load moves, it will work out any slackness you may have left in the strap, and could come adrift if the strap is not absolutely taut. (Illustration, courtesy Indespension)

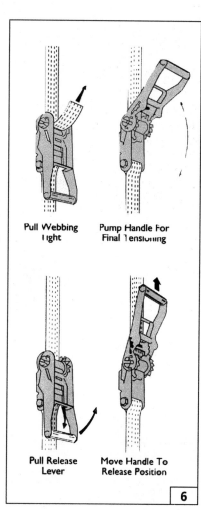

Pull Webbing Tight

Pump Handle For Final Tensioning

Pull Release Lever

Move Handle To Release Position

6

Positioning the strap across the load correctly is a skill which cannot really be learnt from a book, but there are certain principals which you can apply, whatever your load might be. When securing large, solid objects, try to ensure that the strap is fixed in a position where it is not going to be able to slide and become slack. Always bear in mind that movement of the load are your main enemies here. Always use at least one strap to secure the back of the object, and another running across its front. The tension of these two straps where they wrap around the sides of the object should automatically prevent it from sliding sideways but you may need extra straps on the sides. The problem is that even the slightest shift in one direction can allow all the other straps to lose their tension - and when they are no longer under tension, they could slip off the load altogether.

INSIDE INFORMATION: Remember that the biggest stresses on your load appear under braking, while cornering and up-down stresses come next, with pulling away stresses probably least - although this is the most likely way that you can actually lose your load!

MOTORCYCLES

7

7. If you are planning to carry a bike, or a similarly tall, or complicated object with a number of moving parts, correct lashing technique becomes critical. A purpose-made bike trailer is little more than a series of narrow platforms on a chassis - and you will be relying absolutely on the quality of your lashing to stop the bike from moving about and prevent it from falling over, too! Use one strap over the back of the headstock, just in front of the petrol tank, to hold it down vertically; and use at least two other straps to keep the bike from moving forward or back. A strap wrapped low around both the front forks, wedged against the mudguard and leading back to anchors at around the mid-point of the bike, is the most secure way of preventing forward movement. Remember the number of bouncing and pivoting parts of the bike, and avoid using these as lashing points, since their movement could well shift the straps. Try and wrap the straps around, or thread them through, the main frame members wherever possible - and NEVER rely on a strap attached to just one of the front forks or through the front wheel, since the movement of the steering head and the forks themselves will shake the strap off. When tightening the straps, get someone to sit on the bike, or bounce the forks, as you tighten each one. Making sure that the suspension is compressed will make the lashing far more secure. (Illustration, courtesy Indespension)

BICYCLES

8

8. You are more likely to carry a bicycle on a special carrier mounted behind or on the car's tow hitch than on the trailer itself. (Illustration, courtesy Witter Towbars.)

Never load too many bicycles onto the carrier, since over-stacking will risk damage either by bending the carrier brackets, tearing the carrier off, or by damaging the suspension. Always ensure that the bicycles are loaded high enough to avoid obscuring the number plate and lights, if you can. If you cannot avoid covering them, you will have to attach a special number plate and light board - and *not* a trailer board with triangular reflectors! Always use proper tie-downs and check regularly that the bikes are still securely attached - as with any load.

CARS, TRACTORS AND MOWERS

With cars or tractors, move the vehicle back and forth on the trailer until you have achieved the optimum nose weight. Put the handbrake on, if there is one, and engage a low gear. You will need four ratchet straps for a car or tractor - one secured behind each wheel, well bedded in against the axle. Lash the wheels to secure the vehicle, and be sure to secure the chassis too, to prevent the vehicle from bouncing up and down on its suspension.

🔋 **INSIDE INFORMATION: If you experience snaking (see *Part I: On the Road*) when carrying a car or tractor on your trailer, the most likely cause is inadequate nose weight. Stop, and reposition the load further forward on the trailer if you are short of noseweight, to effect an instant cure! For the same reason, don't position the engine-end over the rear of the trailer. 🔋**

SAFETY FIRST!

Observe the following rules when using your tie-downs, and they should give you reliable service:

i) Always match the strength of the straps you use to the weight of the load. If in doubt, always go up in size to the next load rating.

ii) If in doubt, add another strap. You can never use too many straps to secure a load - but you could use too few.

iii) Check the condition of each strap before using it. Make sure that there are no frays or cuts on the strap itself, and that the catch is in good order.

iv) Always protect the straps from sharp edges. If necessary, use protector pads or corner protectors (available as accessories from the strap supplier), or tie a rag around the strap to prevent it chafing on a rough-cornered load.

v) NEVER tie knots in the strap, and never use a strap if it has a knot in it. If you should find any knots, untie them straight away if possible. Otherwise, replace the strap.

vi) NEVER use a tie-down for lifting or pulling.

vii) NEVER attempt to use or repair a damaged strap. Always replace it.

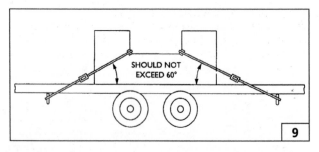

🔲 9. Use tie-downs at as shallow an angle as you can, to maximise their leverage on the load. An angle of not more than sixty degrees, as shown in this diagram of a flat-bed trailer with a single central load, allows your straps to give the best service that they can. (Illustration, courtesy Indespension)

SHORING POLES

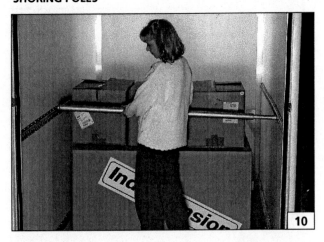

🔲 10. Shoring poles are an ingenious means of wedging loads inside closed box trailers. They simply snap into the tracking slots in the trailer walls, and are spring-loaded, to hold them into position. They are invaluable for wedging piles of boxes, as illustrated.

LOAD NETS

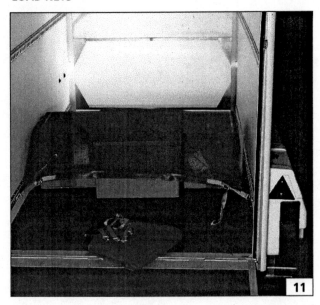

🔲 11. Load nets are handy accessories for closed box trailers, too, and can be used either flat across the top of a load, or mounted vertically to keep the load from shifting from front to back. Their principal advantage is, as with the shoring poles, the ease and speed with which they can be installed and removed. (Illustration, courtesy Indespension)

TARPAULINS

A tarpaulin can be used to keep rainwater and rubbish from building up in the trailer when it is not in use - and can also be used to secure loose materials such as garden waste. When choosing a tarpaulin, make sure that it is large enough to extend 300 mm (a foot) or so down the sides of the empty trailer. This will mean it gives a good seal against the weather - and that you can pile up light material in the trailer, and use the tarpaulin to hold it all down. Tarpaulins are available in cotton canvas, rubberised cotton or thick nylon weave.

Cotton canvas is the most expensive option, but it gives excellent weatherproofing and is extremely strong. Rubberised cotton is vulnerable to sunlight, and goes strangely floppy when the weather is hot - and it can also become brittle in the cold. Woven nylon poses an excellent and cheap alternative, but it does have to be looked after, since the plastic coating will wear away if the tarpaulin is abused, and rainwater will flood in through these unprotected holes. Make sure that around the edges of the tarpaulin there are brass-eyeletted holes to allow you to tie it down.

When securing the tarpaulin over the trailer, zigzag the cord between eyelet holes and rope hooks or buttons, in as neat and regular a pattern as you can, or use elasticated rope for greater ease of use. When you come to the corners, fold a triangular flap. Fold the flap around the corner, and thread the rope or cord through the triple thickness (there will be a hole in each corner for the purpose) of the corner flap and the first hole of the next side.

🛈 INSIDE INFORMATION: For most standard sizes of open-topped trailers, there are ready-made covers and tie-down available from your supplier. 🛈

Securing the Load

┌───┐
│   **SAFETY FIRST!**   │
│   │
│ *SAFETY FIRST!*   │
│ *While it is to be expected that the tyres on a laden trailer* │
│ *should bulge out a little when laden, you should be careful* │
│ *not to over-load them just the same. Make sure you know* │
│ *the recommended axle weight for your trailer, and use the* │
│ *guidelines in Appendix 5, The Plans to estimate the weight of* │
│ *your load.*   │
└───┘

TIMBER

making it easy ❏ 12. *Timber is a commonly carried load, but a difficult one to secure correctly. It always compresses, and so you should check the tension of the tie-downs periodically on any journey. When tying down timber, tension the straps, give the timber a really good shake to help it all bed down together, and then tighten the straps still further. (Illustration, courtesy Indespension)*

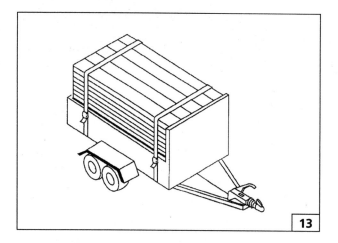

❏ 13. When loading timber, follow these simple rules:

i) Load the timber so that one end is up against the trailer's headboard.

ii) If you have them, fit side supports to stop the package of timber from spreading out sideways.

iii) Lash the package of timber from side to side, as illustrated, and use corner protectors to protect both the straps and the load.

iv) Tie down any overhanging lengths separately to prevent their ends from whipping, and to stop them working loose.

v) When carrying sheet materials, it's best to tie or band them together, with the bands running at right angles to the tie-downs.

Loading Animals

❏ 14. Before leading the animal to the trailer, lower the propstands and ramp, open and secure the door(s), and ensure that any stalls or gates are already held open. Spread a good layer of straw on the floor of the trailer (at least six inches deep, but not much more than a foot), and spread a slightly thinner layer all the way down the ramp. Unless your horse or other animal is well accustomed to getting in and out of this particular trailer, the straw on the ramp can make all the difference between getting them in calmly - or not at all! Tether the animal, and/or install the partitions, and hang up haybags for horses to nibble during the journey. (Illustration, courtesy Ifor Williams).

When unloading a horse from its box, unless you have a horsebox with front door and ramp, you will have to get it to walk backwards down the ramp. If the horse is used to doing this, you should have little trouble: hold the halter rope, or the bottom of the halter itself, close to the horse's nose, and gently pull on it to guide it backwards. If necessary, push against its neck with your forearm for extra encour-

agement. If you experience persistent trouble in loading your horse into its box, seek assistance from an experienced trainer at your local stables.

NEVER shout or use sudden movements when trying to load an animal into a small space.

PART III: HITCHING UP

Hitching your trailer to the car is generally going to be a two-man job - unless the trailer is small enough to be easily wheeled about, in which case you can just drag it to the car. With a large, heavily laden trailer, you may be best to reverse the car to the trailer's hitch - and it's a great help to have someone else to direct you!

Heavy and Fully Laden Trailers

If the trailer is a heavy one, or is fully laden, so that you can't easily manoeuvre it, make sure that the trailer's handbrake is fully on - if it's pointing down a slope, you may want to chock the wheels as well. Make sure that the jockey wheel is sufficiently extended for the trailer's hitch to be two or three inches higher than the top of the car's towball.

❑ 2. The common AL-KO hitch type has a trigger switch which must be released before the handle is lifted. Make sure that the trigger is fully engaged, and the handle lifted as high as it can go. When the towball is in position inside the hitch, release the handle, and the hitch will lock onto the ball.

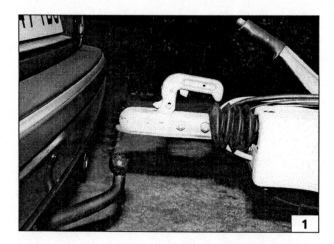

❑ 1. Carefully manoeuvre the vehicle until the towball is directly underneath the hitch and then wind up the jockey wheel so that the hitch is lowered onto the ball.

All Types of Trailer

HITCH COUPLING TYPES

First of all, make sure that the towball has a good coating of grease (BUT NOT if you have a hitch stabiliser fitted). Locking the hitch onto the towball is the final stage of coupling. Some hitches will lock onto the towball automatically, but on others, the locking handle will have to be firmly engaged. Some have a trigger or button which must be operated before the locking handle can be engaged or disengaged.

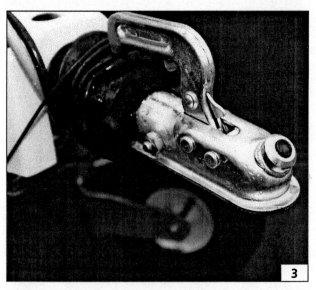

❑ 3. Later AL-KO models have this positive coupling indicator button on the front. You operate the hitch in exactly the same way as the older model, but when the hitch is correctly attached, the red indicator button lets you know that all is well by rising slightly to reveal a green band. When the hitch is unlocked, the green band disappears.

4. Alternatively, you may have the Albe type hitch fitted to your trailer. Knott, Peak and Avonride are just three brands of hitch which work like this. When engaging this hitch, the handle will already be locked in a raised position. When the towball is located correctly, the handle will automatically snap down into position. To disengage the hitch, grasp the handle, lift it as high as it will go, and press it forwards.

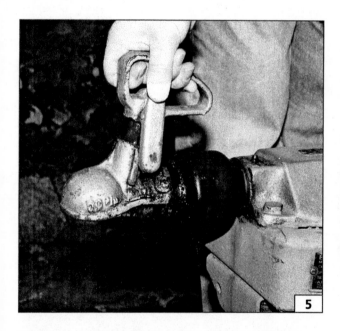

5. The other type of hitch which you could have is the Bradley type. To open the hitch, release the safety catch at the back of the handle, and lift the handle straight up. Lower the hitch onto the ball, then lower the handle and lock it back into position with the catch. To release the hitch, you do the reverse!

INSIDE INFORMATION: If you are unsure whether the hitch has engaged correctly, try winding down the jockey wheel (if fitted) a little way, raising the drawbar and tow vehicle together, to see if it lifts the coupling off the towball. Don't over-do it however, or you could damage the jockey wheel, the drawbar, or both.

FACT FILE: TOWING EYES

Towing eyes are widely used on large, heavy-duty trailers without brakes, such as agricultural or plant machinery.

Towing eyes are also found on Sankey trailers, which were originally designed for military use for towing behind Land Rovers over the roughest terrain - treatment that ball hitch mechanisms could not withstand.

If you should have cause to use an eye-and-pin hitch, you will find it extremely simple to use: just place the eye in between the jaws, and insert the pin. If choosing a towing pin to fit to your vehicle, always ensure that the jaws are sufficiently open to allow the eye plenty of up-and-down movement, otherwise damage to the rear of the vehicle or to the drawbar may result. Also, if looking to combine a jaw and towball arrangement in one unit, opt for the type which has a separate towball built in, and not the sort where a ball is moulded onto the top of the pin. These can prove insecure because the tow ball is only held by the strength of the 'penny' clip holding the pin in place.

IMPORTANT NOTE: 25 mm and 32 mm pins are available. NEVER use a 25 mm pin with an eye for a 32 mm pin!

Now that the trailer and towing vehicle are securely locked together, there are just two more things left to do:

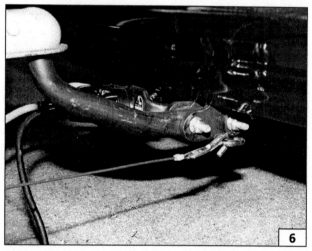

6. If your trailer has brakes, attach the breakaway cable to a solid part of the car - but not to the towing bracket itself (unless there is absolutely nowhere else to clip it).

Now connect up all the trailer's electrical equipment. You will definitely have a black seven-pin connector - and you may also have a grey seven pin connector and/or a flat twin-block connector to connect up too. At last, it's time to raise the jockey wheel, release the handbrake, and remove any wheel chocks!

7. The last job will be to fit a towing mirror to the car, if you need one i.e. if the trailer is too wide for your regular door mirrors to give you a view behind on each side.

Before you drive away, get someone to stand behind the trailer and help you to check that all the lights and indicators are working properly. Look underneath the trailer to ensure that the 12-volt cable is not trailing on the floor, and tidy it up with cable ties if necessary.

i INSIDE INFORMATION: Stop after the first ten minutes or so, and check the following:

• **That the load is still perfectly secure - check for movement and pull on all of the tie-downs.**

• **That the tyres are still properly inflated.**

• **That the wheel centres and tyre walls feel reasonably cool. If the wheel centres feel hot to the touch, it is possible that you have a binding brake, or that the wheel bearing is maladjusted, or starved of grease. If you must continue, drive as slowly as possible, stop and check at regular intervals and beware that the wheel could come adrift! Attend to hub greasing as soon as possible. i**

PART IV: MOVING & PARKING

Moving the Trailer

Unless your trailer has a jockey wheel, it's not a good idea to move a fully laden trailer because of the risk of back injury in lifting the nose of the trailer while pulling it along. If you have to move a laden (lightweight) trailer without a jockey wheel, it's best to have one person holding the hitch-end off the ground (make sure it's not over laden) while someone else concentrates on pulling or pushing the trailer along.

making it easy! 1. Four-wheeled trailers are very easy to push in a straight line but incredibly difficult to get round corners! Overcome the problem by pushing the nose of the trailer down as far as it will go before retightening the jockey wheel. This will lift the rear wheels off the ground and you can then manoeuvre the trailer as easily as any two-wheeled trailer.

Reversing

All modern trailers are fitted with an auto-reverse braking system. Some, such as the Bradley HU12 coupling is also fitted with the manual reverse catch which can be used in particularly difficult circumstances, such as when reversing up a slippery incline, where the slight drag present in the auto-reverse brakes may otherwise cause the wheels to lock. On Ifor Williams' trailers, for instance, manual reverse catches are available as optional extras for other coupling types.

Parking

TRAILER ON LEVEL GROUND OR FACING DOWNHILL

1) Fully apply the towing vehicle and trailer handbrake. 2) Remove the lighting plug and stow in a safe position. 3) Release jockey wheel clamp and lower the jockey wheel to the ground. 4) Firmly re-tighten clamp by hand. 5) Uncouple the trailer using the jockey wheel to raise the coupling free of the coupling ball. (For eye couplings, remove the pin from the towing jaw following the towing jaw manufacturer's instructions.) 6) Detach the breakaway cable.

TRAILER FACING UPHILL

1) Apply the towing vehicle and trailer handbrakes. 2) Return to the towing vehicle and release the handbrake. The trailer should roll back a few inches as the handbrake applies the brakes, overriding the auto-reverse system. 3) Re-apply the towing vehicle handbrake. 4) Check the trailer handbrake is fully applied. 5) Remove the lighting plug. 6) Lower the jockey wheel and clamp securely. 7) Uncouple the trailer using the jockey wheel to raise the coupling free of the ball. (For eye couplings, remove the pin from the towing jaw following the towing jaw manufacturer's instruction.) 8) Detach the breakaway cable.

IMPORTANT NOTE: Never detach the breakaway cable before uncoupling the trailer.

PARKING FOR EXTENDED PERIODS

When parking the trailer for extended periods, it is advisable to chock the wheels and release the handbrake to avoid the possibility of the brake shoes adhering to the brake drum surface.

Handbrake Application

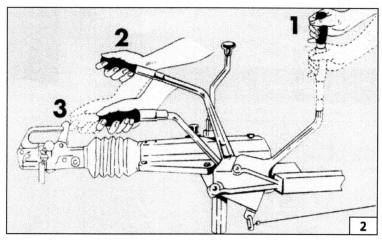

☐ 2. The modern over-centre trailer handbrake has three positions. 3 - the 'off' position, 2 - the normal 'on' position, 1 - the autoreverse 'on' position. The handbrake automatically moves to position '1' if the trailer rolls backwards with the handbrake in it normal 'on' position '2'. This extra movement overrides the autoreverse brake mechanism

and allows the handbrake to hold when the trailer is pointing backwards down hill. Disengaging a trailer handbrake, particularly from autoreverse position '1', can require great strength. The extending handbrake lever illustrated (unique to Indespension products) gives you just enough extra leverage to make operating the brake quite easy. It is spring loaded and automatically retracts out of the way when not in use.

The automatic reversing brake system incorporates a patented device for added safety when parking on a reverse sloping site or a steep hill. A spring cylinder has been added to the link between handbrake lever and centre brake rod.

It should be noted that it is good common practice to chock the wheels of a trailer when parking on steep slopes, or under adverse weather conditions such as loose or slippery surfaces.

IMPORTANT NOTE: When the handbrake is correctly applied it should be almost in a *vertical position*. Full application of the handbrake lever compresses a coil spring inside a steel cylinder and should any movement of the trailer occur following uncoupling the energy stored in the spring is immediately released to lock the wheel brakes. (Illustration, courtesy Indespension.)

PART V: TRAILER & LOAD THEFT-PROOFING

🛈 **INSIDE INFORMATION: Whatever physical precautions you might take, the best theft prevention is not to put your property in the way of thieves. Car parks at motorway services are by far the worst places for car crime, with multi-storey and other public car parks coming a close second. If possible, park your trailer where you can see it. Failing that, park it as close to the busiest part of the car park as you can.** 🛈

Load Theft

Open-topped trailers are extremely vulnerable to theft, so always remove anything of value before leaving the trailer unattended. A padlocked tarpaulin cover is no protection - thieves will simply slit the tarpaulin with a knife to have a look inside. You can buy small trailers with solid lids - or you could make up a solid lid to fit the trailer, yourself.

More substantial enclosed trailers have doors, which can be fitted with a good quality padlock at a moderate cost. You may need to replace the catches with a suitable type to take a padlock - but this is a small expense compared to your load's loss.

Security Posts

☐ 1. If you keep a large and expensive trailer unhitched on an open drive, then you might want to install a security post or tow hitch lock to stop it being wheeled away. The post can be folded flat when not in use, or locked in its vertical position. (Illustration, courtesy Perkson Ltd)

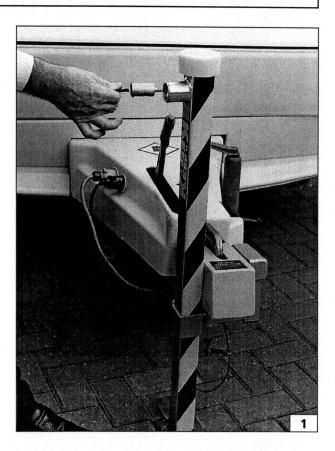

Wheelclamps

2

2. Trailer wheelclamps come in a whole variety of designs and colours but all do roughly the same job. Whichever one you choose you should make sure that it fits right around the wheel of the trailer and, once fitted, can't be slid off, even with the tyre deflated. Also be sure to check that the lock can't simply be removed by hammering a hole punch into it. Stories of thieves removing wheelclamps in under 30 seconds are too common to ignore. (Illustration, courtesy Perkson Ltd)

Locking Hitches

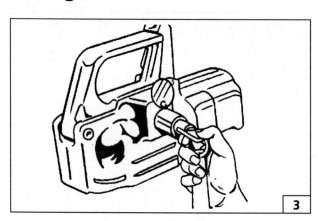

3

3. Locking hitches are an excellent anti-theft measure, and can be retro-fitted. The barrel lock contained within the hitch means that the hitch cannot be released from the towball - or attached to another vehicle - without using the key. On some models, the entire lock barrel is withdrawn when you take the key out - on others, the head locks automatically. (Illustration, courtesy Indespension.)

Hitchlocks

4. Other hitchlocks lock over the hitch of the trailer making them inaccessible to a potential thief's towcar brackets. (Illustration, courtesy Perkson Ltd)

4

INSIDE INFORMATION: Hitchlocks should only really be fitted as an additional security measure along with a wheelclamp as alone they can be quite ineffective as thieves have been known to simply put a rope around the hitch, lock and all, tie the other end to their (stolen?) vehicle and use it to tow the trailer off. And if you do fit a hitchlock, make sure that it covers the bolts that attach the hitch to the trailer's A-frame. Otherwise a thief can simply unbolt and remove the locked hitch, fit an unsecured one in its place and make off with the trailer.

Tracker Units

One of the most effective methods of countering trailer theft is through tracking units designed to be hidden within the walls and chassis of the trailer. These remain inert until the trailer is stolen. Then, when activated, tracer units are used to discover the whereabouts of the trailer. Unfortunately these units are often quite expensive, and only come into their own once the trailer has actually been stolen. It's therefore advisable to use them in conjunction with another more obvious security device, such as a wheelclamp although the retrieval rate of trailers stolen after being fitted with these units is said to be very high.

INSIDE INFORMATION: Whatever methods you choose to make your trailer and load secure, always buy your security equipment from a recognised company, and never try to buy locks or alarm systems 'on the cheap'. The denser (and so stronger) a piece of metal, the heavier it will be - so as a general guide to quality, the heavier the device is for its size the more thief-proof it is likely to be.

Insurance

Unlike cars, it isn't a legal requirement to have a trailer insured. It is, however, a recommended practice. Many insurance companies that deal with car and house coverage will be able to offer a policy for your trailer.

IMPORTANT NOTE: While on the subject of insurance, it is essential that you check that your towcar's insurance covers is for towing a trailer. If not you will be committing a criminal offence when towing a trailer because your towcar's insurance will be invalidated. Check with your insurer and CHECK BEFORE SWITCHING TO A TEMPTINGLY CHEAP CAR INSURANCE POLICY!

PART VI: FITTING A TOWBRACKET TO YOUR CAR

FACT FILE:
TYPE-APPROVED TOW BRACKETS

When fitting a towbracket in the UK, you aren't allowed to fit a DIY towbracket. Cars first registered on or after 1 August 1998 are required to be fitted with an EC type-approved (94/20) towbracket designed to be fitted to mounting points tested and fitted by the manufacturer.

All such vehicles have an 'e' mark on their VIN plates (which also show maximum car load and trailer weight/mass).

If your post-July 1988 car's VIN plate does not specify a trailer weight/mass, the vehicle is not permitted by law to tow (except for a few very low-production cars which fall outside the scope of type approval legislation).

FITTING A TOWBRACKET

This sequence shows how one of the UK's foremost towbracket fitting companies, Towcraft in the West Midlands go about fitting a Witter towbracket.

❏ 1A. First job, as always, is to take everything out of the box, make sure it's all there and identify each piece against the fitting instructions.

❏ 1B. There are almost always mounting brackets to be added in order to spread the stresses from the towbracket. Witter have worked closely with all major manufacturers to develop the correct type-approved fittings.

❏ 1C. In the case of this Saab, as with most vehicles, part of the mountings are situated behind the rear bumper. You can sometimes get away with slackening bumper mountings and easing the bumper away far enough to introduce mounting brackets. If the bumper has to be removed, take care to disconnect any wires that may be attached before walking away with it! Old bumper mounts can become very rusty. You might have to budget for buying new ones - and they're usually main-dealer-only parts.

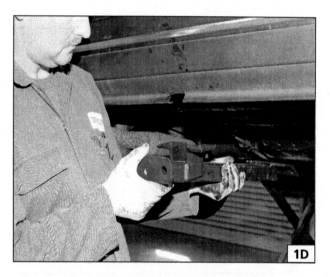

❏ 1D. Here, as is often the case, some bumper material has had to be cut away to allow the bracket to fit correctly. This needs to be done with care and professionalism so that the towbracket fitting looks an integral part of the car.

❏ 1E. Where necessary, holes have been drilled in the boot floor for bolting the bracket support in place. Such holes must be de-burred then treated with primer and rust-proofing fluid after drilling.

When drilling through visible panels, place masking tape over the panel and mark it for accurate drilling. The tape will also help prevent the drill bit from slipping.

The bracket is bolted on ONLY after removing underseal from the mounting area to give a good metal-to-metal contact.

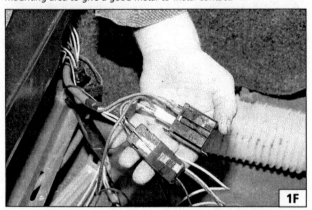

☐ 1F. The next job is to wire in the 7-pin (or, if using Euro-standard caravan plugs/sockets) 13-pin connectors.

These Towcraft connectors include caravan wiring relays for the 'fridge and leisure battery charging circuits - not usually needed on a trailer but useful to have fitted now if you think you may want to tow a caravan in future.

Clip-on electrical connectors are not a good idea. They corrode and should never be used in exposed places.

The vehicle must, by law, be fitted with an audible or visible warning that the trailer indicators are working. Modern cars should come with the warning system ready fitted.

See *Chapter 3, Job 6* for wiring plug/socket connection diagrams.

☐ 1G. Towcraft have their own electrical tester for use in their workshop to check the vehicle's wiring, including the caravan-specific connections mentioned earlier. It takes a little longer but it's just as effective if you connect your trailer and check that everything is working the 'manual' way.

PART VII: USING A WINCH

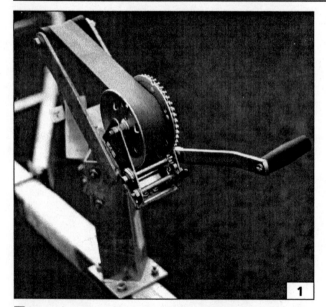

☐ 1. Much of the job of caring for your winch can be achieved simply by using it properly, but see *Chapter 6, Servicing & Maintenance* for details on cleaning and lubrication. If you also make sure you take note of the following basic rules for using the winch, you should never encounter any problems, either with safety, or mechanical failure:

i) Always use the winch to pull in a straight line - never allow the strap to pull over objects, or to go around corners.

ii) Always stand clear of the winch strap or cable when the winch is in use.

iii) Never allow the winch handle to spin as the strap is spooled out - always put the winch gear into its neutral position, if it has one.

iv) Never operate a winch without the strap or cable properly secured to the drum and with less than five wraps of strap or cable around the drum - the strap could break loose under heavy load.

v) When beginning to winch, start off by taking up any slack in the strap.

vi) Do not allow the hook closer than about 600 mm (2 feet) to the winch itself.

vii) Never exceed the rated capacity of the winch.

viii) Never use the winch as a tow-eye, to lift, or to haul animals or people.

ix) When re-winding the strap or cable, always try to do so with it under load. Allowing the strap to wrap round the drum loosely will mean that the inner layers will slip when you do come to use it.

x) Always locate the hook on its keeper bracket, or a handy frame member, when not in use. If allowed to swing about, it could cause all sorts of havoc as you drive along!

CHAPTER 6
SERVICING & MAINTENANCE

It's not only your car or van which needs regular maintenance if you are to get the best out of it over the years. Your trailer will need regular attention too. It's reasonable to assume that having bought this book, you are a responsible trailer owner, and want your outfit to fall into the first of these two categories. You want your trailer to provide reliable and convenient service throughout many years, and this chapter gives all the information you will need to achieve this.

If you want your trailer to be as well looked after as possible, you'll follow the Jobs shown here. If time and financial constraints mean that the entire Service Schedule is too much for you to achieve, then select the most important jobs from those listed here, and carry your selection out faithfully.

Do bear in mind however that *preventative maintenance* is by far the most important kind of repair. And that's why many of our service jobs have the word 'Check...' near the start!

Other special headings are also used. One reads **INSIDE INFORMATION**. This tells you that here is a Job or a special tip that you wouldn't normally get to hear about, other than through the experience and 'inside' knowledge of the experts, such as manufacturers' own professional mechanics, who have the job of servicing hundreds of customers' trailers every year.

Another is **SPECIALIST SERVICE**, which means that we recommend you to have this work carried out by a specialist. One obvious example of this would be the braking system of any braked trailer. There may be other areas about which you don't feel confident, and in those cases, once again, you would be best off leaving it to the experts. Where we think you are better off having the work done for you, we say so! But even then, there is no reason why you shouldn't have a go - as long as you have any work checked thoroughly by a qualified engineer at your home, before taking the trailer out onto the road.

Using The Service Schedules

At the start of each Service Job, you'll see a heading in bold type, looking a bit like this:

❑ **Job 16. Check wheel bearings.**

Following the heading will be all the information you will need to enable you to carry out that particular Job. You will also find other key information immediately after each Job title, and in most cases there will be reference to an illustration - a photograph or line drawing, whichever is easier for you to follow - on the same page. Where we feel that a little background information will make it easier to carry out the work, we include a box of FACT FILE information, relevant to the job in hand.

If the Job shown only applies to certain types, the Job title will be followed by a description of the type of system to which the Job title applies. For instance, where Job 35D applies to LEAF-SPRING SUSPENSION ONLY, the text in capitals tells you so.

SAFETY FIRST!

This special heading is the most important one of all! SAFETY FIRST! information must always be read with care and always taken seriously. In addition, please read the whole of Chapter 1, Safety First! before carrying out any work on your trailer. There are a number of hazards associated with working on a trailer but all of them can be avoided by adhering strictly to the safety rules. Don't skimp on safety!

Working underneath a small trailer will be a simple matter of getting someone to help you turn it upside-down! With a larger trailer, however, it's often necessary to jack the trailer up. It is essential that you follow the correct procedure for this and use the recommended tools. It is also advisable that, whenever working under a trailer, you make sure that somebody nearby knows what you're doing so that they can regularly check on you to make sure that everything's OK.

I. Make sure that the trailer is on firm and level ground.

II. Apply the handbrake, if you have one. If you're carrying out work on the brakes or wheels, however, you will have to jack the trailer up, and then prop it, and/or chock the wheel which is not to be raised off the ground.

III. Lower the prop stands, if you have them, on the side that is going to be raised. DO NOT use the prop stands to raise the trailer - even if they are of the sturdy wind-down type.

IV. Place an axle stand under the axle. DO NOT rely on bricks or odd pieces of wood, as these have a habit of crumbling or giving way.

V. If the trailer has its own jacking points, use these to raise it up. If not, place a jack under the trailer's axle, as close to the chassis as possible, or under the chassis rail itself.

☒ INSIDE INFORMATION: Use a jack especially made for your trailer, if you can get one: it will fit the profile of the axle tube or chassis rail. Modern trailer axle tubes are very often square. ☒

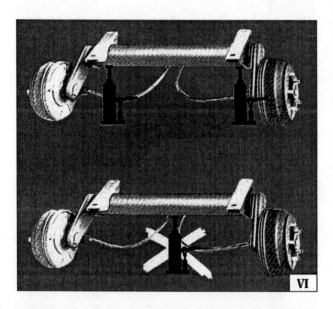

VI. With some trailers, you are able to jack or support the trailer beneath clearly visible axle-to-chassis mounting points. NEVER jack beneath the centre of the axle: you could easily distort it. (Illustration, courtesy Knott)

VII. Further lower the prop stands (if fitted) on the raised side of the trailer so that they just touch the ground.

Changing a Wheel

To change the wheel on a trailer:

I. Ensure that the handbrake is fully applied. If the outfit is parked at the roadside, it is also advisable to leave the car and trailer hitched up.

II. Lower the jockey wheel (if fitted), so that it can take some of the trailer's weight when the wheel is being removed.

III. Chock the wheel on the opposite side of the trailer to the one that you are intending to change.

making it easy! *IV. Using a wheel brace, **just** slacken off - but do not undo any further - the wheel nuts of the wheel to be changed. If you try to do so after the wheel has been raised, the wheel will turn instead of the nut.*

V. Position the jack either at the trailer's specified jacking point, or along the trailer's axle, as close to the chassis as possible. Raise the jack sufficiently to allow the wheel to be removed.

VI. If fitted, lower the prop stands on the same side only as the wheel that you are about to remove. Under no circumstances should you attempt to use the prop stands to jack up the trailer.

VII. Remove the wheel nuts and wheel, and put the wheel under the trailer, just in case it slips off the jack!.

VIII. Put the replacement wheel onto the hub and fasten the nuts or bolts to finger-tightness. Lower the trailer and tighten the nuts or bolts. (Obviously, you're not likely to have your torque wrench with you if you have a puncture on the open road, in which case tighten the nuts as firmly as you can, and then once you're home, UNDO each nut/bolt in turn, and RETIGHTEN to the correct torque setting as soon as you can.)

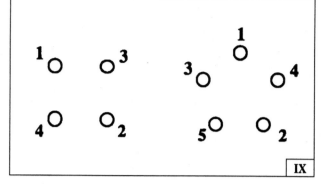

IX. Depending on whether your trailer's wheels have four or five mounting studs or bolts, tighten bolts or nuts in the sequence shown in the appropriate illustration. (Illustration, courtesy Ifor Williams.)

FACT FILE:
WHEEL NUT TORQUE SETTINGS

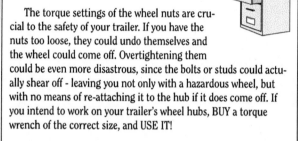

The torque settings of the wheel nuts are crucial to the safety of your trailer. If you have the nuts too loose, they could undo themselves and the wheel could come off. Overtightening them could be even more disastrous, since the bolts or studs could actually shear off - leaving you not only with a hazardous wheel, but with no means of re-attaching it to the hub if it does come off. If you intend to work on your trailer's wheel hubs, BUY a torque wrench of the correct size, and USE IT!

Torque settings from trailer to trailer can be vastly different, and you should check your owner's handbook or with your dealer to see the exact setting required on your own trailer's wheels. THEN ENTER IT ONTO THE DATA-BASE ON PAGE 1 OF THE MANUAL! In an emergency though, you could use the following manufacturers' recommendations as a guide:

AL-KO recommend that their wheel nuts are tightened to 8.0 kg/m (62 lb/ft), and bolts to 9.0 kg/m (65 lb/ft).

Peak Trailers recommend the following settings for wheel nuts:

IMPERIAL STUDS	METRIC STUDS
3/8" UNF - 45 lb/ft	M12 x 1.5 - 75 lb/ft
1/2" UNF - 80 lb/ft	M16 x 1.5 - 145 lb/ft

Indespension's recommendations are as follows:

NUTS	TORQUE SETTINGS
3/8" UNF	42 lb/ft (57 Nm)
7/16" UNF	50 lb/ft (67 Nm)
" UNF	56 lb/ft (76 Nm)
5/8" UNF	85 lb/ft (115 Nm)
BOLTS	
M12	55 lb/ft (74 Nm)
M14	60 lb/ft (81 Nm)

Ifor Williams give the following settings:

4 x M12	65 lb/ft (88 Nm)
5 x M14	81 lb/ft (110 Nm)

X. Raise the prop stands, lower the jack, remove the wheel chocks and raise the jockey wheel.

XI. After driving a further 20 miles or so, it is important to stop and recheck the torque settings of the wheel nuts. Then remember to recheck them regularly, preferably before each journey with your trailer.

INSIDE INFORMATION: A torque wrench only checks the torque when tightening a thread, never when unscrewing it. To check the torque effectively, it is essential that the nut or bolt is backed off, that the thread is clean and free-running, and the torque setting is made as the nut or bolt is being re-tightened.

XII. TO USE A TORQUE WRENCH: You set the scale on the wrench to the torque figure required, and then use the wrench with a regular socket spanner and extension if needed. When the nut or bolt reaches the required torque, the torque wrench 'lets go' and, instead of turning the thread any further, makes a clear clicking sound as the wrench is turned.

Never attempt to use your towcar's spare wheel on your trailer, or vice versa, as the types of wheels and tyres used on cars and trailers are rarely the same. Before fitting a new wheel, always check it for distortion or damage. If you find any, do not fit the wheel.

XIII. As with a car, it is recommended that you always carry a suitable spare wheel and jack with your trailer in case of punctures or wheel damage.

INSIDE INFORMATION: If you can't afford a brand new wheel and tyre, purchase just a wheel (they're surprisingly cheap!) and a second-hand tyre *of the correct rating* for use as a spare.

IF YOU HAVE A PUNCTURE...

...try to get the outfit as far away from other road traffic as you can. A ruined tyre is worth a lot less than a life! Also, use a reflective triangle, so that other motorists are aware in advance that there's a hazard.

Unless there's no choice, don't be tempted to abandon the trailer at the roadside while you go off for help.

PREPARING FOR OCCASIONAL USE

IMPORTANT NOTE: The preparation and checks given in this section should be made as a routine annual service procedure regardless of whether or not the trailer has seen much use during the year. Turn to *Chapter 8, Perform Your Own 'MoT'*, for further details on the essential annual once-over.

If the trailer is stored outside, removing dirt and trapped water from braking systems, suspension, wheel bearings and hitching mechanisms will help to prevent corrosion, and will also help you to see easily when you make a quick visual check on their condition. Also, remember to carry out greasing and oiling at the intervals recommended in this book. Fuller details of how to prepare the trailer for storage will be found in **Jobs 46 to 53**.

Before taking the trailer out on the road once more, there is a little further work for you to do. Check the items listed below, and also carry out the checks listed as *Every Week, or Before Every Long Journey.* You should also make sure that the towing vehicle is properly prepared, as detailed in **Jobs 4 to 10**. When using a vehicle for towing, it is even more important than usual that it has been serviced in accordance with the manufacturer's schedules - for full details, see the Porter Manual or the owner's handbook, for your model. And it's important to bear in mind that with some vehicles, there may be shorter service intervals for driving in 'arduous conditions' - and that includes towing!

☐ Job 1. Check condition of body.

If an open trailer has been standing for any length of time, remove water, fallen leaves and so on that may have gathered in it. Inspect carefully to ensure that structural beams have not been attacked by corrosion, and that wooden panels have not begun to rot.

⚡ INSIDE INFORMATION: If you know that your open-topped trailer is going to have to stand exposed, out of doors, drill holes in the trailer bed rather then allowing a mobile pond to develop. ⚡

☐ Job 2. Check condition of auxiliaries.

Locks, bolts, catches and hinges may have become stiff during storage. Lubricate them before you plan to take the trailer out.

TRAILER TENTS ONLY

If you have a trailer tent, check the condition of the fabric carefully. Take out or erect the tent, checking that all the necessary poles or supports are present and in good condition, and that no mould has formed on the fabric. If there is some mould, which may just appear as a spotty blackening of the fabric, try to brush or wash it off. If the fabric has suffered slight damage from damp or mould, it will need to be re- waterproofed after cleaning. See *Special Equipment* at the end of this chapter for full details.

IMPORTANT NOTE: Only take the tent or awning out if the weather is dry, as putting it away again when wet will cause mould to form, and may well rot the fabric.

For details on boat rollers, winches, and other specialist attachments, see *Special Equipment* later in this chapter.

☐ Job 3. Check electrical wiring and connectors.

Check the 12-volt wiring connectors at the front of the trailer. Unless you have a rather ancient five-pin plug, you will definitely have a black seven-pin connector, known as the 12N plug or socket, which carries wires for the stoplights, indicators and so on. There may also be a grey or white connector, the 12S type, which carries wiring for any accessories, trailer-borne batteries, or interior lights which you may have fitted to your box trailer or horsebox. Ensure that neither has been damaged, and that there is no corrosion around the pins - clean off to bright metal with a soft wire brush or abrasive paper if necessary. Park the towcar near to the front of the trailer and connect up the wiring connector(s). If there is any problem with any of the trailer lights, or with any electrical accessories you may have fitted, open up each connector as appropriate, and check the wiring.

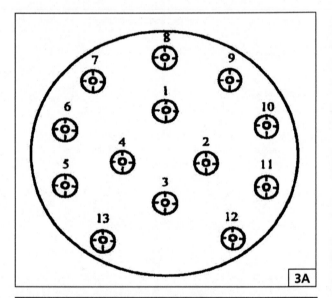

3A

FACT FILE: 13 PIN CONNECTORS

☐ **3A.** Many cars and trailers are now being supplied with 13 pin connectors instead of two 7 pin connectors. Adaptor leads are available to connect a 13 pin connector to twin 7 pin connectors.

---

13 PIN CONNECTOR TERMINALS

1. LH indicator	8. Reversing lights (1)
2. Rear fog lamp	9. Permanent power (4)
3. Earth for 1,2,4 & 8	10. Ignition switch
4. RH indicator	controlled power supply (6)
5. RH side tail	11. Earth for 10 (7)
6. Stop lamp	12. Coding for trailer (2)
7. LH side tail	13. Earth for 9 (3)

3B

☐ 3B. Pin numbers 1 to 7 are the same as on 12N connectors. Pin numbers 8 to 13 are the equivalent of the pins on the 12S connector. These latter numbers are shown in brackets.

Ensure that your car and trailer are wired in this way.
(Sometimes the 'bodgers' may have been at work!)
REMEMBER: Incorrect wiring could cause a fire.

3E. Check each connection to ensure that:

i) None of the wires have pulled loose, or have just a few strands of wire remaining.

3C. Unscrewing the two screws holding the two halves of a 12-volt trailer plug together.

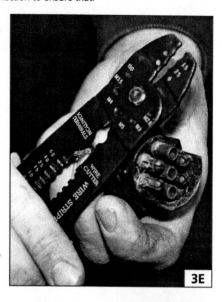

ii) There are no expanses of bare wire - the insulation should just butt up against the entrance to each screw connector.

iii) There is no white or green corrosion in the plug. If there is, clean off thoroughly. Strip off a fresh 'end' if necessary.

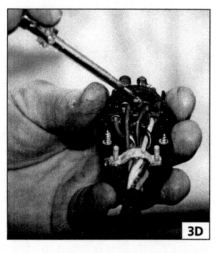

3D. The wiring connections are made to this block, which locates inside each half of the plug.

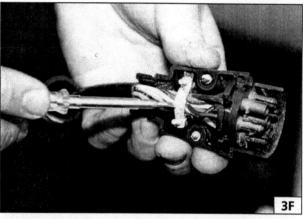

3F. Make certain that the wire clamp is tight, otherwise it is all too easy to pull the wires out of the plug as it is disconnected from the car. In this case, the clamp is placed uselessly over the wires, not the insulation sheath. Also make sure that the rubber shroud seals correctly. Replace if necessary.

FACT FILE: SOCKET WIRING

3G. All cars and trailers with 12S socket from 1999 (and some before!) have the NEW connections shown below. 12N sockets are unchanged. If a continental 13 pin socket is fitted, adaptorplugs/sockets are available.
If car and trailer are different 1) 'OLD' car 'NEW' trailer connections - add separate earth for fridge to the car via pin 7. 2) 'NEW' car 'OLD' trailer connections - add trailer/caravan wiring and relay for aux. battery charging via pin 4.

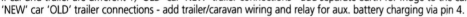

12S SOCKET

No.	Connection	Colour
1.	Reversing light*	Yellow
2. OLD	Battery charger	Blue
2. NEW	Coupled trailer coding.*	Blue
3.	Earth	White
4.	Constant Live	Green
5.	Spare	Brown
6.	Fridge	Red
7. OLD	Spare	
7. NEW	Earth for fridge	Black
* When applicable.		

12N SOCKET

No.	Connection	Colour
1.	L.H.Indicator	Yellow
2.	Fog Lamp	Blue
3.	Earth	White
4.	R.H.Indicator	Green
5.	R.H.Side Light	Brown
6.	Stop lamps	Red
7.	L.H.Side Light	Black

3H. Finally, check the condition of the seven-core cable running along beneath the length of the trailer. Look to see if any part of it is hanging dangerously near the road, and examine the condition of the outer insulation layer to make sure that it has not been scuffed through. If it has been damaged, replace the cable. DO NOT rely on insulation tape for a cheap bodge!

Checks to the Tow car

The following checks should be made in addition to the regular servicing requirements of your car.

☐ Job 4. Check towcar wiring.

4. You can carry this out in conjunction with **Job 3**, of course. You may find a problem inside one of the towcar sockets.

⚡ INSIDE INFORMATION: There are two 'favourite' wiring problems which are commonly found on a tow vehicle's trailer wiring: i) Water may have got in through the backs of the sockets; in which case, clean up the sockets and replace them, if necessary. When refitting the wiring grommet, use silicone seam sealer around the grommet, and around the back of each socket to seal it up properly for the future. ii) Check that the earth lead from the socket has not become dislodged where it is bolted inside the car; usually in the spare wheel well, beneath the car or inside the boot/hatch area. Also, to ensure that there is a good earth connection, remove if necessary, clean up the surfaces to bare metal, treat with copper-impregnated grease, and refit securely. ⚡

☐ Job 5. Check towbracket mountings.

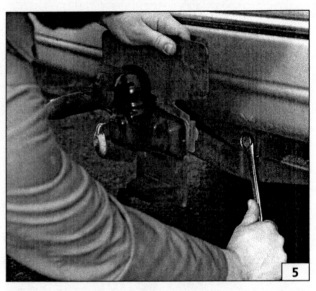

5. Check that all of the towbracket and towball mountings on the car are tight. Also look for evidence of cracking around the mounting points. If any is found, SPECIALIST SERVICE: Have the car professionally repaired before towing, and check with your local main dealer that you have the correct towbracket, made by a recognised supplier, for your car. BEWARE: If selecting a new towbracket, note that some cheap 'n' cheerful makes are believed to put inappropriate stresses on the car.

☐ Job 6. Check rear suspension.

While in this area of the car, check the rear suspension. A car or van which regularly pulls a heavy trailer takes more of a pounding in this area than most, so: check rear shock absorbers for leaks; check springs for sagging. (Measure the ride height of both sides of the car and compare - they should both be the same).

☐ Job 7. Check car tyre pressures.

7. Ensure that the rear tyre pressures are suitable for driving the car when fully laden, if you intend to do a lot of towing. See your car's handbook for details. If you only tow occasionally, do this before each journey and restore pressures to 'normal' afterwards.

Job 8. Check headlight alignment.

If, when you are towing at night, oncoming traffic 'flashes' at you because your headlights are dazzling them, have your headlights set a little lower - but not so low that they are unsafe, illegal or will fail an MoT. This is a *SPECIALIST SERVICE* job and must be carried out by a garage with special beam-setting equipment. DON'T GUESS IT!

Job 9. Check indicator warning.

Check that, when the car is connected to the trailer by the 12N plug, and the indicators are operated, the trailer indicator warning light or buzzer inside the car operates correctly. This is a legal requirement!

Job 10. Check towing mirrors.

10. If your trailer is so large as to make them necessary, dig out those towing mirrors and make sure that they haven't been cracked while in storage, and that all the fixings are still there.

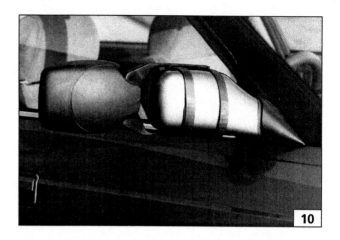

10

Every Week, or Before Every Long Journey

FACT FILE: TYRE PRESSURES

RECOMMENDED TRAILER TYRE PRESSURES. You should always follow manufacturer's figures in preference to the general information given here. But as a helpful guide, or for emergency use, here are some recommended tyre pressures for the most commonly used sizes of trailer wheel. Note that the pressures given are for maximum load. Radial ply tyres have an 'R' in their size rating; cross-ply tyres do not.

Tyre size	Ply rating	Max. axle load @ 80mph (100km/h)	Pressure
4.00 x 8"	4	1190lb (540 kg)	60psi (4.2 bar)
6.50 x 8"	4	1240lb (562 kg)	45psi (3.1 bar)
4.00 x 8"	6	1490lb (680 kg)	75psi (6.2 bar)
4.00 x 8"	8	1675lb (760 kg)	86psi (5.9 bar)
5.20 x 10"	4	1355lb (616 kg)	32psi (2.2 bar)
4.00 x 10"	6	1390lb (630 kg)	45psi (3.1 bar)
145 R10"	4	1525lb (692 kg)	35psi (2.41 bar)
145 R10"	Reinforced	1720lb (781 kg)	42psi (2.89 bar)
145 R10"	8	2200lb (1000 kg)	65psi (4.5 bar)
5.00 x 10"	6	1895lb (860 kg)	50psi (3.5 bar)
5.00 x 10"	8	2200lb (1000 kg)	65psi (4.5 bar)
145 R12"	4	1717lb (780 kg)	35psi (2.4 bar)
155 R12"	4	2000lb (910 kg)	36psi (2.5 bar)
140/70 R12"	Special	1938lb (1060 kg)	62psi (4.3 bar)
155/70 R12"	Special	3853lb (1800 kg)	90psi (6.2 bar)
145 R13"	4	1870lb (850 kg)	36psi (2.5 bar)
165 R13"	4	2310lb (1050 kg)	35psi (2.4 bar)
175 R13"	4	2574lb (1170 kg)	35psi (2.4 bar)
185 R13"	4	2712lb (1232 kg)	34psi (2.3 bar)
175 R13"	Reinforced	2809lb (1276 kg)	45psi (3.1 bar)
6.70 x 13"	6	3096lb (1406 kg)	47psi (3.25 bar)
185 R13"	6	3366lb (1530 kg)	54psi (3.75 bar)
185/70 R13"	Special	4180lb (1900 kg)	87psi (6.0 bar)
7.50 14"	6	3465lb (1574 kg)	47psi (3.25 bar)
185 R14"	6	3584lb (1628 kg)	54psi (3.75 bar)
185 R14"	8	3932lb (1786 kg)	65psi (4.5 bar)
6.00 x 16"	6	3188lb (1448 kg)	47psi (3.25 bar)
6.50 x 16"	6	3465lb (1574 kg)	47psi (3.25 bar)
6.50 x 16"	8	4158lb (1890 kg)	62psi (4.25 bar)
6.50 x 16"	10	4400lb (2000 kg)	72psi (5.0 bar)

You should find the specifications of your trailer's tyres embossed in the rubber on the tyre wall. For further technical information on wheels and tyres, turn to *Appendix 6, Wheels and Tyres* at the end of this book. Information, courtesy Indespension.

☐ Job 11. Check trailer tyre pressures.

Check each of the tyre pressures with the tyres cold, before the trailer is used. As a tyre 'works', it heats up - this increases the pressure inside the tyre, and so will give a false reading. Also check the tyre valves for dirt and damage.

☐ Job 12. Check trailer tyres' condition.

12B

12A

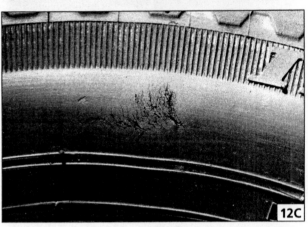

12C

12A. When running on the road, and especially when pulling onto and off the highway, cuts or bulges in the tyres can occur, especially if you happen to go over rough ground or a kerb. Check **both sides** of each tyre with great care, rotating the wheels so that all of the tyres' treads and sidewalls can be examined. If any lumps or bulges appear in the sidewalls, the tyre must be scrapped. If you find any cuts, ask your local tyre dealer to take a look. Very shallow cuts may be OK; deeper ones probably call for a new tyre.

12B. Look for cracking or crazing on the tyre walls. Trailer tyres rarely cover the mileage of car tyres and they are usually scrapped before the treads are worn out. Sunlight and ozone cause all tyres to go cracked and brittle. Check carefully, and if the tyres show signs of starting to deteriorate, replace them.

12C. Also, check for abrasion of the tyre wall, which can take place either in conjunction with bulging, or by itself. This invariably results from an impact, such as the tyre striking the edge of a kerb or a pothole in the road. If you find abrasions on your trailer's tyre you should take advice from a tyre specialist as to whether the tyre will require replacing.

Thanks are due to Dunlop Tyres Ltd for the use of all the tyre photographs used here.

FACT FILE: WHEELS AND TYRES

TRAILER TYRES require the same level of care and attention as those on a car. They are also covered by the same laws. So make sure that there is at least a minimum of 1.6 mm of tread in a continuous band across three quarters of the tyre's width. In practice, you should replace tyres before they get near this level, and certainly if any of the tyre tread falls below the recommended level.

12D. UNDER-INFLATION. If the outer edges of the tread are noticeably more worn than the centre, the tyres have been run under-inflated - which not only ruins tyres, but increases fuel consumption, causes poor handling, and is illegal.

OVER-INFLATION causes the centre part of

12D

the tyre to wear more quickly than the outer edges. This is also illegal, as well as making the tyre more susceptible to concussion damage, and reducing the tyre's grip.

TYRE TYPES Trailers may be fitted with either tubeless or tubed tyres. Make sure that the correct type is fitted to the wheels of your trailer. Tubeless tyres must only be fitted to safety-type rims. For older trailers with non-safety rims, tubes must be fitted with 'tubeless' radial tyres.

SPECIALIST SERVICE: It is not always possible to fit modern tyres to very old rims (wheels). If you have any doubt about which tyres should be fitted to your trailer, consult your local trailer dealer or tyre specialist.

Under NO CIRCUMSTANCES should cross-ply and radial-ply tyres be mixed on the trailer (or car!).

There is more information on wheels and tyres in *Appendix 6, Wheels and Tyres*.

⚡ INSIDE INFORMATION: These wheels must regularly be checked and re-balanced by your local tyre specialist. ⚡

☐ Job 13. Check trailer tyre tread depth.

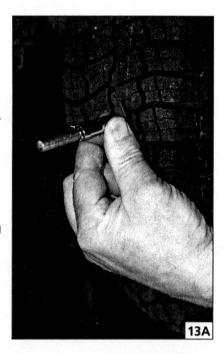

13A. Use a proper tyre tread depth gauge to check the tyre treads. The legal minimum in the UK is 1.6 mm across the central 75% of the tyre's width. (In practice, many police officers regard with a jaundiced eye the sight of *any* of the width of a tyre's tread below 1.6 mm!).

13A

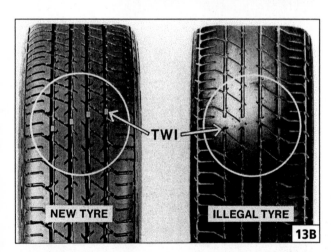

NEW TYRE — TWI — ILLEGAL TYRE

13B

13B. Modern tyres have tread wear indicators built in to the tread grooves (usually about eight of them, spread equidistantly around the circumference of the tyre). When the tread depth wears down to 1.6 mm, these appear as continuous bars running across the tread. There will be a distinct reduction in wet weather grip long before the tread wear indicators begin to show, and in the interests of safety, you really should replace the trailer's tyres well before they get to this stage.

☐ Job 14. Check wheel rims.

14

14. Wheel rims can be damaged surprisingly easily, especially when driving over kerbs or rough ground. Rim damage can cause rapid tyre deflation, with catastrophic consequences. **SPECIALIST SERVICE:** If necessary, have your local tyre centre or trailer dealer check that rims are true. Slight damage can be repaired, otherwise a new wheel will be needed.

🛈 **INSIDE INFORMATION: Unfortunately, it is unlikely that you will find a wheel to fit your trailer at a car scrapyard. Not only are the diameter and stud hole positions crucial, the 'offset' of the wheel - the amount by which the rim sticks out from the line of the hub - is not likely to be the same as anything you can find on a car. In addition, the load requirements are different. It's back to your trailer dealership, it seems!** 🛈

☐ Job 15. Check wheelnuts for tightness.

Use a torque wrench to check that the wheel nuts (or bolts) are sufficiently tight - but not too tight, which can be just as bad, because bolts or studs can shear if over-tightened.

FACT FILE: WHEELNUTS

Trailer wheelnuts are much more prone to coming loose than those fitted to cars. We recommend that you buy a torque wrench - so that the correct tightening force required can be accurately measured.

Be sure to check your wheel nuts regularly, even if it means taking off awkward wheel trims to get at them. Also, check wheel nut tensions a second time, around twenty to fifty miles after you have changed a wheel - and always check their tightness on a brand new trailer as soon as it is delivered.

❏ Job 16. Check fixtures and fittings.

All but the simplest trailers have tail boards, loading ramps, partitions and the like. Check all hinges, springs and catches for security.

❏ Job 17. Check exterior lights.

Connect the towcar electrical connectors to the trailer, and try out all of the exterior lights, both front and rear, not forgetting any auxiliary lights that may be fitted.

If you discover any problems, check the bulbs and holders (see below), and refer to **Jobs 3 and 4** for examination of cabling connections.

⚡ INSIDE INFORMATION: If a rear fog light or fog lights have been fitted to your trailer, they are subject to the same Construction & Use regulations as those fitted to your car or van. Ensure that they work properly, and that the correct wattage bulb is fitted. ⚡

Almost all trailer light lenses are easy to remove, and bulbs are simple to replace. Clean the lenses, inside and out, while they're off, and check that the surrounding seals are effective. If not, the lamp housings and bulb holders quickly deteriorate.

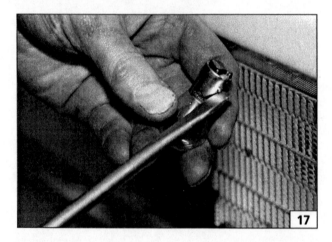

17. Note that tail/stoplight bulbs have offset pegs to prevent their being fitted the wrong way round (brake lights are brighter than tail lights, of course).

Fitting is quicker, once you suss this simple fact! Make sure terminals are clean!

making it easy! Most trailer lighting problems stem from one of two sources: connections to the trailer plug or car socket, or earthing problems within the trailer lamps themselves. To solve the latter problem, remove each lens and check for good connections between the lamp units and the trailer body; check for corrosion-free bulb holders; check that bulb internals have not vibrated themselves to bits; check for sound wiring connections.

❏ Job 18. Check hitch and couplings.

IMPORTANT NOTE: If your trailer has a friction head stabiliser fitted, see the section devoted to *Special Equipment* at the end of this chapter for details of how to maintain it. DO NOT APPLY ANY GREASE.

Use the torque wrench to check that all securing bolts are tightened to the right degree.

With the coupling fitted to your vehicle's towball, check the hitch for wear.

BRADLEY HITCH

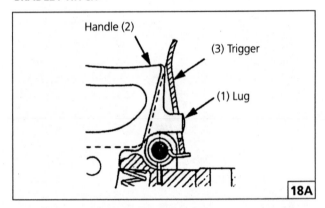

18A. If the square lug (1) at the rear of the head handle (2) resting on the bottom of the slot in the trigger (3), excessive wear has taken place on the coupling head, the coupling ball, or both.

If this is the case, make a further check using a new 50 mm ball.

If the lug remains at the bottom of the slot, the coupling head is excessively worn and should be replaced. However, if the lug is now riding noticeably higher up the slot, your original 50 mm ball should be replaced. (Illustration, courtesy Ifor Williams)

KNOTT KF27 COUPLING

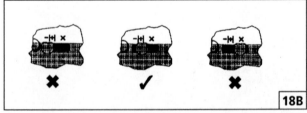

18B. With the trailer attached to your towing vehicle, check the wear indicator on the left hand side of the coupling head (see diagram). The indicator should point to the '+' side of the central line. If it points to the '-' side, excessive wear has taken place on the coupling head, the coupling ball, or both.

If this is the case, make a further check using a new 50 mm ball.

If the indicator still points to the '-' side, the coupling head is excessively worn and should be replaced. However, if it points to the '+' side, your original 50 mm ball should be replaced (Illustration, courtesy Ifor Williams)

BOTH TYPES

If you need to replace your coupling head, carry out the first check once more, as your 50 mm ball may need to be replaced as well. It is recommended that the coupling head and ball are replaced at the same time, as this will increase the service life of both components.

To comply with BS AU 113c, the ball diameter should be between 49.61 mm and 50.00 mm.

Now unhitch the trailer, chock the wheels so that the trailer is firmly parked, and then push the coupling head towards the trailer's body. It should move, but only slowly. If it is stuck solid, or moves very easily, then you are going to have to work on the damper, as detailed in **Job 40**.

18C. Clean out the cup inside the coupling head, and re-grease it thoroughly to prevent wear.

18D. Also remember to lubricate the hitch mechanism.

18E. Look out for torn bellows. This will lead to *rapid* shaft wear: replace immediately!

❏ Job 19. Check breakaway cable.

The breakaway device should be checked every month for signs of damage and wear. Pay particular attention for signs of the cable kinking or splitting.

19. Also, make sure that the clip that attaches the cable is in good order. If any faults or damage are discovered, make sure that the cable is replaced with the correct part. DO NOT be tempted to use some old piece of cable that you might have lying around.

IMPORTANT NOTE: The use of a breakaway cable is a legal requirement on braked trailers.

FACT FILE: BREAKAWAY CABLE

In the extremely unlikely event that the trailer should 'break away' from the car, the breakaway cable will become taut, and will pull on the trailer's brakes. The cable is designed to snap as soon as it has engaged the trailer's brakes. The whole idea is so that the trailer comes to a halt, instead of either careering off down the road out of control - or flailing about behind the towcar while connected solely by a piece of cable.

⚡ INSIDE INFORMATION: Breakaway cable operation is one very good reason why you should choose a trailer with an over-centre brake, rather than the more old-fashioned ratchet type. With an over-centre handbrake, the breakaway cable's initiation of braking will be continued by the brake itself, after the cable has snapped, the over-centre effect pulling the brake on harder and harder. With the ratchet mechanism type of handbrake/parking brake being applied by the breakaway cable, the brakes will fade as they heat up. ⚡

FACT FILE: TRAILER CHASSIS

READ THIS FIRST!

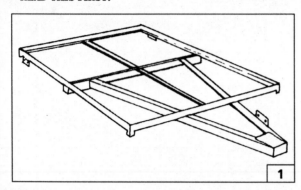

1. All the major trailer manufacturers produce their own chassis, and there is an almost infinite number of versions available. You can even upgrade an existing chassis to carry greater loads. Any modification work must be made with reference to the law, and you can find out all about this in *Chapter 7, Repairing and Upgrading Your Trailer*.

If you should need to replace any particular component on the chassis or running gear, your trailer's original manufacturer should be able to provide the items which you need, straight off the shelf. However, if you have bought one of a number of trailers made abroad, a very old trailer, or one made by a small or 'part-time' manufacturer, finding components may be a rather more difficult job. Turn to *Appendix 2, Specialists and Suppliers* to look up possible suppliers.

☐ **Job 20. Lubricate handbrake and over-run unit.**

20A. With any type of hitch, grease the one or two grease points (depending on model) on the top portion of the hitch.

20B. Check to see if there is a further grease point on the underside of the hitch, and on the over-run lever, and again, treat with a grease gun.

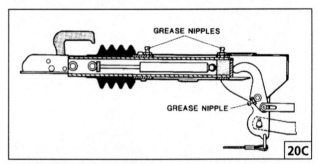

20C. These are the three grease points on the AL-KO hitch. (Illustration, courtesy AL-KO Kober)

The over-run type of handbrake MUST be lubricated every three months:

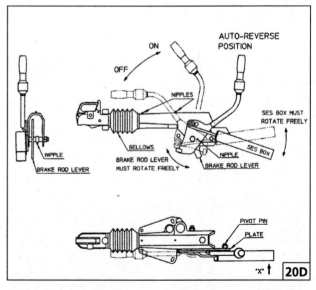

20D. With the trailer on level ground, adjust its height with the jockey wheel until it is quite level. Apply the handbrake, and push the trailer back until the reverse rotation of the wheels throws the handbrake into its auto-reverse position, as shown. (Illustration, courtesy Indespension)

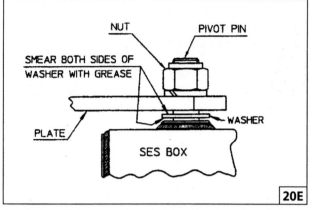

20E.

20E. Slacken off the nut on the end of the pivot pin until it is flush with the end of the thread - BUT DO NOT REMOVE IT. Now, smear both sides of the washer with a generous amount of good quality grease. (Illustration, courtesy Indespension)

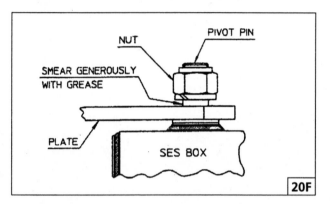

20F.

20F. Push the back end of the energy store (spring pack) inwards, to force its forward end away from the pivot pin so that you can smear this too with a generous amount of grease. The lubrication finished, now tighten the nut back up until it nips against the plate, and then back it off by a maximum of a quarter-turn. Before putting the trailer back into use, check that the energy store's tube rotates freely when the handbrake is operated. (Illustration, courtesy Indespension)

20G.

20G. Take hold of the front of the hitch. If it can be moved an appreciable amount up and down, the shaft is badly worn and might need replacement.

❏ Job 21. Lubricate jockey wheel (if fitted).

21A. Lubricate all moving parts of the jockey wheel using light oil. Locate a small hole in the operating handle of many earlier hitches and apply some oil, and/or lube the top bearing. Wipe off the excess. IMPORTANT NOTE: Some older jockey wheels were fitted with a grease nipple towards the top of the shaft, in which case, apply grease with a grease gun. Apply more oil to the centre of the jockey wheel itself and to the threaded handle...

21A.

21B.

21B. ...and the clamp which holds the jockey wheel to the side of the A-frame.

21C.

21C. Don't forget the wheel itself!

❑ Job 22. Lubricate propstands (if fitted).

Whether your trailer uses telescopic, threaded or flip-out propstands, clean off any dirt and grease the threads and pivot points.

❑ Job 23. Check and lubricate car towball.

IMPORTANT NOTE: If your trailer has a friction head stabiliser fitted, see the section devoted to Special Equipment at the end of this chapter for details of how to maintain it. DO NOT GREASE THE TOWBALL.

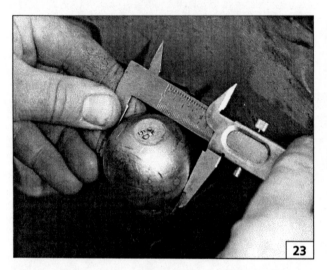

23

23. Before greasing, check the towball for wear. **SPECIALIST SERVICE:** EC-market towing balls should all measure 50 mm when new, and it's advisable to check on wear periodically by using a Vernier gauge to measure the ball's diameter. If you do not possess a Vernier, or similar piece of specialist diameter measuring equipment, have your local specialist measure the ball for you. AL-KO recommend a minimum safe diameter, at any point, of 49.61 mm. If the ball is worn below this point, REPLACE IT BEFORE TOWING THE TRAILER.

❑ Job 24. Lubricate trailer coupling head.

IMPORTANT NOTE: If your trailer has a friction head stabiliser fitted, see the section devoted to *Special Equipment* at the end of this chapter for details of how to maintain it. DO NOT APPLY ANY GREASE.

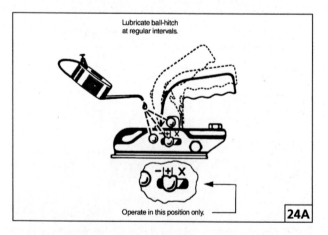

Lubricate ball-hitch at regular intervals.

Operate in this position only.

24A

24A. Wipe out and lightly grease the inside of the towball coupling. Now grease or oil all the other moving parts of the coupling head... (Illustration, courtesy BPW)

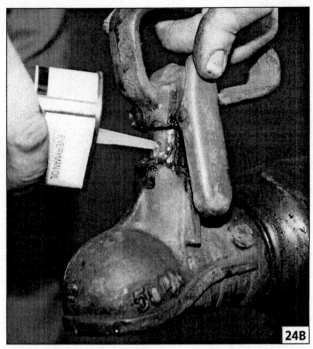

24B

24B. ...paying particular attention to the plunger assembly on the B&B-type hitches. Don't forget the manual reverse lock, when fitted.

❑ Job 25. Lubricate external hinges and locks.

25

25. Take the oil can (or specialist Teflon anti-friction spray) to all catches and locks. Where applicable, push the door key into the lock so that the protective 'door' on the lock is held open (if fitted), and inject a little oil or Teflon into the barrel. If keys are starting to feel stiff in their locks, spray in a little releasing fluid, and leave to soak.

Job 26. Check and lubricate brake operating system.

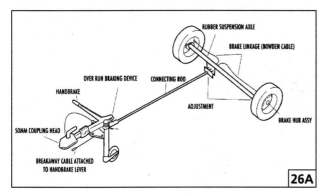

26A. These are the components of a rod-operated braking system. (Illustration, courtesy Conway)

26B. Remove any rust or caked-on dirt from braking system linkages then wash off any remaining dirt with paraffin or releasing fluid. Smear a light layer of grease onto all external moving and sliding parts of the braking system, taking care to keep the lubricant well away from the brake back plate.

IMPORTANT NOTE: Modern Bowden cables almost always have a nylon-lined outer sleeve, and so do not require oiling. In fact, if you do apply oil to a nylon-lined cable, it will damage the lining and cause the cable to wear out prematurely.

SAFETY FIRST!

When lubricating the braking system, it is essential to keep all lubricant well away from the brake back plate and the brake shoes. Should you allow any grease or oil to get onto the brakes themselves, it could be extremely dangerous, since it could well stop them working altogether - and the only remedy for grease-contaminated brake shoes is replacement.

26C. Check condition of brake linings. A visual check of brake linings should be carried out regularly. You may have to remove the brake drum to see the linings, in which case see **Job 32**, but on many types you will find two removable plastic bungs in each back plate, the outer one of which you can remove in order to make a quick check on lining condition. If the linings are less than about 1.5 mm thick, they will need replacing. Should your trailer not be equipped with these bungs, see below for cautions and instructions on working on the braking system. Make sure that the bungs are replaced securely after your check.

Check adjustment of brakes, which may need re-setting due to lining wear and/or the Bowden cables' natural stretching in operation. If brakes do need adjusting, follow the procedure described in **Jobs 28 and 29**.

Job 27. Check and re-grease wheel bearings.

27A. Remove the hub cap...

27B. ...to reveal the castle nut, and check the condition of the grease. If grease looks normal, simply 'top-up' if necessary. If grease looks dirty or emulsified (creamy looking), the bearing will need to be stripped, cleaned, and re-packed with grease. Ensure that hub caps are securely replaced DON'T over-grease!

27C. Unbraked trailers may have a grease nipple to make bearing lubrication an extra simple job. (This hub has been removed from the trailer, of course.)

Every 6,000 Miles - or Every Six Months, whichever comes first

FACT FILE: BRAKING SYSTEMS

IT IS ESSENTIAL THAT YOU READ THIS FACT FILE BEFORE ATTEMPTING TO WORK ON YOUR TRAILER'S BRAKING SYSTEM.

SAFETY FIRST!

SAFETY FIRST AND SPECIALIST SERVICE!
i) Obviously, your trailer's brakes are among its most important safety related items. Do NOT dismantle or attempt to perform any work on the braking system unless you are fully competent to do so. If you have not been trained in this work, but wish to carry it out, we strongly recommend that you have your local trailer specialist or qualified mechanic check your work before taking the trailer on the road. See also the section on BRAKES AND ASBESTOS in Chapter 1, Safety First! for further information. ii) Remember that brake dust can contain asbestos - and in the case of older systems, it most certainly will. Since asbestos can kill: ALWAYS spray a proprietary brand of aerosol brake cleaner on to the brakes after removing the hub (available from your local auto accessory store). ALWAYS wear an efficient particle mask, gloves and a hat, and wash your hands and arms after doing the job. ALWAYS dust yourself off thoroughly out of doors. ALWAYS dispose of the old shoes, wiping rags and wiped-up dust in a sealed plastic bag, and keep children and pets away from the work area. iii) Always replace the brake shoes in complete sets - NEVER replace the shoes on one wheel only. Keep all traces of oil or grease off the friction surfaces. iv) When adjusting the brakes, it is necessary to adjust one side first and then the other. In both cases it will be necessary to work underneath the trailer, and it is therefore essential that the correct safety procedure is followed for raising and supporting the trailer. See the section on Raising A Trailer Safely earlier in this chapter. v) Always specify and use ASBESTOS FREE brake linings.

Although exceptions do occur, you will probably find one of three main makes of braking systems on your trailer. Those which used to be made by AP Lockheed (and are now produced by Peak Trailers) are likely to be encountered on some older models, while some may have the modern Peak version fitted. Some Lockheed brakes are rod operated, while others will be controlled by the equally effective Bowden cable.

The two other makes - which you are far more likely to come across - are 'AL-KO', and 'Knott'. (NB. In trailer circles, the 'K' in Knott is pronounced.) You are most likely to find Knott brakes on boat trailers, car transporters and so on made from about 1990 onwards, while AL-KO brakes occur more frequently on agricultural trailers and horseboxes, made up until 1990 or so. You can generally recognise an AL-KO brake by the fins on the drum. These identification details are intended as general guidelines only, however - and you should confirm your brakes' type and maker before starting work. If you are unsure of your brakes' type and specifications, refer to your specialist trailer dealer, or to the manufacturer themselves, to find out. And always go to your trailer's manufacturer or a specialist dealer when the time comes to buy replacement components.

NEVER, on any account, try to fit car or van brakes to your trailer; they are quite different in design, and would make the trailer extremely dangerous to use. Just as importantly, they would contravene both Construction and Use and European Type Approval regulations, and could make your trailer illegal. Some manufacturers supply special axles for use with vehicle wheels - but even these are not designed to be used with the quite different braking systems found on vehicles.

All trailer brakes feature a basically similar type of system, designed to respond to the braking of the towcar. The trailer's tow hitch is mounted on a shaft which moves inside a tube which is an integral part of the chassis' A-frame. The hitch is spring-loaded, so that it is normally pushed as far forwards as it can go by the spring. When the towcar brakes, the weight and momentum of the trailer cause it to press forwards against the force of the spring, pushing the shaft back into the A-frame. This movement is transmitted through the trailer's braking system by a mechanism made up of rods and/or cables, causing the brake shoe mechanisms at the wheels to operate. Modern versions incorporate a damper (or 'shock absorber') inside the drawshaft to eliminate short, sharp movements and rebounds, and it's important to make sure that this works efficiently.

When the trailer is unhitched, the handbrake mounted on the A-frame is engaged to lock the brakes in position. It is essential that you follow the instructions in the handbook supplied with your trailer when applying the handbrake. Also, see *Chapter 5, Using a Trailer*, page 47.

Trailer Braking Systems

Adjusting the brakes is a matter of adjusting BOTH the brakes at the wheels AND the handbrake/over-run linkage, because both are interconnected, and have to work in conjunction with one another. The brakes at the wheels are adjusted first, then you follow the sequence of brake operation back through to the coupling head. See the information below.

IMPORTANT NOTE: When adjusting the brakes, turn the wheel only in the direction in which the wheel will turn when the vehicle is travelling forwards along the road. The automatic reverse facility, disabling the brake, comes into operation when the direction of rotation is reversed and you will not be able to adjust the brakes when turning the wheel backwards. And remember that braking adjustment mechanisms are relatively fragile, so do not use excessive force. (Illustration, courtesy AL-KO Kober)

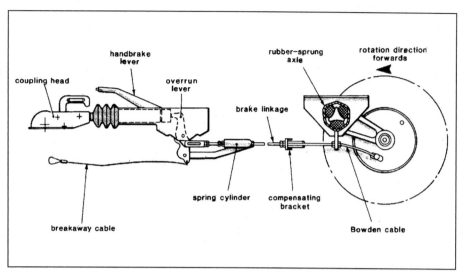

❑ **Job 28. Adjust brakes at the wheels.**

FACT FILE: PEAK TRAILERS AND LOCKHEED BRAKES

At one time, AP Lockheed brakes were commonly fitted to many trailers, and to caravans with the popular B&B chassis (hence their sometimes being incorrectly referred to as 'B&B brakes'). B&B were eventually taken over by AL-KO, who manufacture their own braking systems, and the B&B name disappeared. AP Lockheed later concentrated on car and motorcycle braking systems.

Most Lockheed trailer brake components continue to be available, and where original stocks have been exhausted, many parts are now manufactured under licence by Peak Trailers, using Lockheed's original tools - there are even brand-new Peak brakes now in production. All are now 'Peak Trailers' brakes since they own the licence to produce them.

PEAK TRAILERS/AP LOCKHEED AUTOMATIC REVERSING BRAKE (EARLY MKI) MODELS ONLY

28A. Park the trailer on level ground and raise the side of the trailer, as described in the section *Working Safely on the Underside* earlier in this chapter.

28B. Disengage the handbrake and pull the trailer drawshaft fully forwards, away from the A-frame. Make sure that there's slack in the brake rod and cables (loosen locknuts if necessary), and ensure that the handbrake is fully disengaged.

EARLY LOCKHEED ('B&B') BRAKES ONLY

28C. If the trailer is fitted with the original wheels, locate a small hole towards each wheel's centre. If there's not a hole in the wheel (or if the wheel has been put back in the wrong place!), remove the wheel and locate the hole in the drum behind.

Turn the wheel/hub until the hole in the front of the hub exposes the adjuster screw. Turning the screw pushes both brake shoes outwards, until they push against the sides of the drum. Use a large screwdriver, and keep turning until the brake shoes are firmly pressed to the drum wall, and the hub is locked.

28D. Operate the handbrake a couple of times, and then fully release it again to centralise the shoes. Then try the adjuster screw again. Now back off the adjuster one 'click' stop at a time, until the brake drum is just completely free to rotate when turned only in a forwards direction.

⚡ INSIDE INFORMATION: The very slightest amount of rubbing at one or two points around the drum is acceptable - but no more. ⚡

IMPORTANT NOTE: Should the amount of adjustment required seem excessive, remove the brake drum and ensure that the carrier shoe is in the correct position. See **Job 32**.

⚡ INSIDE INFORMATION: The adjuster screw bears directly on the front shoe, but the rear shoe is only pushed outwards by the sliding expander (See *Job 32, Part I*). If there is corrosion, or a build-up of brake dust on the back plate, this can be difficult to move by the action of the adjuster alone, which is why you need to centralise the shoes using the handbrake. ⚡

Don't forget to examine the rubber boot (gaiter) on the backplate (when fitted), and renew if necessary.

Replace the wheel, lower the trailer and repeat the procedure on the opposite wheel.

'STANDARD' AP LOCKHEED - NON-AUTOMATIC REVERSE BRAKES ONLY

These brakes predated the 'automatic' AP Lockheed brakes. Not all spares are available, and we would recommend replacement with auto-reverse wheel hubs wherever possible.

1. Adjuster
2. Expander
3. Rubber boot
4. Brake shoes
5. Pull off spring
6. Backplate

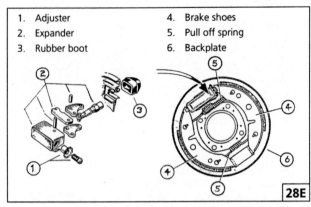

28E. In the unlikely event that you have seven-inch brakes fitted, adjustment is by a starred wheel adjuster (see AL-KO brakes), accessed from the front of the drum, with the wheel removed. (Illustration, courtesy Peak Trailers.)

1. Adjuster
2. Expander
3. Rubber boot
4. Brake shoes
5. Pull off spring
6. Backplate
7. Abutment block

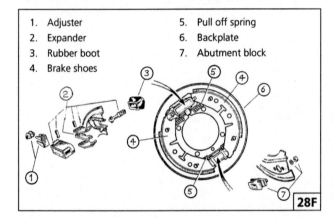

28F. When 8, 9, or 10 in. brakes are fitted, the adjuster is identical to that used in the automatic-reverse brake system. (Illustration, courtesy Peak Trailers.)

FACT FILE: AUTO-REVERSE BRAKES

28G. Incorporated into the trailer's braking system is an ingenious mechanism which automatically allows the trailer to be reversed without the braking system engaging itself. As the car starts to reverse, the drawbar shaft is compressed as normal - but rather cleverly, the brakes un-apply themselves.

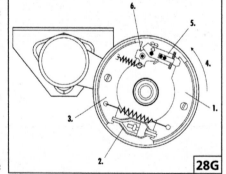

What happens is that, as the brake shoes (1 and 3) are forced against the brake drum by the expander (2), they start by 'gripping' the brake drum, as normal. If the wheel was travelling in a forwards direction (4), the brake would operate as normal. As it is, the brake shoes try to rotate backwards with the brake drum. This causes the spring-loaded reverse lever (6) to collapse, and the brake shoes are moved away from the brake drum. There is inevitably a tiny amount of friction taking place (to maintain the reverse lever in it collapsed position) but this is negligible.

As soon as the wheel/brake drum move in the forwards direction, the coil spring attached to the reverse lever snaps everything back to its normal braking position. For reference, item 5 is the adjuster box.

On older trailers, someone would have to physically over-ride the over-run brake, using a reversing catch on the tow hitch, before reversing could be carried out. With this system, you couldn't reverse out of danger rapidly, in an emergency, and there was always a possibility that the operator might forget to re-engage the brakes before driving away. If your trailer is not equipped with an auto-reverse facility, we would suggest that you contact one of the suppliers listed in *Appendix 2, Specialists and Suppliers* and have more modern, replacement auto-reverse brakes fitted. (Illustration, courtesy Conway)

AL-KO TYPE BRAKES ONLY

IMPORTANT NOTE: AL-KO point out that all servicing must be carried out by an authorised dealer throughout the period covered by any applicable chassis warranty.

Ensure that there is some end float in the brake rod and spring cylinder. Make sure that the drawshaft is fully extended - pulled out as far as it will go - and that the handbrake is fully disengaged.

Jack the trailer up, make it secure, and remove the wheel, following the lifting procedure as described before for adjusting the AP Lockheed brakes with an axle stand underneath the outer end of the axle, and positioned on a good firm, level surface.

28H. At the back of the wheel hub, remove the inner of the two plastic blanking plugs. Take a look at the back of the hub and you will see an arrow stamped there. (You may first have to clean off some dirt, or rust!) Insert a flat-head screwdriver into the hole revealed by having removed the blanking plug, and turn the star wheel inside...

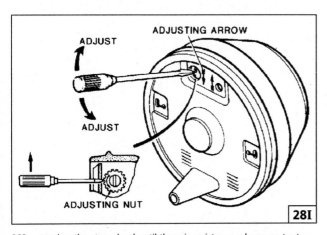

28I. ...turning the star wheel until there is resistance when you try to rotate the road wheel by hand.

IMPORTANT INFORMATION: Always rotate the roadwheel in the forwards direction - NEVER backwards.

Now slacken the star wheel once again, until the road wheel just begins to turn freely in the FORWARDS direction.

Repeat the procedure on the other side of the trailer. (Illustration, courtesy AL-KO Kober.)

ADJUST BRAKE COMPENSATOR

AL-KO-TYPE BRAKES

28J. Next, locate the brake compensator, where the brake cable outers are fixed to a bracket located on the centre of the axle (the anchor plate), and the inners secured to another, moving bracket, which is pushed and pulled by the brake operating rod (the compensator itself). Using a pair of pliers on each cable in turn, pull the inner cable out. It should extend between 5 and 8 mm. This applies to

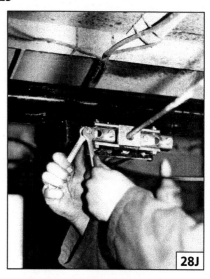

every Bowden cable which leads to the compensator from a road wheel. IMPORTANT NOTE: this check and adjustment (see **Job 28M**) does not apply when a gas strut handbrake is fitted.

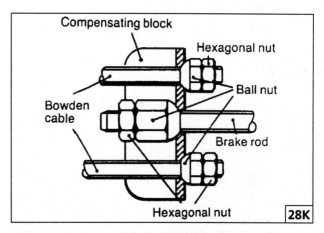

28K. Ensure that the compensator is pulled evenly by all the brakes. To do this, apply and release the handbrake three or four times to centralise the brake shoes, then adjust the brake rod so that the over-run lever butts up against the end of the towing shaft, leaving no clearance. Tighten up all brake rod locking nuts as shown in 28J. (Illustration, courtesy AL-KO Kober.)

28L. Adjust the locking nuts to give 1 mm clearance ONLY on the spring cylinder. (Note that, as said above: if the over-run is fitted with a gas strut handbrake, this does not apply because there is no spring cylinder fitted.)

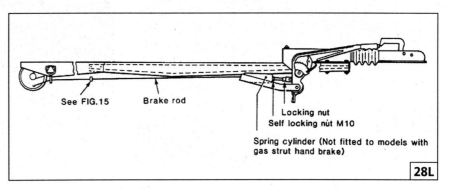

Correct adjustment of the linkage is checked by operating the handbrake lever so that a slight braking force is felt when you attempt to turn the wheels by hand, with the handbrake lightly applied (just on, if over-centre; on the second or third tooth if it is of the ratchet type). IMPORTANT NOTE: if either the wheel brakes or linkages are over-adjusted, reversing will be difficult or impossible. (Illustration, courtesy AL-KO Kober.)

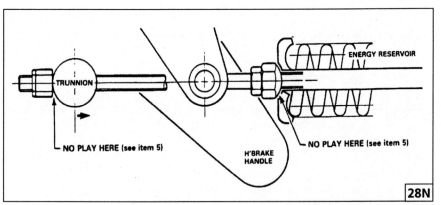

28N

Before replacing each wheel, remove the second (outer) plastic plug at the rear of the wheel hub (see Job 26C) and check the condition of the brake shoes. If they appear damaged, or worn down to a thickness of less than about 1.5 mm, replace them as shown in **Job 32, Part 2**.

Assuming that all is well with the brake shoes, replace the wheel, and retighten using a torque wrench (to 65 lb/ft or 90 Nm on all M12 wheel bolts - see *FACT FILE: WHEEL NUT TORQUE SETTINGS on page 53* for more recommended wheel nut/bolt torques) in the correct sequence of north, south, east, west. Now lower the trailer back to ground level.

KNOTT BRAKES, PLUS LATER (MKII) LOCKHEED BRAKES ONLY

IMPORTANT NOTE: Where Knott brakes are fitted in conjunction with their standard Bowden cable brake system, follow the cable adjustment procedures for AL-KO brakes, above.

N.B. The type of adjustment at the road wheels shown here is also applicable to Lockheed trailer brakes *with automatic reverse*. Note that the adjuster on these later Lockheed brakes is a small squared shaft, and is best adjusted with a proper brake adjuster tool, available from your auto. accessory store.

28M

28M. After lifting both trailer wheels off the ground and supporting the trailer with an axle stand under the end of each axle, and lowering each prop stand, turn the brake adjusting nut, as illustrated, with a 17 mm ring spanner in a clockwise direction until the wheel locks up. Do not force it! (Illustration, courtesy BPW)

⚡ **INSIDE INFORMATION: Because this type of adjuster is external, there is a chance that the thread may have rusted solid. To be sure of freeing it, spray it with a little releasing fluid the day before commencing work.** ⚡

28N. When these brakes are fitted in conjunction with the Peak Trailers 4700 Series coupling, the linkage has next to receive some attention. Check that the linkage is free and properly lubricated, and ensure that the linkage is free from slack. Pull the central brake rod forwards to take up all the free play, and at the same time, push the brake rod trunnion (illustrated) on the hitch back to its rear position. There should now be no clearance between the rear of the nut and the trunnion (as shown). Adjust the nut as necessary to take up any clearance.

Also check the spring pack assembly, and adjust the domed nut as necessary, so that there is no clearance between it and the locating plate, as shown. IMPORTANT NOTE: The overall length of the spring pack is set by the factory, and should not be interfered with.

Now, go back to the wheels and back off each adjuster until each wheel just turns freely with no binding. Check the adjustment by pulling on the handbrake one or two 'clicks', until the brake is just starting to work.

⚡ **INSIDE INFORMATION: With the Knott system, it is advisable to gently tap the adjuster with a hammer to ensure that it has seated correctly.** ⚡

There should now be an identical amount of 'drag' from each brake. If not, only effect an adjustment by slackening off the 'tight' brake - not by tightening the 'loose' one. Binding brakes can be dangerous and damaging. Also, DO NOT compensate by adjusting the brake cables. Adjusting the brakes in this way, with this system, ensures that the correct amount of play is present in the linkages. (Illustration, courtesy Peak Trailers.)

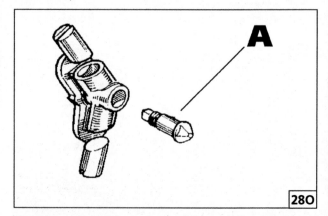

28O

28O. Adustment of Sankey (ex-military) trailer brake shoes is by the square headed stud (A), which protrudes from the outside of the brake backplate. *USE THE CORRECT BRAKE ADJUSTER TOOL* from a car accessory store - a spanner can easily 'round' the stud. If the adjuster is seized, the brakes assembly has to be stripped, the assembly shown here has to be removed and heat used to free the stud.

FACT FILE: BRAKE ROD CLEARANCES

As you will see in **Job 30**, the modern over-centre handbrake requires that all slack should be adjusted out of the brake operating linkages - which, fortunately, is an easy job to judge. However, many early hydraulically damped couplings, and many makes of ratchet handbrake still commonly found, depend on very precisely measured adjustment of the brake operating rod if they are to work properly. The diagrams shown here (courtesy, Indespension) show the areas which must be measured on the popular Bradley and Knott couplings, along with the figures which you will need to set the rod properly. If this all appears too confusing for you to attempt yourself, visit your local trailer specialist! He will also help to establish the make and model of your own trailer's coupling, if necessary.

IMPORTANT NOTE: The Knott couplings shown here are also to be found in use with non-auto-reverse brakes. If this is the case with your trailer, the part numbers will be the same, but there will be no energy store fitted. You should set these types to a clearance of zero.

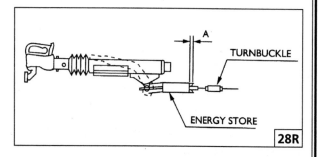

28R. Bradley

Model	Weight (kg)	Application	A (mm)
MXR	2250-3000	auto-reverse, cable	1-5

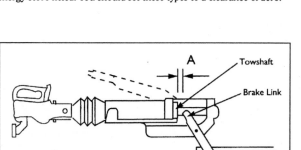

28P. Bradley

Model	Weight (kg)	Application	A (mm)
HU5M	650 - 1350	Non-autoreverse	12
HU6M	1080-2200	non-autoreverse	12
5MR	600-1350	auto-reverse, rod	18
6MR	1100-2600	auto-reverse, rod	18
MKX	2250-3000	non-autoreverse	0

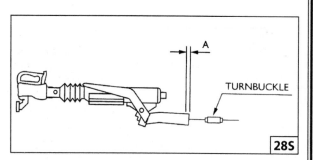

28S. Bradley, with gas strut handbrake.

Model	Weight (kg)	Application	A (mm)
HU3LR	450-900	auto-reverse, cable	1-3
HU3HR	850-1700	auto-reverse, cable	1-3
HU3HER	1650-2600	auto-reverse, cable	1-3

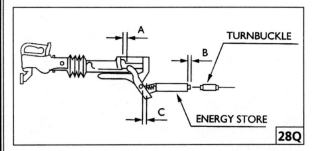

28Q. Bradley

Model	Weight (kg)	Application	A (mm)	B (mm)	C (mm)
5MKR	912-1900	auto-reverse, cable	10	1-3	30
6MKR	1456-2500	auto-reverse, cable	10	1-3	30
HU3S80RL	875-1350	auto-reverse, cable	10	1-3	30
HU3S80RH	1130 - 1800	auto-reverse, cable	10	1-3	30

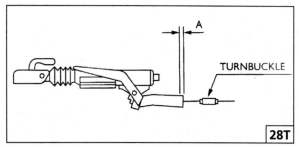

28T. Knott

Model	Weight (kg)	Application	A (mm)
KF7.5C	375-750	auto-reverse, cable	3
KRV7.5C	375-750	auto-reverse, cable	3
KF13C	800-1300	auto-reverse, cable	3
KRV13C	800-1300	auto-reverse, cable	3

❑ Job 29. Adjust handbrake and over-run.

IMPORTANT NOTE 1: Before adjusting any of the handbrake systems shown here, it is essential that the wheel brakes, cables and compensator are correctly adjusted, as described in **Job 28**.

Until recent years, it seemed as though there were as many different types of brake operating mechanism as there were trailer manufacturers. However, the Lockheed system described here is one of the most common older types, and can be taken as a guide. If necessary, obtain specific information from the original manufacturer (see list towards the back of this book), or from your local trailer dealership.

FACT FILE: TRAILER HANDBRAKES

The flexibility of settings offered by a ratchet handbrake is ideal for hill-starts and so on, while driving a car - but on a trailer, most advantages of a ratchet are wasted.

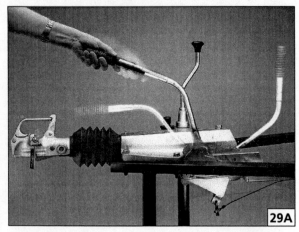

29A

29A. By far the commonest sort of handbrake to be fitted to trailers in the past few years is the 'over-centre' type, and these have taken over from ratchets almost completely. The over-centre brake is a far simpler mechanism than the ratchet, but it offers many advantages over its predecessor. With an over-centre brake there is no need to adjust the brake operating mechanism itself - and linkage adjustment is simplified too: you simply adjust all play out of the operating linkage. (Illustration, courtesy Indespension.)

There are two other significant advantages to using an over-centre brake:

i) The brake can be used to carry out a simple and reliable test of your wheel brakes' adjustment. See **Job 30**, below.

ii) The brake increases the efficiency of the breakaway mechanism enormously (see **FACT FILE: BREAKAWAY CABLE** on page 61 for full details). For this reason alone, we would always recommend that you choose a trailer fitted with an over-centre handbrake.

The only area where a ratchet might be preferred to an over-centre brake is where the person to operate it is not very big or strong. Generally, rather more effort is required to release an over-centre brake than a ratchet - but Indespension have developed a telescopic handle for their over-centre brakes, as shown in picture **29B**, which solves even this problem!

SAFETY FIRST!

The compression spring used with the over-centre handbrake is extremely strong, and should you dismantle any part of the braking train without first securing the handbrake lever, it could fly up and might cause serious

---

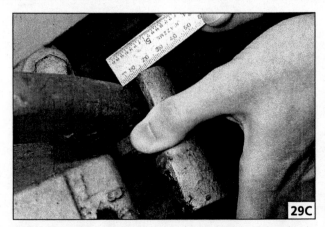

Handbrake locking screw

Do not tow trailer witht he locking screw in place as the breakaway system and handbrake will not operate

29B

29B. Manufacturers of trailers using an over-centre handbrake often supply a special locking pin or screw with which you should fasten the handbrake lever before working on the braking train. Always use this pin if you have it, otherwise lash the lever down securely with strong cord. (Illustration, courtesy Ifor Williams Trailers Ltd.)

LOCKHEED/PEAK-TYPE RATCHET HANDBRAKE ONLY

Once you have adjusted the drum brakes and linkage, don't forget to check the handbrake. The handbrake/over-run mechanism is an important part of the system, and works in conjunction with the wheel brakes. Make sure that the drawshaft is fully extended, and that the brake rod is in good condition and not bent or twisted.

29C

29C. Pull back the over-run lever and measure the distance between it and the handbrake. Ideally it should be 5 - 10 mm.

29D. If necessary, adjust it by repositioning the nuts on the front end of the brake operating rod.

Once you've done this, check the brakes by engaging the handbrake and pushing the trailer backwards on smooth, level ground. A 'click' should be heard from each brake, and then you should not be able to move the trailer any further. If the brake fails to hold the trailer, readjust the brake rod until it does so.

If you do have to readjust the brake rod, check that, with the brakes disengaged, there is no drag when the trailer is pulled forwards. Best of all, raise each wheel in turn from the ground and check for 'drag' when turning each wheel forwards by hand.

29E. Locate any grease nipples on the brake linkage, such as behind the wheels beneath the trailer, and at the front (depending on the type of linkage fitted). Also grease any grease nipples which may be fitted to brake cable 'outers'.

AL-KO TYPE RATCHET HANDBRAKE ONLY

IMPORTANT NOTE: It is essential before beginning that the brakes are adjusted correctly at the wheel, and the brake compensator is correctly set. Do NOT attempt to adjust the handbrake until these jobs have been correctly carried out.
The handbrake will be 'right' when, with both wheels off the ground, there is a braking effect when the handbrake is on its second or third 'click' of the ratchet. It is important that the braking effect you can feel (by turning each wheel in the direction it will go in when the trailer is travelling forwards) is equal on each wheel. If one wheel is tighter than the other, back that brake off at the wheel (not at the cables or rod) until the 'tight' brake just matches its colleague. DON'T adjust by tightening the 'loose' brake, because you may end up causing the brakes to bind, which can be extremely dangerous.

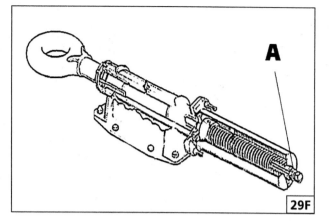

29F. The Sankey (ex-military trailer) over-run is very easy to adjust, consisting of just mechanism and a lock nut.
• Apply the handbrake, then slacken off the lockut (A).
• Adjust the bolt head until it contacts the handbrake mechanism, then tighten the lock nut.

☐ Job 30. Brake adjustment with over-centre handbrakes.

 If you find it difficult to let off an over-centre handbrake - and it can be difficult! - carry a length of tube to act as an extension and avoid hernias and other lesser embarrassments.

The modern, over-centre type of ratchetless handbrake makes little difference to the procedures described above for adjusting the wheel brakes, and does not need elaborate servicing (see **Job 20**). It does however have one or two special implications which you should be aware of:

Ratchet handbrakes will tolerate a certain amount of play in the cable and rod operating mechanism before their operation is seriously affected. Over-centre handbrakes will only operate efficiently if there is no play whatsoever along the rod and cable train. So, proper adjustment is doubly important if you have an over-centre handbrake on your trailer.

FACT FILE: BRAKE TEST

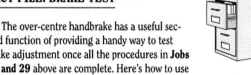

The over-centre handbrake has a useful second function of providing a handy way to test brake adjustment once all the procedures in **Jobs 28 and 29** above are complete. Here's how to use it to test brake adjustment:

Apply the handbrake, and then, to test the wheel brakes' adjustment, turn each wheel in the reversing direction until it locks. All brakes should lock firmly, since the over-centre handbrake is designed to over-ride the auto-reverse mechanism. If the wheels do not lock, their brakes' adjustment is not tight enough. If the wheels lock satisfactorily, release the handbrake and tighten the locknuts...

⚡ INSIDE INFORMATION: To check that the brakes haven't been over-tightened, couple the trailer to the towing vehicle, take the handbrake off, and reverse the trailer. If the brakes lock now, then you know that the brake rod has been over-tightened. Re-adjust the brake rod, and re-test to check that adjustment is now correct. ⚡

It is essential that you read this before doing any work on the braking system.

When carrying out any work which involves dismantling any part of the braking system - basically, anything more ambitious than adjusting the brakes' settings - you must be sure to abide by all the safety warnings given in Chapter 1, Safety First! of this book, and in the relevant sections of Job 32.

If your trailer is equipped with an over-centre handbrake, it is also important that you remember to SECURE THE HANDBRAKE before dismantling any part of the braking train. It has a powerful compression spring which will force the handbrake lever to fly up in the air once tension is released, and this could potentially be very dangerous.

AL-KO and Knott over-centre brakes come with a special handbrake locking pin or screw, which is inserted into the appropriate holes in the handbrake to prevent it from springing up when the brakes are dismantled.

If your over-centre brake does not have such a pin - or if you have mislaid it - lash the handbrake lever firmly down in the 'off' position before any part of the braking system is interfered with.

And, once you have finished working on the brakes, remember to remove the pin or untie the handbrake before attempting to tow the trailer - with the pin or screw still in place, the breakaway system and handbrake will not operate.

❑ **Job 31. Replace a bowden cable, when necessary.**

FACT FILE: BOWDEN CABLES

31A. The correct name for any cable with a stranded steel inner sliding in a protective-coated steel spiral outer is 'Bowden' cable (after the chap who invented them many decades ago) and they still present the cheapest and simplest way of operating the brakes. There are two problems which you

should watch out for with Bowden cables:

i) The steel inner cable will stretch in use. This is quite normal, but you must keep a close eye on adjustment, and replace the cables when necessary.

ii) The ends of the cables terminate in 'nipples', which can sometimes pull off. Over-tightening your brake cables will not only stretch them, it will put undue stress on their vulnerable ends. Allowing dirt to build up around a cable nipple, and neglecting to oil or grease the nipple seating regularly, increases friction - which could result in the steel strands onto which the nipple is clamped being 'sawn through' as the cable is used.

It is recommended that brake cables should be replaced as a set every six thousand miles or every five years if the trailer is used regularly. Even when regularly replaced, fraying of cable strands, partial detachment of cable nipples, and scuffing through of cable outers require immediate replacement.

KNOTT BRAKES ONLY

31B. This type of cable can be replaced without dismantling - just lift off the upper shroud, as shown. (Illustration, courtesy BPW.)

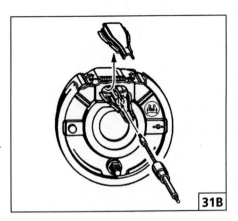

AL-KO BRAKES ONLY

31C. AL-KO cables of the type fitted to the later-type brakes can also be inserted externally. After removing the steel sleeve from the support collar, the upper part of the cable support can be detached.

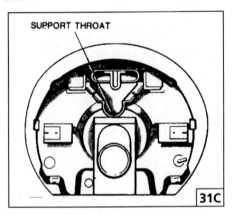

31D. The nipple is then pressed into the insertion eye; pull back the cable outer as you apply it, so that you can see when the nipple engages correctly.

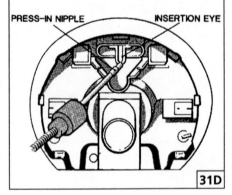

31E. The upper part of the cable support is inserted into the brake plate opening, flush with the lower, welded part of the brake support.

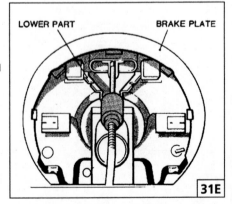

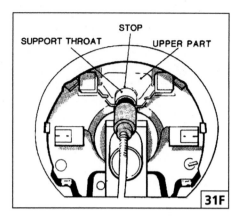

31F. Now the cable end-bush is pushed over the support throat as far as it will go.

31F

Labels in figure: SUPPORT THROAT, STOP, UPPER PART

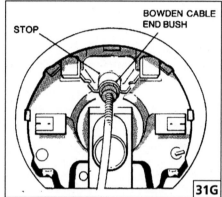

31G. Once you are certain that the nipple is inserted correctly, it only remains to adjust the cable inner's free length at the compensator end. (All five illustrations, courtesy AL-KO Kober)

31G

Labels in figure: STOP, BOWDEN CABLE END BUSH

AP LOCKHEED MKII AUTO REVERSE, & EARLY KNOTT BRAKES

Raise the trailer and remove the brake drum. (You will find instructions on how to remove the drum under **Job 32.**) Having ensured that it is safe to do so (see *Working Safely on the Underside*), get underneath the trailer to disconnect the forward ('pulling') end of the cable from the compensator, and release the cable outer from the anchor/abutment plate. Now, working at the brake itself, prise the expander lever towards you. This should allow you to release the cable eye. Withdraw this from the rear, fit the replacement cable, and then reassemble by following these instructions in reverse order. Finally, don't forget to readjust the brakes!

⚡ **INSIDE INFORMATION: Pull the handbrake on hard, several times, to centre the brake before final adjustment.** ⚡

☐ Job 32. Replace brake shoes, when necessary.

32A. If there are any signs of excessive wear, or any damage or if any of the friction material (the linings themselves) have worn down to a thickness of 1.5 mm or less renew the brake shoes as a complete set.

⚡ **INSIDE INFORMATION: Older brake shoes can sometimes be a bit more difficult to get hold of. If this is the case, the recommended route is to contact your local AP Lockheed service centre (or see Peak Trailers, listed in *Appendix 2, Specialists and Suppliers*), where it should be possible to have your existing brake shoes relined quite inexpensively.** ⚡

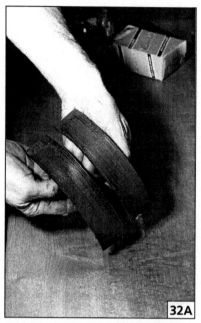

32A

PART ONE: BRAKE OVERHAUL - EARLY KNOTT AND LOCKHEED MK2 BRAKES ONLY

┤ SAFETY FIRST! ├

i) Obviously, your trailer's brakes are among its most important safety-related items. Do NOT dismantle or attempt to perform any work on the braking system unless you are fully competent to do so. If you have not been trained in this work, but wish to carry it out, we strongly recommend that you have a your local trailer specialist workshop or qualified mechanic check your work before taking the trailer on the road. See also the section on BRAKES AND ASBESTOS in Chapter 1, Safety First! for further information.

ii) Remember that brake dust can contain asbestos and in the case of older systems, it most certainly will. Since asbestos can kill: ALWAYS spray a proprietary brand of aerosol brake cleaner onto the brakes after removing the hub (available from your local auto. accessory store); ALWAYS wear an efficient particle mask, gloves and a hat, and wash your hands and arms after doing the job; ALWAYS dust yourself off thoroughly out of doors; ALWAYS dispose of the old shoes, wiping rags and wiped-up dust in a sealed plastic bag, and keep children and pets away from the work area.

iii) Always replace the brake shoes in complete sets - never replace the shoes on one wheel (or one axle on a twin-axle trailer) only. Keep all traces of oil or grease off the friction surfaces.

iv) When adjusting the brakes, it is necessary to adjust one side first and then the other. In both cases it will be necessary to work underneath the trailer and it is therefore essential that the correct safety procedure is followed for raising and supporting the trailer. See the section on 'Working Safely on the Underside' earlier in this chapter.

v) Always specify and use ASBESTOS FREE brake linings.

IMPORTANT NOTE 1: Before dismantling the brake shoe assembly, take notes, sketches and even a photograph or video of the spring assembly. It is *essential* that all springs are re-attached in their correct locations. As well as examining the brake shoes for wear, carefully examine the brake springs. If any appear stretched - if the coils appear uneven, or open at any point; or if the hooked ends appear open - replace them with a complete new set of branded parts. DO NOT substitute any other springs! Also look carefully for oil staining on the brakes and backplate. If any is found, the oil seals will have to be renewed.

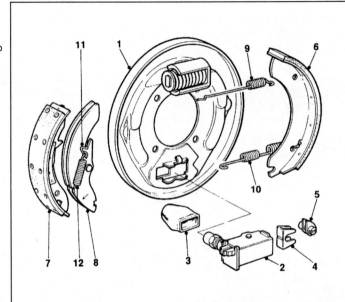

1. Backplate
2. Expander
3. Rubber boot
4. Mask
5. Micram adjuster
6. Leading brake shoe (2)
7. Trailing brake shoe (2)
8. Trailing shoe carrier
9. Pull-off spring (Black) Single coil R.H.
9. Pull-off spring (Red) Single coil L.H.
10. Pull-off spring double coil R.H.
10. Pull-off spring double coil L.H.
11. Carrier link (2)
12. Carrier spring (4)

32B

IMPORTANT NOTE 2: When removing and replacing a wheel hub (brake drum), it is absolutely essential that the hub nut is neither over-tightened nor under-tightened. DO NOT attempt to replace a wheel hub without using a torque wrench at the correct setting to tighten it up again. If you do not have a suitable torque wrench, take the trailer to a specialist dealer or manufacturer to have the work done. Even if you have the right equipment and are sufficiently confident to carry out the work yourself, we would still recommend that you have a trailer specialist check that the wheels and brakes are properly set up once you have finished.

IMPORTANT NOTE 3: Another important safety precaution is always to use a brand new split pin to secure the hub's castellated nut each time that it's removed. Alternatively, if a nut collar is used, then this should be replaced every second time the wheel is removed; some hub nuts should be renewed each time too. See **Job 39** for details.

INSIDE INFORMATION: Before replacing the brake drum, check it for any damage, such as cracking, or excessive scoring from brake shoes. If the drums are scored, see if you can have them lightly skimmed by an engineering workshop. Otherwise, replace them with new drums. IF THE SCORING IS DEEP, OR IF YOU SUSPECT THAT THE DRUMS HAVE PREVIOUSLY BEEN SKIMMED, REPLACE THEM WITH NEW.

MKI Rod Operated Version

32B. The Peak/Lockheed brake has a conventional mechanical expander with sliding links, a micram type adjuster on the leading shoe, and a carrier on the trailing shoe. When the trailer is travelling in a forwards direction, as the brakes are operated the shoes are forced into contact with the brake drum, and by virtue of the trailing shoe moving in the carrier and the expander being able to slide on the backplate, a duo-servo braking effect is achieved.

The fitting opposite the expander is fixed for the leading shoe, but the trailing shoe seats onto a powerful coil spring which acts as a torque limiter. During heavy forwards braking, reaction through the trailing shoe/carrier assembly compresses the spring at a given torque, so allowing the shoe to move away from the drum and limit the brake. Note that the whole assembly is often fitted in a different position to the one shown here, with the spring usually on the right-hand side rather than at the top.

BRAKE DRUM AND SHOE REMOVAL

Securely chock the trailer's other wheel, and slightly loosen the nuts on the wheel which is about to be removed. Jack the trailer up, and then use axle stands to securely support the trailer's weight. Lower the prop stands (if fitted) for extra security before releasing the handbrake fully, ensuring that the hitch is fully extended, and then remove the road wheel from its hub.

making it easy! Brake drums are machined from cast metal, and so are prone to cracking if abused. If you carry on using a cracked brake drum, there is a good chance that it will shatter in use - with predictably catastrophic results. In their early stages, these cracks are not always immediately visible, and a good way to check for invisible cracks is this: hang up each drum on the end of a piece of string, and tap it gently with a hammer. You should hear a clear ringing sound. If the sound is dull and flat, the drum is cracked and should be scrapped immediately and replaced with new.

32C. Line up the hole in the brake drum with the slotted head of the micram adjuster. Back off all brake adjustment, with a screwdriver, by turning the adjuster fully anti-clockwise.

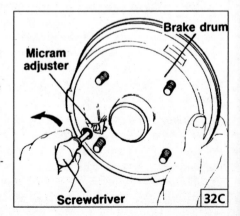

32D. Prise the grease retainer cap off the hub, and remove the split pin, hub nut, washer and bearing. Withdraw the brake drum from the stub axle. BEFORE PROCEEDING MAKE A CAREFUL NOTE OF THE SPRING AND SHOE POSITIONS.

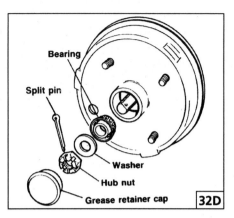

Bearing

Split pin

Washer

Hub nut

Grease retainer cap

32D

making it easy! If you can't grip the split pin's head with pliers, straighten the ends as well as you can, and use the pliers to push it out.

32E

32E. Release the *double coil* pull-off spring, indicated here, from behind the hook on the back plate, adjacent to the expander.

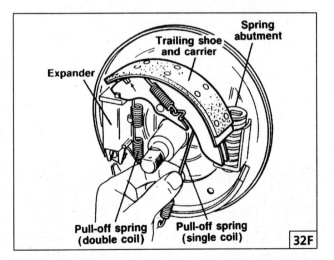

Spring abutment

Trailing shoe and carrier

Expander

Pull-off spring (double coil)

Pull-off spring (single coil)

32F

32F. At the opposite end, lift the carrier and shoe away from the spring abutment and disconnect the single coil pull-off spring, as shown, from the leading (lower) brake shoe.

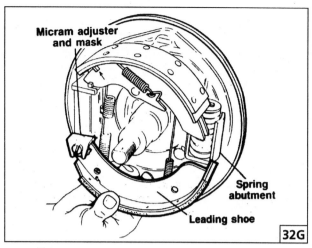

Micram adjuster and mask

Spring abutment

Leading shoe

32G

32G. Lift the leading shoe from the spring abutment and slide the adjuster and mask off the expander body. Remove both shoes from the backplate.

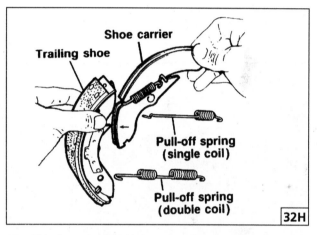

Shoe carrier

Trailing shoe

Pull-off spring (single coil)

Pull-off spring (double coil)

32H

32H. Slide the carrier assembly from the trailing shoe to expose both pull-off springs. Note their positions, and remove them.

 INSIDE INFORMATION: The double coil spring is not interchangeable with the one fitted to the opposite brake.

32I. This is the way in which the trailing shoe is seated in the carrier.

32I

EXPANDER REMOVAL AND REPLACEMENT

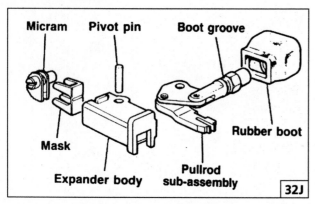

32J. Disconnect the pullrod and remove the rubber boot. Withdraw the expander assembly from the backplate, push out the pivot pin and extract the pullrod sub-assembly from the expander body. Remove all dust and deposits from the backplate using a special aerosol car brake cleaner and a clean rag. *Do not blow out with an air line. Do not use petrol or paraffin.*

Before replacing, lubricate the pullrod sub-assembly *using only approved brake grease*. Fit the assembly into the expander body, and insert the pivot pin. Fit the expander assembly onto the backplate, and check that it slides freely in the slot. Pack the rubber boot with Lockheed Rubberlube (Part No. LPK 102), and slide this over the pullrod up to the backplate. Ensure that the boot lips locate correctly over the backplate tabs, and also seat into the pullrod boot groove.

BRAKE SHOE REPLACEMENT

32K. Assemble the new shoes, carrier and springs by reversing the removal procedure.

⚡ **INSIDE INFORMATION: The easiest way of doing so is to put springs in place on the trailing shoe and carrier (top) and the leading shoe, then hook the shoes onto the expander without the adjuster assembly in place.** ⚡

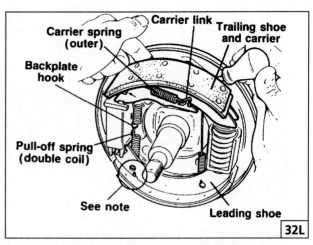

32L. Using only an approved brand of brake grease (not ordinary grease), very lightly smear all metal to metal contact points such as brake shoe and carrier tips, the abutment faces, the areas of the backplate against which the shoe webs rest, also the surface of the carrier roller. *Avoid contact of grease with shoe linings, rubber parts and the friction surface of the brake drum.*

32M. You can then pull the brake shoe assemblies into place on the spring assembly, one shoe at a time. Don't despair if it takes a few goes before you manage to get the shoes back on with the springs still in place; it's a difficult job even for an expert! But take some consolation from the thought that trying to fit the springs once the brake shoes are in place is a completely hopeless task.

You will also have to lever the expander end of the lower shoe away from the expander in order to fit the adjuster assembly.

making it easy! Taking care **not to clamp onto the friction lining material,** use a mole grip or adjustable spanner to grip one end of the last brake shoe to be fitted. This should give you the extra leverage needed to pull it into place against the force of the spring.

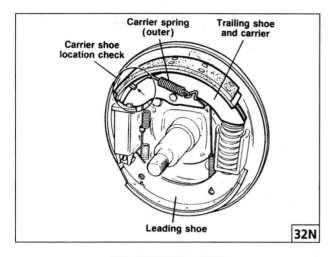

Carrier shoe
location check
Carrier spring
(outer)
Trailing shoe
and carrier
Leading shoe

32N

32O

32O. Before re-fitting the drum, attend to the lubrication of the hub centre bearing. As a general guide, the bearings should be liberally coated, with a good quality high melting point hub grease. BUT: do not overpack the hub because surplus grease could be forced onto the braking surface, causing the brakes to fail. (Illustration, courtesy Indespension.)

Refit the drum, bearing, washer and hub nut as described in **Job 39**. Adjust the brakes - see **Job 28**.

KNOTT AND BPW BRAKES ONLY

INSIDE INFORMATION: Always rotate the drum forwards whilst tightening the hub nut. This ensures that the taper roller bearings are seated correctly and unlikely to become loose.

Carry out the brake shoe adjustment procedure, but remember to turn the drum in the forwards direction only when doing so.

AP Lockheed Auto-Reverse MKII Cable Operated Version

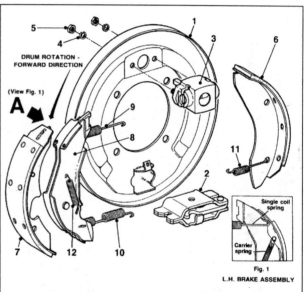

DRUM ROTATION -
FORWARD DIRECTION

(View Fig. 1)

A

Single coil spring

Carrier spring

Fig. 1
L.H. BRAKE ASSEMBLY

1. Backplate
2. Expander assembly
3. Adjuster assembly
4. Shakeproof washer (2)
5. Hexagonal nut (2)
6. Leading brake shoe (2)
7. Trailing brake shoe (2)
8. Trailing shoe carrier
9. Pull-off spring single coil (2)
10. Pull-off spring double coil (Red)
10. Pull-off spring double coil (Black)
11. Bias spring (2)
12. Carrier spring (4)

32P

32P. The Peak/Lockheed cable-operated brake has a conventional mechanical expander, into which are fitted the toe of the leading shoe, and the trailing shoe carrier. When your trailer is travelling forwards and the brakes are applied, the cable operates the expander lever, which causes the shoes to be forced into contact with the brake drum. By virtue of the trailing shoe's movement in its carrier, and the expander being able to slide on the backplate, a duo-servo braking effect is achieved.

The brake features a single point adjuster with an aluminium body, housing two sloping tappets and a threaded square stem which protrudes behind, out through the backplate.

BRAKE SHOE REMOVAL

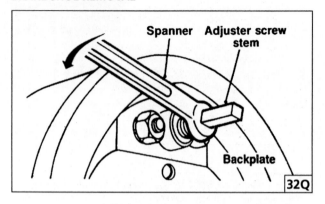

32Q

32Q. Securely chock the trailer's other wheel, loosen the wheel nuts on the side you are working on, and jack up the trailer before installing an axle stand to support the trailer's weight securely while you work. Lower the prop stands for extra security. Fully release the handbrake, ensuring that the hitch is fully extended, and finally, remove the road wheel.

With a suitable spanner, back off all brake adjustment by turning the square adjuster screw stem behind the backplate anti-clockwise as far as it will go.

making it easy! The brake adjuster frequently seizes solid, and this can mean that the stem rounds off. Spray a generous amount of releasing fluid onto the adjuster thread several times during the day before you plan to start work. Don't try to undo it straight away, but gently try easing it backwards and forwards just a little each way, until it begins to free. Always use a proper brake adjusting tool on these adjusters; you can buy one from your local auto-accessory shop. If all the above fails, you will be able to buy a replacement adjuster from your local dealer. This can be fitted quite simply, by removing the two nuts which hold the adjuster onto the back plate.

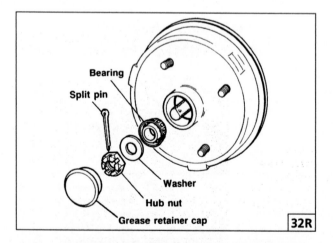

32R

32R. Prise off the hub grease retainer cap and remove the split pin, hub nut, washer and bearing. Withdraw the brake drum from the stub axle.

NOTE: A different design of double coiled pull-off spring and a new design bias spring are incorporated in Spring kit LK 17056. For details of their correct location refer to picture 32Q.

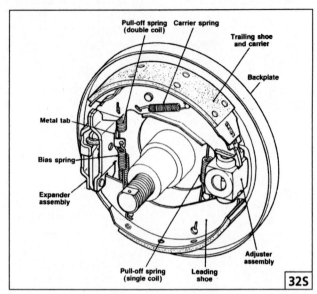

32S

32S. After taking careful note of the spring and shoe positions, pull the heel of the leading shoe, then the toe of the carrier, out of the adjuster tappet slots. Disconnect the single coil spring from the leading shoe web. Release the *double coil* spring from behind the metal tab on the backplate, and then ease the leading shoe out of the expander slot. Remove the bias spring, and the double coil spring from the leading shoe web. *Make a written note of the spring hook positions,* then remove the springs from the carrier. Disconnect both carrier springs, and remove the trailing shoe from the carrier.

EXPANDER REMOVAL AND REPLACEMENT

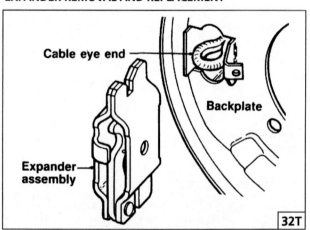

32T

32T. Disconnect the eye end of the operating cable, and remove expander from backplate. Remove all dust and deposits from the backplate. *Do not blow out with an air line or your own breath, since it could be dangerous to inhale the dust. Always use a proprietary aerosol car brake cleaner and a damp cloth. Do not use petrol or paraffin.*

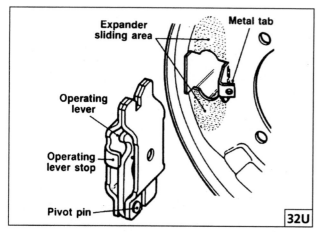

32U. Before replacing the expander, lubricate the expander operating lever and pivot pin *using only an approved brake grease* (not ordinary grease) and also smear a *very* small amount onto the area of the backplate on which the expander slides. Fit the expander against the backplate. It is particularly important to check that the brake shoes are fitted the correct way round. In the case of the left-hand brake assembly (illustrated), the expander operating lever stop faces towards the adjuster assembly. On the right-hand brake assembly, it faces away from the adjuster. The shoes are fitted accordingly.

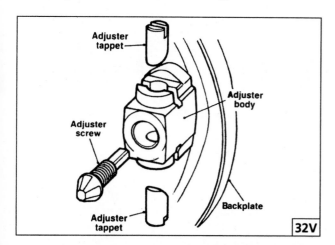

32V. If the adjuster is thoroughly seized, you should replace with new. Even if you have managed to re-use it, strip and rebuild each adjuster. Extract the adjuster tappets - they just pull (or fall!) out - and unscrew and withdraw the adjuster screw from the front of the adjuster. Thoroughly clean the parts, then smear tappets and adjuster screw threads *very lightly* with brake grease, or with copper impregnated grease. Then, in readiness for re-fitting the brake shoes, screw the adjuster fully into place (so that it is at minimum adjustment). Insert the tappets into the adjuster body, the sloping ends matching the tapered angle of the adjuster screw.

 *To help prevent seizing in future, ensure that the threads of the adjuster stem exposed behind the backplate are well coated with grease after assembly.*

BRAKE SHOE REPLACEMENT

32W(i). Using only an approved brand of brake grease (not ordinary grease), very lightly smear all metal to metal contact points such as the brake shoe and carrier tips, the carrier roller, the areas of the backplate against which the brake shoe platforms rest, and the adjuster tappet slots. *Be certain not to get even the slightest amount of grease on the brake shoe linings or the friction surface of the brake drum.*

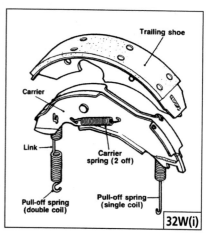

Fit the trailing shoe to the carrier, and secure with the two carrier springs. Refit the shoes, carrier, and pull-off springs by reversing the removal procedure.

IMPORTANT NOTES:

i) It is important that the brake shoes are fitted the correct way round. On the left-hand brake assembly (illustrated), the operating lever stop faces towards the adjuster. On the right- hand brake assembly, it faces away from the adjuster.

ii) Ensure that the double coil pull-off spring link is located behind the metal tab adjacent to the expander assembly.

iii) Check that the single coil pull-off spring is hooked into the carrier correctly, as shown in illustration **32R**. This is a view from the direction of arrow 'A', with the brake shoe assembled to the carrier.

iv) Certain chassis manufacturers fit the brake with the leading shoe in the top position. In this case the bias spring (Item 11 in illustration **32R**) is unnecessary, and is not fitted.

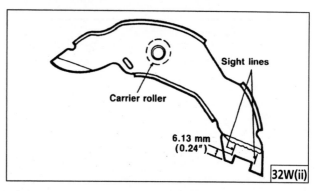

32W(ii). IMPORTANT NOTE: BRAKE SHOE CARRIER. Two types of shoe carrier design have been used with this brake assembly. The later design has an increased adjuster location recess depth of 6.13 mm (0.24 in.), as illustrated. It is important that the newer carrier is only used with the later type adjuster assembly, which has deeper body slots to accommodate the new carrier shape. The new adjuster assembly, if required, is available under AP Lockheed Part No. 4158-133, and can be identified by the Body Casting No. 3144-310 C.

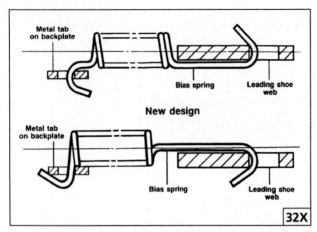

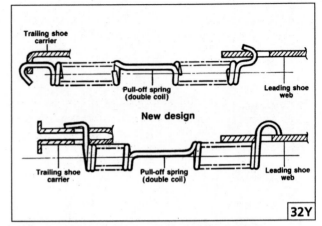

32X. LOCATION OF LATER TYPE OF BIAS SPRING. The design and method of fitting of the bias spring has been changed from the original design. Compare your spring with those shown, and assemble accordingly.

32Y. LOCATION OF LATER TYPE OF PULL-OFF SPRING. The design and method of fitting of the pull-off spring has also been changed from the original design. Compare your spring with those shown, and assemble accordingly.

Now refit the drum, bearing, washer and hub nut as described in **Job 39**. Adjust the brakes - see **Job 28**.

AP Lockheed ('Standard') Non-Automatic Reverse Brake Shoes Only

Please see the drawings and parts lists detailed with **Jobs 28E and 28F**, and read carefully all of the instructions contained within **Job 32**.

Thanks are due to AP Lockheed/Peak Trailers for their kind permission to use the information and drawings in this section. See Appendix 2, Specialists and Suppliers for information on where to obtain parts for Lockheed brakes.

PART TWO: BRAKE OVERHAUL AL-KO BRAKES ONLY

AL-KO brakes are a popular choice for heavy-duty trailers. The main types are covered here. The greatest differences arise between the earlier brakes, and those fitted to the newer models, known as Euro-Axle brakes. See below for details.

IMPORTANT NOTE 1: Before dismantling the brake shoe assembly, take notes, sketches and even a photograph or video of the spring assembly. It is *essential* that all springs are re-attached in their correct locations. As well as examining the brake shoes for wear, examine the brake springs carefully too. If any appear stretched - if the coils appear uneven or open at any point, or the hooked ends appear open - replace them with a complete new set of branded parts. DO NOT substitute any other springs! Also check carefully for oil staining on the brakes and backplate. If any is found, the oil seals will have to be renewed.

IMPORTANT NOTE 2: Do not attempt to carry out any work on your brake drum without having a torque wrench of the correct type to hand. It is *essential* that the hub nut is neither over-tightened nor under-tightened, and you will need a torque wrench to be sure of this. If you do not have access to a torque wrench, or are unsure as to how it should be used, entrust the job to your local trailer specialist. Even if you are equipped and confident enough to do the work yourself, we would still recommend that you have a qualified mechanic or trailer expert check the work once you have finished - and before you take the trailer on the road. This is especially important with those requiring extremely high torque settings. The types of wrench found in most home workshops only go up to around 150 Nm, or 110 lb/ft, and will be inadequate for heavy-duty hub nuts. If in doubt, always entrust the job to a professional!

It is also *essential* that a new split pin, lock nut or nut collar is used (as used originally) on the hub castellated nut each time it is removed. See **Job 39** for details.

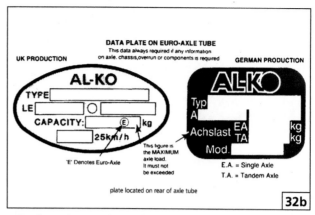

32b. All AL-KO Euro-Axles can be identified by looking for the data plate on the rear of the axle tube. In addition, the brake backplate has a gold coloured finish. (Illustration, courtesy AL-KO)

AL-KO NON-EURO AXLE BRAKES ONLY

32c. Taking one side of the trailer at a time, loosen the wheel nuts on the side which you are going to tackle first. Chock the opposite wheel, jack the trailer up, and then support it securely using axle stands and its own prop stands, as described earlier in this chapter. Release the trailer's handbrake, and check that the hitch assembly is fully extended. Now remove the wheel.

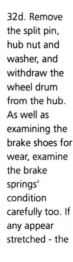

32a. In the case of the Euro-Axle, no split pin is fitted. Instead, a 'one-shot' locknut is used, and it is important that a new one is always fitted after the old one has been removed. DO NOT RE-USE THESE HUB NUTS as they could then come loose, and allow the wheel/hub assembly to be shed as the trailer is travelling along.

SPECIALIST SERVICE: Work on the Euro-Axle hub - and therefore brake replacement - is beyond the scope of most DIY repairers, because the locknut (32c, item 13) requires a massive torque tightening figure (214 lb/ft, or 290 Nm, both plus or minus about 3%), which is well beyond the capacity of any 'domestic' torque wrenches. (Illustration, courtesy AL-KO.)

IMPORTANT NOTE: See **Job 28** on brake adjustment, and following the general instructions given there, turn the star wheel as far as it will go in the opposite direction to the arrow on the backplate - so that the brakes are backed right off.

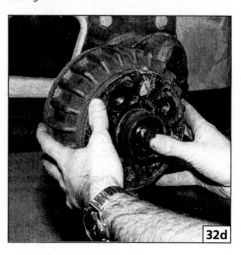

32d. Remove the split pin, hub nut and washer, and withdraw the wheel drum from the hub. As well as examining the brake shoes for wear, examine the brake springs' condition carefully too. If any appear stretched - the coils appear uneven, or open at any point — or the hooked ends appear open, replace them with a complete new set of branded parts. DO NOT substitute any other springs!

Wash off the brake backplate assembly with a proprietary brand of aerosol brake cleaner before dismantling, and once again when all the parts have been removed.

1. Backplate
2. Bowden cable
3. Link
4. Tension spring (handed)
5. Transmission lever (handed)
6. Brake shoe
7. Tension spring
8. Expanding clutch
9. Inner bearing
10. Brake drum
11. Outer bearing
12. Split pin
13. Castle nut
14. Grease cap
15. Wheel bolt
16. Brake shoe (right)
17. Oil seal
18. Pivot pin
19. Split pin
20. Pressure spring
21. Leaf spring
22. Adjusting screw
23. 'Starred wheel' adjuster
24. Pressure clip
25. Screw
26. Cover plate
27. Cable cover (upper not shown)
28. Bush
29. Lockwasher (not fitted to 2051 brake unit)

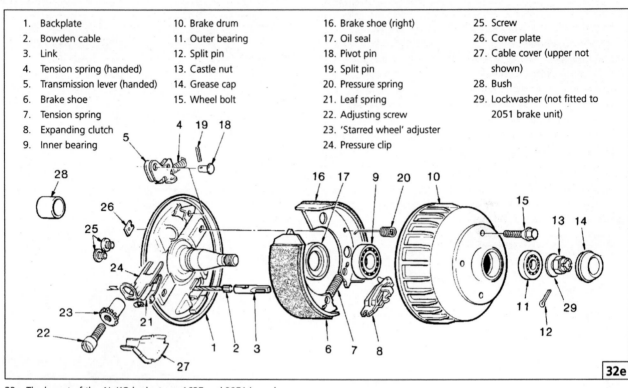

32e

32e. The layout of the AL-KO brake types 1637 and 2051 is as shown here. NOTE THAT PART NO. 29 IS NOT FITTED TO THE 2051 BRAKE. This drawing is applicable to several different sizes of brake.

INSIDE INFORMATION: Be sure to take the old parts with you to your AL-KO stockist when ordering new parts. (Illustration, courtesy AL-KO.)

32f. This is the layout of the following AL-KO brake types: 1635, 1636, 2035, 2050 and 2350. (Illustration, courtesy AL-KO.)

1. Brake drum
2. Wheel bolt
3. Castle nut
4. Grease cap
5. Lock washer
6. Split pin
7. Outer taper roller bearing
8. Expanding clutch
9. Tension spring
10. Brake shoe
11. Cover plates
12. Backplate (handed)
13. 'Starred wheel' adjuster
14. Adjusting screw
15. Pressure spring
16. Transmission lever (handed)
17. Split pin
18. Pivot pin
19. Oil seal
20. Inner taper roller bearing
21. Bowden cable tension spring

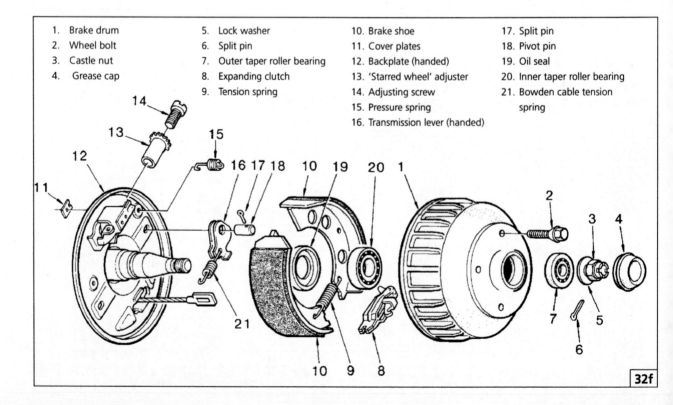

32f

32g. Push in the brake shoe retaining springs and remove the sprung retaining clips at the rear of the hub. Take care not to lose these clips.

32h. You can now remove the brake shoes from the hub.

32i. Replace the old shoes with the new ones, making sure that you put them on the right way up. Look out for the embossed marking arrows on the Type 1625 and 1627 brake shoes. *The brakes will not work if the shoes are fitted to the wrong side.* For brake Types 2051 and 2361, the left and right shoes are identical. See **32e** and **32f** to help you identify which type of AL-KO brakes you have and, if in any doubt, consult your dealer.

Reposition the brake shoes on the hub, and replace the retaining springs and their retaining clips. Ensure the CORRECT POSITIONS OF BRAKE SHOE SPRINGS! Refer to the other side of the trailer, if necessary.

Use a *very small* amount of specialised *brake grease* on all metal contact areas - don't use ordinary grease, and DON'T get any lubricants onto any of the friction areas or the inside of the brake drum.

making it easy! Before replacing the brake drum, check it for damage, cracking, or excessive scoring from brake shoes. If there is excessive scoring, you will need to replace the drum. Cracking is not always easily visible - but if it's left unchecked, tiny hairline cracks can eventually lead to a spectacular shattering of the drum while in use, with predictably disastrous results. So here's a good way of spotting if a drum is cracked, and replacing it in plenty of time: hang the drum up on the end of a piece of string, and tap it gently with a hammer. You should hear a clear ringing sound. If the sound is dull and flat, the drum is cracked, and should be scrapped immediately.

Replace the drum, washer, hub nut and refit a new split pin. See **Job 39** for details. Replace the wheel and carry out the same job on the trailer's other wheel, then readjust the brakes.

SAFETY FIRST AND SPECIALIST SERVICE!

*i) Obviously, your trailer's brakes are among its most important safety related items. Do NOT dismantle or attempt to perform any work on the braking system unless you are fully competent to do so. If you have not been trained in this work, but wish to carry it out, we strongly recommend that you have a your local trailer specialist workshop or qualified mechanic check your work before using the trailer on the road. See also the section on **BRAKES AND ASBESTOS** in **Chapter 1, Safety First!** for further information.*

ii) Remember that brake dust can contain asbestos and in the case of older systems, it most certainly will. Since asbestos can kill: ALWAYS spray a proprietary brand of aerosol brake cleaner onto the brakes after removing the hub (available from your local auto accessory store); ALWAYS wear an efficient particle mask, gloves and a hat, and wash your hands and arms after doing the job; ALWAYS dust yourself off thoroughly out of doors; ALWAYS dispose of the old shoes, wiping rags and wiped-up dust in a sealed plastic bag, and keep children and pets away from the work area.

iii) Always replace the brake shoes in complete sets - never replace the shoes on one wheel only. Keep all traces of oil or grease off the friction surfaces.

*iv) When adjusting the brakes, it is necessary to adjust one side first and then the other. In both cases it will be necessary to work underneath the trailer and it is therefore essential that the correct safety procedure is followed for raising and supporting the trailer. See the section on **Raising A Trailer Safely** earlier in this chapter.*

v) Always specify and use ASBESTOS FREE brake linings.

Please read the cautions relating to working on brakes at the beginning of **Job 31** before starting work, and REMEMBER TO SECURE THE HANDBRAKE.

32j. Knott's popular braking systems are pretty similar to the less commonly found arrangements detailed above, so follow the instructions

given for AL-KO brakes (**Jobs 32e and 32f**), to remove the road wheel and brake drum.

Shown below is the layout of Knott's most commonly used brake system. (Illustration, courtesy Knott)

Clean the brake backplate and shoes off thoroughly, using a proprietary brake cleaner and a damp rag, before embarking on shoe removal. Record the exact positions of all springs and other components (as detailed in the Important Note just before **Job 32c**), examine the springs for any open coils or opening of the spring hooks, and then release the shoe-steady spring (32j.12) which holds the leading shoe against the backplate.

making it easy! You'll have to pull and twist at the same time to get the shoe-steady spring out, so use a pair of pliers. They will help you grip the spring - and to twist it through ninety degrees as you pull.

NOTE: Earlier steady springs took the form of a toggle which bridged a slot in the backplate. The location of the steady springs has since changed: newer brakes have a recessed slot, which allows the spring hook to engage with the rim of the recess.

It is often recommended that you use a screwdriver to lever brake shoes off their adjusters, but working against such strong springs can result in a nasty wound if the screwdriver slips. Use a self-grip wrench on the metal part of the shoe if you need extra leverage.

Ease the brake shoes off the adjuster assembly. Try to avoid stretching the springs any more than you have to, otherwise they will have to be replaced. Fold the shoes together, and release the spring at the expander (item 7 in illustration **32j**) end. You can now lift the shoes away from the backplate.

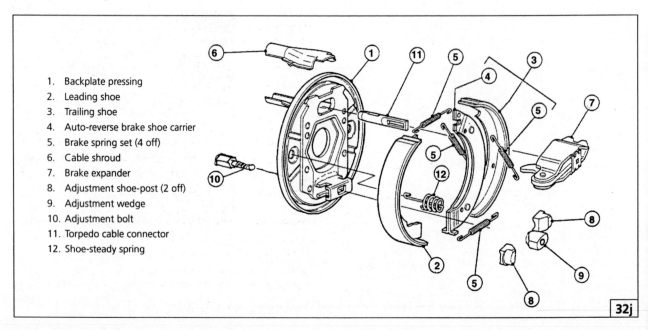

1. Backplate pressing
2. Leading shoe
3. Trailing shoe
4. Auto-reverse brake shoe carrier
5. Brake spring set (4 off)
6. Cable shroud
7. Brake expander
8. Adjustment shoe-post (2 off)
9. Adjustment wedge
10. Adjustment bolt
11. Torpedo cable connector
12. Shoe-steady spring

32j

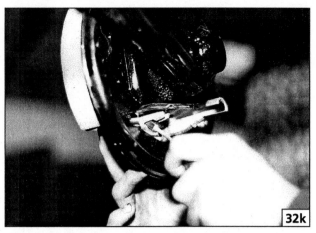

32k

32k. Ease the cable ferrule off the abutment, and lift off the removable half to reveal the cable nipple in its seat in the torpedo connector (Illustration **32j**, item 11). Unhook the nipple from its eye, and lift the cable away. Now pull the expander from the backplate. It should be free moving. If its action is at all stiff, clean it thoroughly, so that the lever can pivot easily. Apply a little copper-rich grease to the area of the backplate where the expander locates so that its movement is as smooth as possible. A sticking expander will prevent the shoes from operating equally, and so will waste brake linings and impair braking efficiency.

SAFETY FIRST!

While it is important to ensure that the expander operates correctly, it is ESSENTIAL that no stray grease gets onto the braking surfaces. Be sparing when using lubricants on or near the brake drum or friction surfaces.

If the brake shoes are worn to 1.5 mm thick or less, or if their rivets are almost flush with the linings' surface, the shoes will have to be replaced.

Examine the adjuster wedge (Illustration **32j**, item 9) and the shoe posts on either side (Items 8). If any of these appear scored or ridged, these too will need replacement. They must move perfectly freely against one another to allow easy adjustment of the brake.

Examine the movement of the auto-reverse shoe (the trailing shoe, (32j.3) in the carrier (32j). No lubrication is necessary, but cleaning might be called for: it should be able to slide freely against the tension of the springs.

Once you are satisfied that every component is in good condition, the brake can be reassembled. Check the positioning of all components against illustration **32j**, and/or your own notes. Reassembly is essentially a reversal of the dismantling procedure.

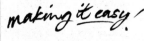 Before replacing the brake drum, check it for damage, cracking, or excessive scoring from brake shoes. If there is excessive scoring, you will need to replace the drum. Cracking is not always easily visible - but if it's left unchecked, tiny hairline cracks can eventually lead to a spectacular shattering of the drum while in use, with predictably disastrous results. So here's a good way of spotting if a drum is cracked, and replacing it in plenty of time: hang the drum up on the end of a piece of string, and tap it gently with a hammer. You should hear a clear ringing sound. If the sound is dull and flat, the drum is cracked, and should be scrapped immediately.

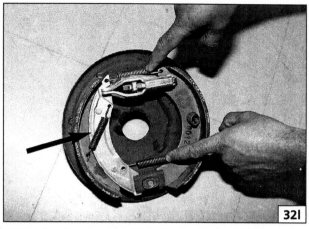

32l

32l. Link the shoes together with their springs, and ease them onto the expander. Fit the wedge and shoe-posts. Position the wedge at its minimum adjustment, to allow the shoe posts on either side to close to minimum width. Pull the auto- reverse shoe on its carrier onto its post, and then prise (with either a screwdriver or small tyre lever) the leading shoe around the other post. NB: Watch your knuckles!

Next, press the shoes down flat against the backplate, and finally, refit the steady spring to the leading shoe (arrowed).

32m

32m. Check again that the adjuster wedge is backed off completely before replacing the brake drum. Replace the nut collar if necessary, and tighten the hub nut to the appropriate torque setting (This can be as high as 260 lb/ft, but check manufacturer's specifications for your own model).

NB. Anything much over 100 lb/ft will be beyond most DIY-use torque wrenches. If the required figure is higher, you will have to have the nut/s tightened to the correct figure by your local garage.

32n. Don't forget to punch in the nut collar, or re-fit the split-pin, to secure the nut. Now all that's left to do is re-pack the hub with grease, re-fit the grease cap, and replace the wheel. (Illustration, courtesy Ifor Williams)

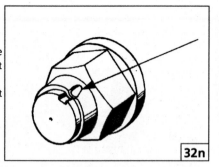

IMPORTANT NOTE: Don't forget to re-adjust your brakes (according to the shoe adjustment procedure shown in **Job 28**) after dismantling them! And remember to turn the drum only in the forwards direction when doing so. This ensures that the taper roller bearings are seated correctly, and are unlikely to work themselves loose.

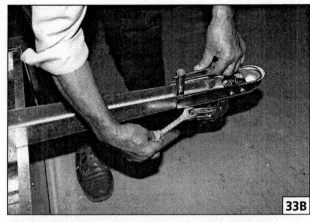

33B. Check all of the chassis assembly and mounting bolts for tightness. This is the hitch mounting on an inverted small trailer.

You should also check the axle tube (when fitted) for straightness, corrosion or damage.

❏ Job 33. Check for chassis damage.

33A. A trailer's chassis should last the life of the trailer itself. However, it's certainly worth checking it occasionally for evidence of damage. If your trailer has a painted, rather than galvanised, chassis, then it is particularly important to keep a close eye on its condition, since paint is nowhere near such a good protector of steel as the more expensive alternative. However, there is some small compensation to be derived from having a painted chassis: if any damage is discovered, then it will be possible to take the trailer along to any competent welder and have it repaired relatively inexpensively.

SAFETY FIRST!

ON NO ACCOUNT should you, or any friendly welder, attempt to work on galvanised material. The fumes given off by the zinc coating when heated are highly toxic, and could seriously damage your health.

🔍 INSIDE INFORMATION: Check the tyres for even wear. Severe chassis damage - such as would be caused if the trailer had been involved in a road accident - could lead to one or more wheels running 'out of true'. This will make the trailer ungainly and difficult to tow - and would eventually show up clearly in the tyres, with one side's tyre(s) worn much more heavily than on the other side. 🔍

❏ Job 34. Check for chassis corrosion.

NON-GALVANISED CHASSIS

Examine the chassis to see if there is any evidence of corrosion - especially likely on earlier (or cheaper) painted chassis. If any is found, wire brush, sand, or scrape the rust off until you are back to shiny metal, and apply a coat of wax-based chassis protection (brush-on or aerosol versions are both available).

GALVANISED CHASSIS

**FACT FILE:
GALVANISED CHASSIS CORROSION**

One problem which has caused concern for owners of trailers with galvanised chassis is 'white rust' which refers to the formation of a soft, porous, light grey surface layer of oxidisation and, although it's not entirely to be welcomed, it is actually evidence that the zinc galvanising is doing its job. For this reason, it's wise to use 'white rust' as a warning mechanism; clean off the metal and treat with a wax-based underseal.

❑ Job 35. Check suspension.

Nearly all trailers come equipped with rubber block, or leaf-spring suspension. Coil springs are not designed to cope well with wide variations in load, and they are not well suited to trailer use.

Rubber Suspension

There is very little to go wrong with rubber suspension - but when it does go wrong, the only remedy is replacement. Firstly, check that the steel housings for the suspension rubbers have not corroded. Now, check the rubber suspension blocks for brittleness, perishing or softness. Standing on level ground and evenly loaded, the body of a trailer whose suspension rubbers have begun to go soft will be noticeably lop-sided. DO NOT APPLY OIL TO RUBBER SUSPENSION UNITS, since it will attack and destroy the rubber.

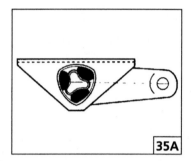

35A. This is a typical 3-block suspension in the normal-laden position.

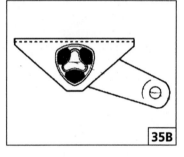

35B. This is the rebound, or free position...

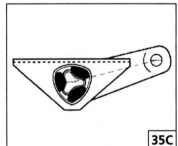

35C. ...and this the maximum load (or maximum bump) position. (Illustrations, courtesy Conway)

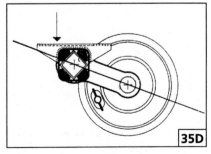

35D. This is the alternative BPW 4-block suspension.

SPECIALIST SERVICE: While it is easy to tell if a rubber suspension block needs to be replaced, it is not always so easy to carry out the work. Ask your dealer for his advice: some replacement rubber blocks are supplied integral with their steel housings, in which case you may feel confident to tackle the job yourself. Otherwise, refer the work to your specialist.

ℹ INSIDE INFORMATION: The life of the suspension rubbers, like that of the tyres, will be prolonged by supporting the trailer's weight on axle stands or similar for any period when it is not in use. ℹ

Leaf Spring Suspension

SEE CHAPTER 7 FOR DETAILS OF LEAF SPRING AND BUSH REPLACEMENT

Leaf-spring suspension remains popular with trailer manufacturers for its simplicity of construction, low maintenance needs, and versatility in coping with varying load sizes. Rust could cause the springs on a long-unused trailer to rust-weld them together but the commonest problems by far are leaf or clamp breakage, loose mountings and worn shackles.

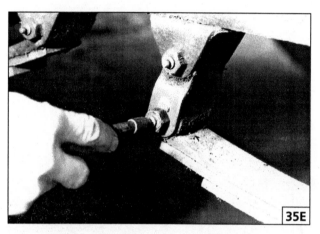

35E. You should pay close attention to the spring end bushes, lubricating them if there is provision. You'll have one of two arrange-ments, - see 35F and 35G. The bushes used will be of the 'Metalastic' type: that is, rubber sandwiched between inner and outer metal bushes. These are subject to softening, spreading and disintegration. Replacement will be called for if any problems are found.

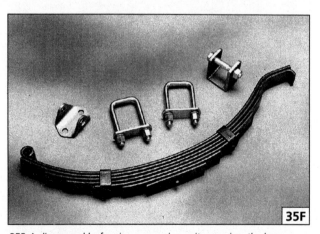

35F. A slipper end leaf-spring suspension unit comprises the large, multi-layered spring itself (1), plus two U-bolts (4) for attaching the centre of the spring to the axle mounting plate, a spring eye fixing bracket (3), and a slipper fixing bracket (2) for attaching the two ends to the chassis. The spring eye could also have a metalastic bush through its middle. (Illustration courtesy Indespension.)

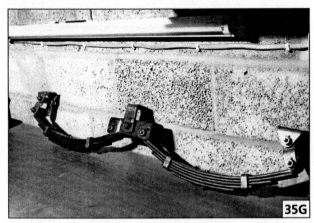

35G. This is the arrangement of a double-eye spring - or rather, a pair of them, for a 4-wheel trailer.

If springs are found to be broken or rusted solid, or the shackle pins are badly worn replacement will be called for. See **Chapter 7, Repairing and Upgrading**. Also, check the tightness of all of the U-bolts securing each spring to the suspension cross-member because they can come loose in use.

36A.

❏ Job 36. Check hydraulic shock absorbers (when fitted).

36A. Check the body of each shock absorber for leaks or for corrosion. In either case, it will need replacement.

36B.

36B. Check the condition of rubber bushes at the top and bottom end of each shock absorber. Grasp each end of the shock absorber in your hand and try to move it, TAKING CARE NOT TO PULL THE TRAILER OFF ITS SUPPORTS. If the bush has 'spread', is missing, or if any wear is evident, fit new bushes.

Every Twelve Months, or At The End of Every Season

❏ Job 37. Attend to all lubrication points.

At the end of a season's use, or annually if you use the trailer all year round, it is important to grease and/or oil all your trailer's recommended lubrication points.

37A. During the annual lubrication service, pay the jockey wheel some extra attention. Remove the wheel or stand, and unscrew the handle until it comes in two. Clean off and grease the threaded jockey wheel shaft.

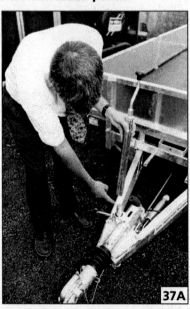

37A.

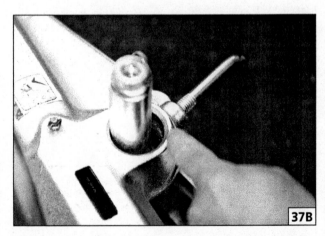

37B.

37B. Take care not to dislocate-locate the pad at the end of the clamp screw.

☐ Job 38. Check wheel bearings for wear.

```
┌──────────── SAFETY FIRST! ────────────┐
```
*Follow the safety information at the start of this chapter and in **Chapter 1, Safety First!** regarding safe procedure when working underneath a trailer supported off the ground.*

Following the safety instructions given at the beginning of this chapter, lift each wheel in turn off the ground, and try spinning it. If you hear a rumbling sound, it is very likely that a wheel bearing has worn and will need replacement.

38. Grip each of the trailer's wheels firmly, with your hands at nine o'clock and three o'clock across the wheel, and pull and push on it to see whether the wheel bearings are in good condition. Cup-and-cone taper roller bearings will move just slightly; caged ball bearings should not allow the wheel and lateral movement at all. If there is more movement than there should be, the first remedy is adjustment. If adjustment has no effect, then you will have to replace the bearing.

INSIDE INFORMATION: Check around the bearing housing for discolouration, which could be an indicator that too much heat is being generated. This could make the housing brittle so that it begins to crack - and it will certainly accelerate wear of rollers or balls and the hub centre itself. The most likely causes of overheating are over-tightening of the bearing, or lack of grease.

SPECIALIST SERVICE 1: If you suspect that there is too much free movement in a bearing, have your specialist take a look. It really needs the eye of experience to tell for sure just how much play is too much!

☐ Job 39. Replace wheel bearing, when necessary.

```
┌──────────── SAFETY FIRST! ────────────┐
```
Brakes are commonly fitted with brake shoes containing asbestos, and these can produce asbestos dust. When removing the dust from the wheel: i) NEVER use a brush or blow the dust out with an airline or your own breath. ii) ALWAYS spray a proprietary brand of aerosol brake cleaner onto the brakes and wipe with a damp cloth. ii) Seal dust and used wet cloths in a plastic bag immediately after you have finished with them, and dispose of safely. iii) Always wear an efficient particle face mask. ASBESTOS DUST KILLS!

FACT FILE: HUB AND BEARING TYPES

Non-DIY Serviceable Hubs

There are two types of hub which are not serviceable at home. They are as follows:

SEALED-FOR-LIFE

The AL-KO Euro-hub cannot be serviced and when the bearing is worn out, the hub as a unit is replaced. AL-KO Euro-hubs have a bronze or gold backplate whereas earlier types have a black backplate.

Ifor Williams sealed hubs all have wheel bolts whereas the serviceable type have wheel nuts.

HIGH-TORQUE HUB NUTS

Several hub types require a torque setting which runs into the hundreds of lbs/ft. It is *essential* that the correct figure is adhered to and a very special and expensive torque wrench has to be used. There is no way of identifying these nuts except to say that if a domestic torque wrench set to around 110 lbs/ft won't undo them, they are probably high-torque nuts. If necessary, telephone the trailer manufacturer or consult your nearest trailer dealer.

Serviceable Hubs

Most of these are fitted with a pair of taper roller bearings as described below, while some are fitted pair of parallel, or cage bearings.

HUB NUT TORQUES

Once the slip pin is removed, it should be possible to undo the nut on a taper roller bearing with the fingers - see instructions below. With a parallel ball bearing, the hub nut will have to be tightened to a specified torque. See **39P**.

Hub Identification

i) Telephone the trailer manufacturer to find out what type you have.
ii) Take your trailer to your nearest trailer dealer and ask their advice.
iii) Stripdown and look. Sealed hubs typically have a centre tube which is pressed into a flange at each end holding the bearings in place.

BRAKED AND UNBRAKED HUBS

Jack the trailer up following the procedure given earlier in this chapter, and remove the wheel.

INSIDE INFORMATION: It is *essential* that you slacken off the brake adjusters so that the brake shoes don't prevent removal of the drum. See *Job 28.*

39A. Remove the grease cap, levering and tapping until it comes free. Renew it if damaged.

39B. Take out the split pin, or lever open the punched-in section of the nut collar, and remove the hub nut.

Taking care not to lose the central collar (when fitted), remove the brake drum (where appropriate). The drum may need to be tapped free using a soft-faced mallet, used ONLY on the edge of the drum. Using a proprietary brand of aerosol brake cleaner and a rag, wipe away any brake dust from the brake drum and wheel hub. DO NOT BLOW THE DUST OUT, AND ALWAYS WEAR AN EFFICIENT PARTICLE FACE MASK. Check the condition of the brake shoes. If they appear worn or damaged, or if the rivets are near to the surface of the shoes, replace them. See **Job 32**.

CHANGING THE CONE

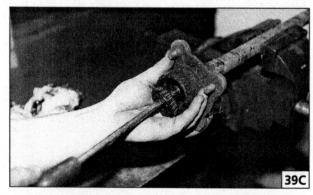

39C. After wiping out all of the old grease and 'rescuing' the thrust washer, the front bearing will now be accessible and generally can be easily withdrawn by sliding the hub forward off the stub axle.

The rear bearing and grease seal is accessed by removing the hub/brake drum completely.

39D. The rear bearing will EITHER i) stay on the stub axle in which case it should be removed by applying gentle forward pressure, OR ii) if it is left in the hub it can be removed by pushing the bearing out. Where a separate grease seal is fitted it must be prised out of the inner bearing bore for access to the cone. This almost always damages the seal, necessitating its renewal on re-assembly. Most inner bearings have an integral seal.

CHANGING THE CUPS

39E. This is a slightly more difficult operation since the cups are normally inserted under pressure and are an interference fit.

39F. Drift each one out in turn, tapping slowly, carefully and evenly around the circumference. This type of hub is easily ruined!

39G. New bearings ready for fitting. Note the oil seal on the inboard bearing.

39H. Ensure the cup is in the correct position (i.e. the diameter of the taper should always decrease towards the centre of the hub).

making it easy! *39I. It is ESSENTIAL that it goes in perfectly evenly. Use a vice (with jaw guards) to press the cup flush with the hub.*

Carefully drift cup into hub working evenly around the circumference of the cup. Take care not to damage the ground surface of the cup or the hub casting.

i INSIDE INFORMATION: Use the old bearing cup, as a drift, to seat the new one. i

i 39J. It is vital to ensure that the cup is firmly down against the collar of the casting. Fit the inner cup in the same way as described in 39I. Now fit both cones 'dry' and, using a long bolt and a pair of washers, draw the bearings towards each other until the cups are fully seated on their bases. Remove the cones and use a drift to finish off, if necessary. DON'T overtighten the bolt! i

REFITTING CONES

39K. Now remove the cones and smear the cups and cones with a liberal coating of grease. If the trailer is to come into contact with water we suggest using Aqualube Grease. Push bearing cones into the cups until they are seated. Tap new grease seal into it bore where required.

39L. Slide the hub onto the stub axle.

39M. Place the thrust washer over stub axle.

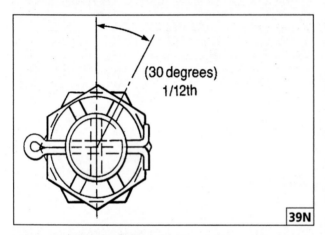

(30 degrees)
1/12th

39N. Tighten the castellated nut until all slack is taken out of the bearing. DON'T over-tighten! Then back the nut off one flat (30 degrees) and make certain that the hub can spin without feeling tight or impaired. If it does feel tight, back off one more flat until it *just* runs free. Always fit a new split pin. (NEVER reuse the old one!) (Illustration, courtesy AL-KO)

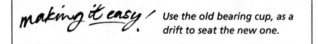

making it easy! Use the old bearing cup, as a drift to seat the new one.

SPECIALIST SERVICE: If the bearings, or bearing cups, are a pressed fit, you may not be able to remove or replace them at home. A specialist engineering workshop should be able to press out and replace them for you.

Place a thick smear of grease around the inside of the hub cap and re-fit.

IMPORTANT NOTE: In the case of some hubs, including some AP Lockheed units without taper roller bearings, you should tighten the hub nut up to 26 lb/ft (3.7 kg/m) using a torque wrench. Different types of hub have different tightening torque requirements. Check with your trailer's handbook, the original manufacturer, or your local dealership for details. Incorrect adjustment will result in excessive wear and bearing damage. If you don't opt to have the bearing set up by a professional, we recommend having a trained mechanic check your work before taking the trailer on the road.

1. Backplate and brake shoe assembly, mounted on stub axle.
2. Brake drum, or hub.
3. Outer bearing; cup still fitted to (2).
4. Inner bearing taper-roller 'cone'.
5. Inner bearing 'cup'.
6. Hub-nut washer.
7. Hub nut.
8. Split-pin.
9. Grease cap.
10. Wheel nuts.
11. Wheel nut protective caps.

39O. These are the components of a typical Knott hub assembly equipped with auto-reverse brakes. (Illustration, courtesy Indespension)

39P. Parallel, or caged, bearings also come in pairs. They sometimes come out of the hub freely; they sometimes need careful drifting out. When being fitted, or adjusted, they are often torqued up tight (typically 30 lbs/ft) then backed off and retightened to a lower figure (typically 15 lbs/ft). CHECK THE TRAILER MANUFAC-TURER FOR CORRECT FIGURES. (Illustration, courtesy Conway)

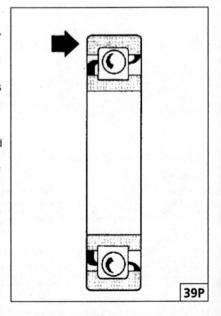

☐ **Job 40. Check damper condition, and replace as necessary.**

🛈 **INSIDE INFORMATION:** Damper failure is most frequently caused by poor, or irregular, adjustment of the wheel brakes - and can even cause rapid brake wear - so should you find that your damper needs to be replaced, it's wise to carry out a thorough overhaul of the braking system at the same time. 🛈

40A. Remove the rear damper mounting bolt (through drawbar, at the A-frame end of the hitch).

i) Indespension Triplelock

ii) Bradley

iii) Knott

Turn to **Jobs 18B and 18C** for instructions on how to check that the damper is operating properly. There are many different makes of couplings, but for all of them the procedure for changing a damper unit is basically the same. However you must ensure is that you fit a damper of the right specification for your trailer. Check with your manufacturer or dealer to find out which one you need. Fit new replacement bolts and self-locking nuts.

40B. Remove front damper mounting bolt (on coupling head itself).

i) Indespension Triplelock

ii) Bradley

iii) Knott

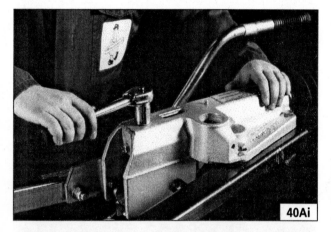

40Ai

40Bi

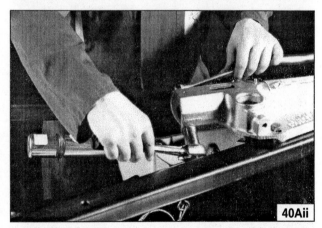

40Aii

40Bii

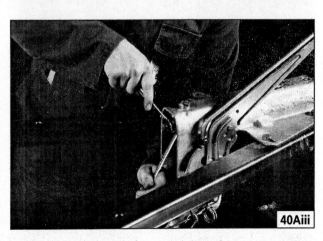

40Aiii

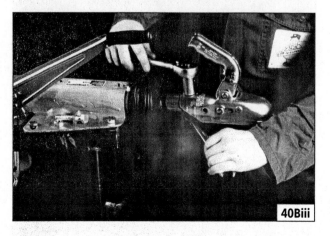

40Biii

40C. Draw out the old damper, being sure to keep any extension piece which might be fitted to re-use with the replacement.

i) Indespension Triplelock

ii) Bradley

iii) Knott

iv) Keep the extension piece but throw away the old damper.

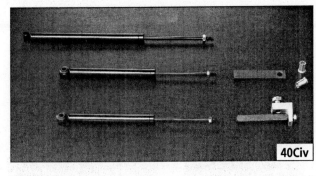

40Civ

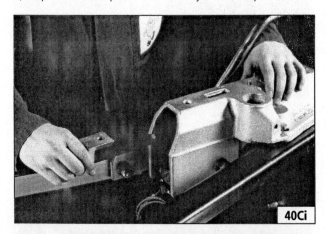

40Ci

40D. Slide new damper unit into the drawbar tube, and secure using a NEW bolt and NEW locknut.

i) Indespension Triplelock

ii) Bradley

iii) Knott - see 40Aiii)

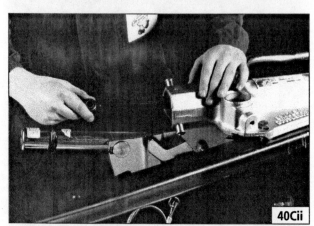

40Cii

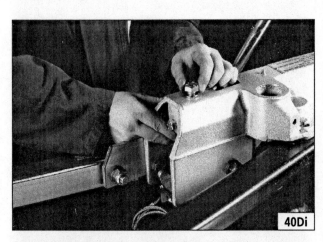

40Di

40Ciii

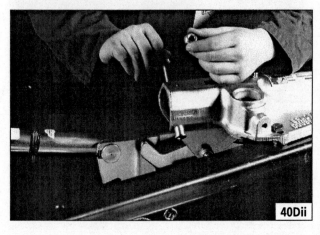

40Dii

40E. Compress the damper, and bolt it into the coupling head using a NEW bolt and a NEW locknut.

i) Indespension Triplelock

ii) Bradley

iii) Knott

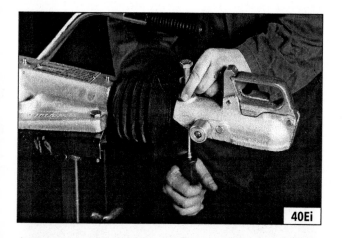

40Ei

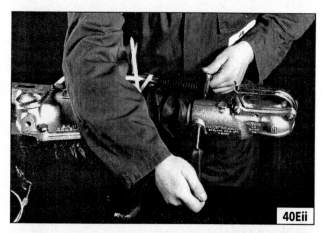

40Eii

40Eiii

All of the text and illustrations for Job 40 were kindly supplied by Indespension.

☐ Job 41. Check ratchet handbrake.

AUTO-REVERSE BRAKE TYPES ONLY

Make an annual check that the handbrake is working properly. Apply the brake fully - this will mean making two distinct pulls: one to apply it, the second to compress the spring pack all the way. Now push the trailer backwards until the wheels lock. If they don't lock, then the handbrake's mechanism will have to be adjusted or overhauled. In view of the essential safety role played by the handbrake, this is a **SPECIALIST SERVICE** item.

NON-AUTO-REVERSE TYPES

Earlier types without auto-reverse can be checked with a single application. *Gently* try to drive off (but DON'T DO SO!). Does the handbrake hold?

☐ Job 42. Check body seams for leaks, where appropriate.

If appropriate - and this is only likely to apply to box trailers whose contents need to be kept dry - check all the seams minutely for cracking, and replace sealant where necessary with mastic applied with a 'gun'.

RUBBER SEALING STRIPS

Some seam seals are simply rubber strips sandwiched between two bolted-together body panels. If your trailer features these and they need replacing, make sure that you buy the correct part-numbered strips from your specialist dealer or the original manufacturer.

☐ Job 43. Polish windows.

Any minor scratches can be polished out, using a small amount of mild cutting compound, such as T-Cut, on a soft cloth. You'll need a lot of elbow grease to go with it, and it won't remove deep scratches - but it should go a long way towards curing any clouding of the acrylic, and should also improve the general clarity of the window.

☐ Job 44. Check window seals.

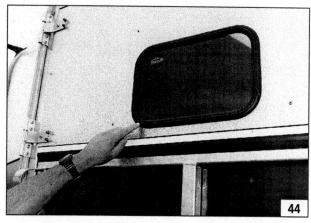

44

44. While you're at it, examine the rubber seals that run around the horsebox window for cracking and perishing. Buy replacements from your trailer dealer and have your local windscreen specialist fit them.

❏ Job 45. Check bodywork.

ALUMINIUM BODY PANELS can become pretty battered throughout a trailer's life, and minor damage is not at all simple to beat out. Do not overdo your amateur panel beating, since there is a good chance that an over-enthusiastic pounding will simply stretch the aluminium and make the dent worse, rather than better. If the damage is too severe, turn to *Chapter 7, Repairing and Upgrading Your Trailer,* or contact your trailer's original manufacturer for a replacement panel.

45. Serious body damage will be a **SPECIALIST SERVICE** job - especially if it is the result of an accident, since the chassis could be affected.

PLASTIC BODY PANELS A small crack, can be filled by using a flexible mastic sealant Anything any larger really requires the panel to be replaced although cracked fibreglass could be repaired from the inside using a fibreglass repair kit and smoothed on the outside with body filler.

❏ Job 46. Lubricate hinges and catches.

Apply a small amount of light oil to the hinges and catches on any doors, windows, ramps, boards or lockers, and check that all are working satisfactorily. Replacements are generally available.

46. DO NOT oil plastic runners or those with plastic bearers on roller shutter doors. Silicone spray should be OK.

Preparing to Store the Trailer

❏ Job 47. Prepare storage area.

Choose a suitable area for storing your trailer, preferably somewhere away from children and animals. And make absolutely sure that the trailer will be securely supported if you intend to remove the wheels.

⚡ INSIDE INFORMATION: If its surface finish is important do not store your trailer under trees. Not only is there the added risk of storm damage, the resin from some types of tree can cause permanent damage to paintwork. ⚡

❏ Job 48. Clean trailer, as necessary.

Corrosion problems can be minimised by ensuring that the trailer begins its period of storage thoroughly clean.

If your trailer has an open box, clean out any bits of debris which may have found their way in. Cover it with a tarpaulin or purpose-made cover, either pulled taut on the trailer's own rope hooks, or supported by something placed inside the trailer. This way you can make sure that any rainwater runs off, rather than collecting in the middle of the cover and dragging it down.

STOCK TRAILERS ONLY

48. If your trailer is used to carry stock, whether farm animals or horses, you will of course have been hosing it down regularly anyway. If you are planning to lay it up however, it is always a good idea to give the whole thing an extra-thorough clean out before storage.

Use a pressure-washer, or a hose with a concentrated nozzle, to give every corner of the trailer a good hose down. Use a stiff broom, too, to scrub at any particularly stubborn patches, if necessary.

Job 49. Prepare chassis.

Damp will strike up from beneath, particularly if your trailer is parked outside on anything permeable, such as soil or gravel. Wash the chassis thoroughly, using a hose or pressure washer, taking particular care with corners and crevices, and being sure to remove any caked-on mud that can cause a 'poultice' effect when soaked with water and salt.

Job 50. Prepare fittings for storage.

12V BATTERY

If the trailer has a battery fitted for any reason, remove it to prevent it from discharging itself - but do not store it on a concrete floor, since this too will cause it to discharge. While the battery is in storage, give it a trickle charge every so often to keep it in good condition.

TRAILER TENTS

If the tent part of your trailer tent is put away damp, it will go mouldy and rotten. Make sure that it is left opened out until it is thoroughly dry, before packing it away. An electrical convection heater placed inside would hurry the job, but ensure that there is no risk of fire if you do use artificial heat. And now, of course, would be the time to have any necessary repairs or restitching carried out.

Job 51. Prepare electrical connections.

51. Apply some water repellent spray, or a light coating of Vaseline, to the 12N (and 12S, if fitted) plugs and sockets, to stop them corroding. You can then cover the plugs with a plastic bag if you wish - but be sure to make some holes in the bottom of the bag to stop the build-up of condensation.

Ensure that the seals on the 12-volt sockets on your car are sound, and that the springs holding the lids closed are working.

Job 52. Measures to preserve tyres.

52. The surest way to ensure that your tyres emerge unscathed is to actually remove the wheels, and use axle stands, (or these proprietary 'tyre savers'), to support the chassis in their stead.

If you leave the wheels in place, remember to rotate the wheels periodically to keep the bearings lubricated. This should also prevent the tyres from becoming misshapen if they are touching the ground. If you

choose to store the trailer without taking any of the above precautions, simply taking the trouble to move it backwards and forwards every so often should at least ensure that you don't find yourself towing on 'square' tyres the next time you take it out!

INSIDE INFORMATION: If you remove the wheels, with the chassis supported, tie a plastic bag around the hubs to protect them from the ingress of water. (Illustration, courtesy Safe and Secure Products)

Job 53. Protect hitch.

53. Grease the hitch and place a cover over the hitch area of the trailer - a bin liner is ideal! - to protect it from the elements and to stop insects crawling inside. You can also buy ready-made covers like this one to protect your hitch in style!

Job 54. Protect winch, as necessary.

If your trailer has a winch fitted, whether manually or electrically operated, it is a good idea to lubricate (where appropriate) and cover the winch.

Every Two Years

❏ Job 55. Repack hub grease.

Because the brakes are in the wheel hubs, a binding or overheating brake may cause the hub grease to thin out and require replacement. You should replace it every two years anyway, as a matter of course. See **Job 39**. If your trailer is ever used in water, see the boat trailer information given under 'Special Equipment', in the next section.

❏ Job 56. Check exterior lamp seals.

Over a period of time, lamp seals deteriorate, damp gets in and lighting problems become endemic. Inspect the seals and replace them, or carefully apply a smear of non-setting silicone sealer to the lamp seals, if new ones are not available.

🛈 56. INSIDE INFORMATION: If you have trouble with lamp compartments filling with water, try drilling a small hole in the bottom of each light bulb compartment to let out any water that may gather there. 🛈

56

Servicing Special Equipment

Stabilisers

The commonest (and least expensive) type of stabiliser you're likely to come across is the blade variety. This reaches from the towing vehicle's towing bracket to the side of the trailer's A-frame. It's important to make sure that the adjuster bolt on this sort of stabiliser is always set correctly.

❏ Job 57. Check and adjust stabiliser.

57A. Tightening the nut (turning it clockwise) will increase the resistance; loosening the nut (turning it anti-clockwise) will slacken the blade's resistance off.

57A

57B

57B. Use a set of bathroom scales to measure resistance, and set the damper according to the manufacturer's recommendations. For most makes, something in the region of 60lbs (or 28 kgs) of pressure on the scales is about right.

FRICTION-TYPE STABILISER

When caring for your hitch-type stabiliser it is essential that you DO NOT GREASE THE TOWBALL OR HITCH. This will decompose the brake pads and make the hitch damper completely ineffective.

57C. The AL-KO AKS2000 stabiliser is just one of a number of hitch type stabilisers on the market, but the information given here applies to all. It has a set of brake pads contained within it. There are three numbers marked on the side: two on the casing, and one on the pivot. If, as the handle on the

57C

stabiliser is engaged, No.1 is between No.2 and No.3, then the pads need replacing.

SPECIALIST SERVICE: Servicing the hitch-type stabiliser is a job requiring specialist tools, and so you should refer pad replacement and overhauling to the appropriate dealer. (Illustration, courtesy Indespension)

Boat Trailers

Exposure to water - and salt water particularly - will rapidly accelerate corrosion and wear.

❏ Job 58. Inspect and lubricate over-run.

58

58. Make sure that the over-run mechanism does not become neglected - on boat trailers, it has not been unknown for these to seize solid - with the result that all braking action is then lost. This degree of rust occurred because the bellows are split and brittle - and missing!

Look closely at all parts of the over-run braking mechanism for signs of corrosion. Clean off any encrusted dirt, salt or corrosion with a wire brush, and treat with water-repellent grease.

❏ Job 59. Lubricate and check boat rollers.

59. Squirt releasing fluid into the centres of the rollers and along their shafts. This will not only make loading easier; it will also slow down wear. Check the rollers' condition and replace if necessary.

59

❏ Job 60. Re-grease wheel bearings.

60. Boat trailers' wheel bearings have a terribly hard life, and must be better cared for than normal. Adhere to normal greasing schedules religiously, and check the presence and condition of the grease as often as is practicable in-between times.

60

⚡ INSIDE INFORMATION: When applying grease to boat trailer bearings, always choose a water-repellent variety, such as Century's 'Aqua Lube', and use sealed bearing savers as shown if at all possible in place of the normal grease cap. ⚡

Car Trailers and Other Vehicle Carriers

Because of the weights - and values - of their loads, it is more important than normal to keep a close eye on the condition and fixings of the axle(s), wheel bearings, tyres and suspension.

Pay close attention to the lubrication and cleanliness of your ramp hinges, securing catches and tie-down hooks.

TIE-DOWNS

❏ Job 61. Care for your tie-downs.

61

61. Tie-downs are often the most neglected part of any trailer's equipment - but in many ways, they're among its most important part!

i) Allowing webbing to get soaked with rain will cause it to weaken - and rust on the catches could make them useless.

ii) Always neatly coil the straps when not in use to avoid knotting. If allowed to tighten to the point where they can't be undone, knots will mean that the straps have to be replaced. NEVER use a knotted strap - the knot will seriously weaken the strap.

iii) Give the catches a good spray with water repellent every so often to keep them working well and rust free. (Illustration, courtesy Euroweb Lashing Systems)

WINCHES

We could never hope to cover every winch type in this manual, and detailed information on servicing and repair will be readily available from your winch supplier. For this reason, we have only included the most basic manual winch types.

❑ Job 62. Clean and lubricate the winch.

62A. The commonest type of winch will be a manually-operated model. Worm drives are generally trouble-free. The geared type, shown, needs more regular cleaning.

Clean and lubricate the winch mechanism every time you perform a normal lubrication

62A

service on your trailer: using generous amounts of paraffin on an old paintbrush, scrub away all clogged-up grease and dirt from the gear, drive, and ratchet mechanisms. Dry thoroughly before re-greasing every moving part (except the drum itself!). A water-repellent grease is recommended for all external winches. Wind the winch back and forth a couple of times to ensure that the grease covers all of the mechanism.

ⓘ INSIDE INFORMATION: If the winch has a wire cable, you should unreel it periodically and spray or brush it well with a light oil. Clean off first if it's very dirty. BUT: See the note below about re-spooling the wire. ⓘ

62B

62B. Always observe the cautions and limitations stamped onto the side of your winch. Winch safety is, a prime consideration - and should any component other than the handle or line break, or become so excessively worn as to compromise the winch's operation, fitting a complete new replacement winch is the recommended remedy.

❑ Job 63. Replace a winch strap or cable.

WINCH STRAP REPLACEMENT

63. Hauling line replacements, whether in polyester webbing or steel

63

cable, are available from any winch manufacturer or plant dealer. Be sure to check that the breaking strength of the new line and the strap width are matched to the load limits of your winch.

Unwind the old strap completely, unbolt the old strap, and check that the bolt has not bent or stretched, before threading the looped end of the replacement onto it. Now wind the new strap around the winch spool at least five times to provide proper anchorage - and it's ready to use! (Illustration, courtesy Euroweb Lashing Systems)

WINCH CABLE REPLACEMENT

If your winch cable is frayed, corroded, crushed or damaged in any other way, then you MUST replace it. Most winch cables have a looped end, and are attached in the same manner as the strap, described above. However, some others have plain ends, and these are attached to the winch drum by locating the plain end of the cable in the appropriate hole, and inserting and tightening a bolt which clamps the cable into place. As with a strap, wind at least five layers of cable onto the drum, taking out any slack, before using your boat or car to fully rewind the cable under load.

Horse Boxes and Stock Trailers

Trailers which are used to carry animals are subject to certain laws regarding how much space each animal is allowed, and the conditions under which they are carried. See *Chapter 4, Rules & Regulations* for information on these regulations, and always comply with them. The laws are clear cut - and so are one's moral duties, of course!

❑ Job 64. Maintain partitions, gates and stalls.

64. An animal travelling in a trailer will almost certainly be injured if a partition should come adrift - and the distress inevitably caused by a journey will be much magnified if a stall partition is able to rattle or flap about. Partitions, fixings, the ramp, and any halter rings, will need to be carefully maintained - and properly used.

❑ Job 65. Attend to ramp.

65. Always ensure that the ramp is scrupulously clean, and that any batons screwed to it are not broken or coming loose. Grease the hinges and/or securing bolts at every normal lubrication service.

❑ Job 66. Clean trailer.

The law requires that, if you are delivering animals on a turnover basis, the trailer is thoroughly hosed down and disinfected after every trip - and regardless of what the law says, it's obviously a sound idea to observe basic hygiene for your stock.

Tipper Units

❑ Job 67. Clean and lubricate tipper mechanism.

67. With the simplest tilt mechanism, located on the drawbar beneath the trailer floor, use a wire brush to clean off road dirt, with a stiff-bristled brush. Apply grease or light oil.

If you have a hydraulic pump, apply a little light oil to the pump handle pivot every so often, and if it has an electrical motor fitted, include all the wiring and switches for this in your electrical servicing schedule.

❑ Job 68. Service hydraulic pump.

SPECIALIST SERVICE: Whether operated by a manual pump-handle or electric motor, the hydraulic tipper unit should be serviced annually by a qualified hydraulics engineer.

☐ Job 69. Roller shutter doors.

SPECIALIST SERVICE: Roller shutter doors are complicated assemblies, controlled by powerful springs located in the top roller housing - and you should NEVER attempt to take one apart. Should anything go wrong with your roller shutter, refer it to the manufacturer of the trailer or door for service or repair. The only tasks which you can safely undertake on these doors are:

i) Applying grease to any operating chain.

ii) Using a releasing fluid or light oil on metal roller shutters to eliminate squeaks and stiffness. Do not apply any oil or grease to a roller shutter door with plastic components.

Trailer Tents

The subject of trailer tents can be a huge one, encompassing under-floor heating, fridges and gas appliances, as well as the simple canvas-over-frame construction covered here.

☐ Job 70. Examine and care for the canvas.

For re-proofing small areas, for example if you have treated mildew or wet patches, and need to re-proof a limited area, you can obtain silicone proofing compounds, such as 'Fabsil', from your local camping shop. For the periodic all-over treatment however, it's best to take advantage of your trailer tent dealer or camping shop's proofing service. Repairs, too, are best trusted to a specialist, and proofing time is the ideal opportunity to have them done.

☐ Job 71. Frame care.

Zinc passivated or powder-coated frame members can be wiped down with a damp cloth for cleaning, although should any 'white rust' appear on a galvanised pole, rub down with fine wire wool.

71A. The springs in those ingenious snap-together poles can be stretched or damaged. These springs are quite strong, and their anchor ends are sharp, so watch out! The springs are pushed into the ends of the poles with a screwdriver, as shown in the diagram. (Illustration, courtesy Conway)

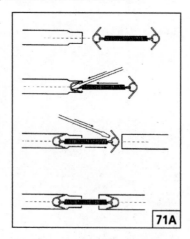

71A

71B. Button clips are used to adjust the lengths of the poles, and these too are sprung. The V-shaped metal clip is tensioned against the insides of the pole, allowing the button to pop in and out as it locates, and then rides past, the holes in the other pole. These little clips can sometimes be damaged, or they can disappear up inside the pole. Again, replacements are easily obtained - and easily fitted -

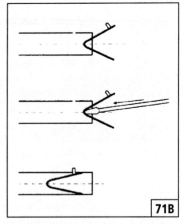

71B

as shown in diagram **83B**. (Illustration, courtesy Conway)

Hinges may be secured with special fasteners: either a bolt with a nylon nut, or a metal pin secured by a domed cap. The technical names for these when buying replacements are 'quickals', or star lock washers.

☐ Job 72. Clean inner tents, linings and loose covers.

All these items should only ever be dry-cleaned. If their hanging clips should get lost or damaged, replacements are cheap and easily obtained from your trailer tent dealer, or local camping shop.

☐ Job 73. Prepare tent for storage.

73. If your trailer tent has a removable canvas, remove it - and all other removable textile items - and pack them separately from the trailer for winter storage in a dry, warm place. With a folding camper, the whole

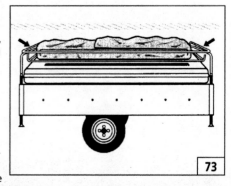

73

trailer must be kept somewhere warm and dry to preserve the in-built textiles. If you can't keep the textile components of your trailer in ideal circumstances, make sure you check on them regularly throughout the winter to make sure that condensation and mildew have not struck. In all other areas, you should prepare the trailer for storage as detailed in **Jobs 47 to 54**. (Illustration, courtesy Conway)

CHAPTER 7
REPAIRING & UPGRADING
YOUR TRAILER

Repairing your trailer will be an easy job by comparison with working on other, more complicated vehicles. All parts of any trailer made by a well-know firm will be easily available from the manufacturer - but always ensure that you use only branded components from an approved source. If you want to use second-hand running gear or braking components, always check their make and part number against the part you intend to replace, and reject anything which is not exactly the same as the originals.

PART I: REPAIRS

SAFETY FIRST!

*Before carrying out any work on your trailer, carefully read and act upon the advice in **Chapter 1, Safety First!***

Brakes

See the relevant parts of *Chapter 6, Servicing & Maintenance* for full details on overhauling all of the braking system.

Wheel Bearings

See **Job 39** in *Chapter 6, Servicing & Maintenance*.

The Over-Run Damper

See **Job 40** in *Chapter 6, Servicing & Maintenance*.

The Jockey Wheel and Prop Stands

☐ 1. Luckily, these are simple bolt-on items. It's always a good idea to fit new nuts and bolts when fitting new components - and in the case of 'Nyloc' self-locking nuts, it's essential.

Leaf Springs and Bushes

If any of leaves in the leaf springs are broken or the straps which go around them have rusted through; if they have rusted solid or the swivel pins have worn so that there is movement in the spring eyes, you will need to replace springs and/or swivel pins as appropriate.

---
making it easy! At least a day before starting work, wire brush all the mud and corrosion on all of the mounting bolts and soak them in releasing fluid. Repeat the dose on several occasions during the day, so that it soaks in well.

☐ 2. Support the trailer chassis securely on a set of axle stands. The axle will also have to be supported because it will be left hanging free once the spring mountings are removed. After undoing the shackle pin retaining nuts, take the weight off the axle with your jack so that the pin can be more easily knocked out. If you intend re-using the pin, take great care not to damage the thread.

3

making it easy! ❏ 3. U-bolts shear really easily! Use a butane torch to apply heat to each U-bolt nut before undoing it. If it still looks as if it's going to shear the U-bolt, use a nut splitter to burst the nut open rather than have to replace the U-bolt.

4

❏ 4. If the shackle pin/s is severely worn, you will need to replace it, along with the spring eye bush.

ℹ **INSIDE INFORMATION:** Spring eye bushes can be the devil of a job to get out! Try hack sawing through at two different points before using an old spanner socket to drift the bush and metalastic rubber surround out of the spring eye. ℹ

SAFETY FIRST!

Don't be tempted to burn the rubber out of the eye: it certainly burns well, but it can explode, throwing molten, burning rubber through the air. The heat of the burning rubber will also probably destroy the temper in the end of the spring and cause it to break.

5

❏ 5. These are the mounting points of a 4-wheel trailer's springs. The principle of all types remains the same.

ℹ **INSIDE INFORMATION: Take special care when fitting a new pin (or re-fitting the old) that you don't damage the thread on the end of the pin as it is pushed through the shackle plate. The answer is to line the spring eye bush holes are perfectly with the shackle plate before inserting the pin.** ℹ

6

❏ 6. IMPORTANT NOTE: Through the centre of each spring is a clamp bolt. Make sure that the bolt head locates in the hole in the centre of the U-bolt plate.

The springs can now be re-fitted to the axles, as before. Do take great care to keep grease off the rubber of the Metalastic bushes in the spring eyes because otherwise the rubber will rapidly go soft and disintegrate.

PART II: UPGRADES

There is an almost limitless choice of upgrades and accessories to enhance your towing capabilities. We have selected the ones that we have found most useful - but there are many others!

Towbracket Improvements

❏ 1. A bumper guard bolts between towball and bracket and protects against damage when hitching up. Also from Witter is the shock-absorber towball, mounted in a rubber shock absorber to make towing more comfortable for the driver.

Fitting a Stabiliser

Fitting a stabiliser is an excellent way of adding stability to a heavy trailer and to make it less susceptible to snaking caused by cross-winds or overtaking heavy goods vehicles.

Fitting a stabiliser to counterbalance a serious defect in the trailer itself - or incorrect trailer loading - will only push the 'snaking' point higher up the speed scale and make the outfit even less safe to use than it was before.

A stabiliser is a damping device, fitted either to the towing hitch or to the trailer's drawbar, which minimises the swaying motion encountered when towing the trailer in strong winds, or when being overtaken by heavy vehicles. The commonest (and least expensive) type is the blade variety shown here and in the Heading Picture. It's important to make sure that the adjuster bolt on this sort of stabiliser is always set correctly.

FITTING A BLADE-TYPE STABILISER

❏ 2. The Safe & Secure stabiliser is typical in that its mounting bracket is fitted beneath the towball. You may need longer bolts. The stabiliser bar then slots into this bracket, and is held with a thumbscrew.

❏ 3. Getting the guide bracket positioned properly on the A-frame is particularly important if the blade is to be able to slide through it freely. Follow the fitting instructions supplied with the stabiliser to get its position along the A-frame exactly right for the model of blade concerned, either clamping or drilling and bolting it in place.

The Safe and Secure stabiliser is fitted with the handle provided - see this chapter's Heading Picture.

┌─── **SAFETY FIRST!** ───┐

Consult the trailer manufacturer before drilling any holes in the 'A' frame. The 'A' frame is highly stressed and could crack with disastrous results.

See *Chapter 6, Servicing & Maintenance Job 57*, for information on how to check and set the stabiliser's adjustment.

Winches

If you intend upgrading your boat or car-transporter trailer with a winch, or a replacement, it is essential that: i) you follow the following guidelines when selecting a suitable winch for the intended application, and that ii) you fit the winch securely following the manufacturer's instructions supplied with the winch.

SELECT AND FIT A WINCH

Winch selection will be largely determined by the weight of load the winch is needed for. When choosing your winch, you will find its maximum load described in one of two ways:

MAXIMUM LINE PULL

This is the maximum dead weight which the winch could lift off the ground. This figure is given as an indicator of the winch's strength only - you should NEVER use a winch for lifting.

ROLLING PULL

This is the maximum weight of load (carried on wheels) that the winch could pull up a slope of a given gradient and surface resistance. This is measured according to a variety of different variables, and manufacturers' claimed rolling pulls should, on the whole, be taken with a pinch of salt unless the gradient and surface are specified.

⚡ **INSIDE INFORMATION: While you should NEVER use a winch for lifting, maximum line pull is the figure which you should rely on as your guide to which winch to choose.** ⚡

FACT FILE: CALCULATING THE PULL

As a rough-and-ready calculation, the relationships between the weight of a vehicle being pulled by a winch and the rolling pull required can be calculated as follows, but ONLY ASSUMING that the ground is level, the brakes are not binding and that there are no other adverse factors at work:

Surface Type	Effort required to move vehicle as a percentage gross weight
Hard surfaced road	4% total weight of Vehicle
Grass	15% total weight of Vehicle
Sand (hard wet)	17.5% total weight of Vehicle
Gravel or sand (soft wet)	20% total weight of Vehicle
Sand (soft/dry/loose)	25% total weight of Vehicle
Shallow mud	35% total weight of Vehicle
Bog, Marsh or Clay (clinging)	50% total weight of Vehicle

Thus the pull required to move a vehicle weighing about 1,000 kg along a flat sandy beach of hard wet sand is Vehicle Weight x Coefficient Percentage = Line Pull Required, or 1000 x 17.5% = 175 kg, plus an allowance for adverse factors.

Two-speed geared winches are by far the most suitable for boat or vehicle applications, and should come with a neutral position to prevent the winding handle from spinning round when the line is unspooled. Make sure, if you choose a geared type, that the winch is equipped with a braking mechanism, too. If you will be hauling large, heavy items, then a worm-drive winch may be the best choice for you, although they are rather rare and specialised. The big advantage with a worm drive is that when you stop winding the winch, the worm drive automatically holds the load firm. Far more common is a work winch with a ratchet to hold the spool at any given point when under tension.

For mounting any fixed winch type, measure up the mounting plate dimensions, and make up another matching plate. Weld this plate onto the chassis or frame to avoid weakening structural members by drilling them.

☐ 4. To use a winch safely, it is important that it should be fitted in such a position as to allow the cable or webbing an unobstructed run when hauling. For this reason, you should select a position - or make up a pillar of a suitable strength and height - which will keep the winch high enough to ensure that the line does not brush against, or run over, any part of the trailer. You must ensure that the hauling line forms an unobstructed, perfectly straight line when in use. (Illustration, courtesy Warne winches)

CHAPTER 8
PERFORM YOUR OWN 'MoT'!

With rumours of an official, annual 'MoT' test for trailers on the distant horizon, now's the time to get into the habit of carrying out an organised check on the condition of your trailer and its equipment.

Let's make it quite clear, however:
1. There is no MoT test for trailers in the UK.
2. There is, at the time of writing, no proposed introduction date.
3. These are our personal views as to what a trailer 'MoT' test *might* comprise...

Make sure that your trailer does not become one of the 'failures' and keep it safe, by adhering to all our recommendations for servicing, and by making the following condition checks on an annual basis. It's an excellent idea to photocopy

these pages, and actually tick off each item as you check it - just like a real MoT tester would! That way you'll be absolutely sure you don't miss anything.

Unless otherwise indicated, if your answer to one of the following questions *YES,* then this is a pass. If the answer is *NO,* then the trailer has failed on that point. If you do find a problem with any of the items listed below, you will find details of how to put the problem right in *Chapter 6, Servicing & Maintenance.*

PART I: LIGHTING CHECKS

Connect the trailer to the towing vehicle, and plug in the 12N electrical socket.

❑ A. Do both indicators work?

❑ B. Apply brake while indicators are on. Do brake lights pulse? (Yes = Fail)

❑ C. Can you hear audible warning indicator or see warning light?

❑ D. Do brake lights work?

❑ E. Does fog light work (if fitted)?

❑ F. Do all number plate bulbs work?

❑ G. Are all rear lenses clean and intact?

❑ H. Are all front/side lenses clear and intact? (White light = Fail)

❑ I. Do lights flicker when tapped? (Yes = Fail)

❑ J. Are all connections sound?

❑ K. Is seven-core cable sound?

❑ L. Are all light fittings positioned correctly? (Not, in fact, a 'fail' in the car test!)

❑ M. Does the tailboard obscure the rear lights when lowered? (Yes = Fail)

❑ N. Are all light fittings properly secured?

❑ O. Are both red reflectors correct and intact?

PART II: HITCH & SUSPENSION CHECKS

See *Chapter 6, Servicing & Maintenance* and *Chapter 2, Buying a Trailer,* for information on how to examine the suspension units and other components tested here.

❑ A. Does hitch shaft show wear when hitch lifted up and down? (Yes = Fail)

❑ B. Does hitch mechanism lock positively when fitted to towball?

❑ C. Is any part of hitch mechanism loose or worn? (Yes = Fail)

❑ D. Does the over-run hydraulic damper (if fitted) operate satisfactorily?

❑ E. Is there sufficient clearance between wheels and body?

❑ F. Do the mudguards cover the full width of the tyres?

❑ G. Are the mudguards complete and securely fitted?

❑ H. Are all suspension mountings points secure?

❑ I. Is there any excessive wear in the suspension? (Yes = Fail)

❑ J. Are suspension leaf springs, shackles and pins in serviceable condition?

❑ K. Are suspension rubber blocks sound?

❑ L. Are wheel bearings showing signs or noise or excessive wear? (Yes = Fail)

PART III: BRAKES CHECKS

Professional MoT testers use special measuring equipment to assess the performance of braking systems. Without access to this equipment, you will only be able to make the basic checks detailed in *Chapter 6, Servicing & Maintenance*.

☐ A. Does drawbar compress and re-extend?

☐ B. Does over-run brake operate satisfactorily?

☐ C. Does handbrake operate satisfactorily?

☐ D. Does handbrake hold trailer firm?

☐ E. Is linkage in good mechanical order or corroded?

☐ F. Is linkage properly adjusted?

☐ G. Are both/all wheel brakes in balance?

PART IV: WHEELS & TYRES CHECKS

☐ A. Are tyres all marked with sizes and load ratings and are they all the same?

☐ B. Are tyres all of a sufficient rating for GVW of trailer?

☐ C. Are all tyres of same type (i.e. radials and cross-ply not mixed)?

☐ D. Are tyre tread depths all over 1.6 mm for 75% of width?

☐ E. Are tyres walls perished or cracked? (Yes = Fail)?

☐ F. Are there any cuts more than 25 mm long? (Yes = Fail)

☐ G. Are there any lumps, bulges, tears, exposed ply or cord? (Yes = fail)

☐ H. Have the treads been recut? (Yes = Fail)

☐ I. Are the tyres seated correctly on the rims?

☐ J. Are the valves in good order and properly aligned?

☐ K. Are the tyres well clear of all parts of the vehicle?

☐ L. On twin axle models, is there the possibility of tyre tread contact? (Yes = Fail)

PART V: GENERAL CONDITION CHECKS

A vehicle MoT tester has discretion in his assessment of the general condition of a vehicle, and can fail it on just about any point if he thinks it is serious enough to warrant it. Go over the whole trailer, making an impartial judgement about any other items you may find; any insecure catches, untoward corrosion on chassis members, and so on - any of these things could bring about a fail in our mock 'MoT'.

☐ A. Is number plate properly secured?

☐ B. Is number plate of the approved type?

☐ C. Is chassis corroded? (Yes = Fail)

☐ D. Is chassis distorted?

☐ D. Are all rope hooks, etc, securely fixed?

☐ E. Are all hinges in good order?

☐ F. Do all catches latch securely?

☐ G. Is the winch securely mounted?

☐ H. Is the tipper unit in safe order?

* Some rust is tolerated, but in the car MoT, small rust holes must not be within 30 cm of key structural points.

APPENDIX 1
RECOMMENDED LUBRICATION POINTS

A Hub Bearings

NON-BOAT TRAILERS
Use a regular high melting point grease such as Castrol's LM.

BOAT TRAILERS
Use a water-repellent grease such as Century's 'Aqua Lube'.

E Over-run Brake Activation Mechanism

High melting point grease applied to all grease nipples with greasing gun.

B Suspension

RUBBER BLOCK
DO NOT lubricate rubber block suspension.

LEAF SPRING SUSPENSION
Units should be protected from corrosion and dirt with a spray-on lubricant such as WD40, or with light oil such as Castrol's 'Everyman', or even engine oil, avoiding the metalastik rubbers in the spring eyes and shackles.

C Brake Cables and Rod

High melting point grease or light oil to be applied to all external moving parts.

Grease to be applied to external adjuster on rear of backplate, if applicable.

On areas of metal to metal contact in the braking system, a very light application of specialist brake grease, such as Castrol's 'PH'.

D Handbrake

High melting point grease from gun, and/or smeared onto components, as appropriate.

F Hitch and Towball

DO NOT lubricate a hitch (friction) stabiliser or the towball used with it. Otherwise, high-melting point grease.

G Jockey Wheel and Prop Stands

Frequent external application of light oil.

Periodic disassembly, all-over smearing of high melting point grease, and light oil or spray lubricant into internal threads.

H Winch and Other Accessories

High melting point grease on winch winding mechanism, tipper pivots, ramp abutments, hinges, catches and all other moving components.

I Boat Trailers

On boat trailer, use water-repellent grease for all applicable lubrication. For enquiries on suitable types of lubricant, please contact Castrol - *see Appendix 2, Specialists and Suppliers.*

APPENDIX 2
SPECIALISTS AND SUPPLIERS

AL-KO Kober Ltd, South Warwickshire Business Park, Kineton Road, Southam, Warwickshire, CV47 0AL. Tel: 01926 818500.

British Canoe Union, John Dudderidge House, Adbolton Lane, West Bridgford, Nottingham, NG2 5AS
Tel: 0115 982 1100.

British Horse Society, British Equestrian Centre, Stoneleigh, Kenilworth, Warwickshire CV8 2LR. Tel: 01203 696697.

British Motorcyclists Federation, Conwyn House, 14-16 Briton Street, Leicester, LE3 0AA
Tel: 0116 254 8818.

British Ropes Ltd (winch cables and ropes) Bridon International, Carr Hill, Doncaster, South Yorkshire DN4 8DG.
Tel: 01302 344010.

Bulldog Security Products Ltd, Units 1-4 Stretton Road, Much Wenlock, Shropshire TF13 6DH. Tel: 01952 728171.

Caddy Trailers Ltd, 151-183 Holme Lane, Sheffield S6 4JR.
Tel: 0114 250 3025.

Carlight Trailers Ltd, Church Lane, Sleaford, Lincs NG34 7DE.
Tel: 01529 302120.

Castrol (UK) Ltd, Burmah House, Pipers Way, Swindon, Wiltshire SN3 1RE. Tel: 01793 512712.

Conway Leisure, Chester Street, Accrington, Lancs, B35 0SD
Tel: 01254 385991.

Dunlop Tyres Ltd., TyreFort, 88-98 Wingfoot Way, Birmingham, B24 9HY
Tel: 0121 306 6000

DVLA Customer Enquiries: 01792 782318.

Ifor Williams Trailers (agricultural, horse and heavy trailers), Cynwyd, Corwen, Clwyd LL21 0LS. Tel: 01490 412626.

Indespension (leisure and light trailers), Head Office, Paragon Business Park, Chorley New Road,, Bolton, Lancs, BL6 6HG. Tel: 0800 720720 for details of your nearest Indespension stockist.

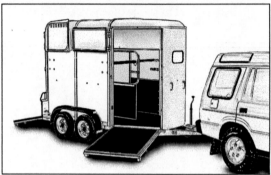

Organisaton of Horsebox and Trailer Owners, 38 Newton Road, London W2 5LT.

Peak Trailers Ltd, Unit 2a-2b, Waterloo Industrial Estate, Waterloo Road, Bidford-on-Avon, Warwickshire B50 4JH. Tel: 01789 778041.

Perkson (George Dyke Ltd.), Imperial Works, Darlaston, W. Midlands, WS0 8LP
Tel: 0807 444 2820

Raydyot Limited (towing accessories), Waterfall Lane, Cradley Heath, Warley, West Midlands, B64 6QB.
Tel: 0121 559 2471.

Ryder International (Winch Division), 215 Knowsley Road, Bootle, Liverpool L20 4NW.
Tel: 0151 922 7585.

Safe and Secure Products (security), Chestnut House, Chesley Hill, Wick, Nr Bristol, BS30 5NE
Tel: 0117 937 4747

SMMT, Forbes House, Halkin Street, London SW1X 7DS.
Tel: 0207 235 7000

Tow Sure Products Ltd, 151 - 183 Holme Lane, Hillsborough, Sheffield S6 4JP. Tel: 0114 250 3025.

Tyre Services Great Britain (Tyron Safety Wheels), 11 Chapel Ash, Wolverhampton WV3 0TZ. Tel: 01902 420234.

Watsonian-Squire Ltd (motorcycle-towed trailers and sidecars), Northwick Business Centre, Blockley, Nr Moreton-in-Marsh, Gloucestershire GL56 9RF. Tel: 01386 700907.

Witter Towbars, Drome Road, Deeside Industrial Park, Deeside, CH5 2NY
Tel: 01244 284500.

APPENDIX 3 - VEHICLE TOWING LIMITS

The maximum weight unbraked trailer you can tow is restricted by law to 50% of your vehicles kerb weight, or 750 kg., whichever is less. Some car manufacturers (especially the Japanese) sensibly suggest lower unbraked limits than this, and you should be warned that towing an unbraked trailer of maximum legal weight can increase your safe stopping distance.

Arriving at a safe maximum is not as straightforward as you might think. The towing capacities quoted by vehicle manufacturers are largely a measure of the vehicle's ability to hill start with that load attached. However, for modern vehicles with their relatively high power to weight ratios the safe handling of the combination is likely to constrain pulling capacity long before engine power.

Many factors affect the handling of a combination: on the vehicle, wheelbase, wheel track, centre of gravity and springing: on the trailer, length, width centre of gravity and suspension.

Vulnerability to cross winds and motorway side draught further complicates behaviour.

However, as a general rule, the major handling factor is the relative weight of the towing vehicle and the load.

The National Caravan Council recommends that trailer gross weight should not exceed 85% of the kerb weight of the vehicle, and we agree. Under exceptional circumstances with a carefully loaded trailer an experienced tow person may feel happy towing at 100%, but this should be an absolute upper limit for private use. Four wheel drives will tow carefully designed and loaded trailers at over 100% acceptably. In the tables below we use the 85% figure for domestic cars wherever possible, but for 4 wheel drives we quote only manufacturers figures.

Vehicle manufacturers' maximum limits - quoted in the handbook, on the VIN plate or available from the manufacturer - are LEGAL maxima, and to exceed them is an offence.

Manufacturer & Model	Kerb Weight kg	Maxm. Bkd. kg	Nose Weight kg	Maxm. U/bkd kg
ALFA				
155 1.8 Twin Spark	1205	1025	50	600
155 2.0 Twin Spark/Lusso	1215	1030	50	605
155 2.5 V6	1290	1095	50	645
155 Cloverleaf 4	1390	1180	50	590
164 2.0i Twin Spark/Lusso	1200	1020	50	510
164 3.0i 24v Super	1295	1100	50	550
164 24v Cloverleaf	1425	1210	50	605
AUDI				
80	1185	1005	50	590
80 TID	1270	1080	50	635
80 TDi	1270	1080	50	635
80 2.0E	1230	1045	50	615
80 16V	1270	1080	50	635
80 2.6E	1430	1215	50	715
80 2.8E Quattro	1425	1210	50	710
Coupe 16V	1190	1010	50	585
Coupe 2.6E	1305	1110	50	650
Coupe 2.8E Quattro	1320	1120	50	660
100 2.0E	1325	1125	50	660
100 2.6E	1400	1190	50	700
1100 2.6E Quattro	1500	1275	75	750
100 TDi	1320	1120	50	660
100 TDi 6.Sp	1420	1205	50	710
100 2.0E Est.	1375	1145	50	685
100 2.8E Est.	1450	1230	50	725
100 TDi/6.Sp Est.	1470	1250	50	735
100 2.8E Quattro Est.	1550	1315	75	750
V8	1710	1450	75	750
A4 Avant 1.8 manual	1225	1040	75	660
A4 Avant 1.8 auto	1225	1040	75	660
A4 Avant 1.8 T manual	1235	1050	75	665
A4 Avant 1.8 T auto	1235	1050	75	665
A4 Avant 2.6 manual	1285	1090	75	640
A4 Avant 2.6 auto	1285	1090	75	640
A4 Avant 2.8 manual	1285	1090	75	640
A4 Avant 2.8 auto	1285	1090	75	640
A4 Avant 2.8 quattro man	1400	1190	75	700
A4 Avant 2.8 quattro auto	1400	1190	75	700
A4 Avant 1.9 TDI manual	1240	1050	75	620
A4 Avant 1.9 TDI auto	1240	1050	75	620
A4 Avant 1.9 TDI I 10 man	1240	1050	75	620
A4 Avant 1.9 TDI I 10 auto	1240	1050	75	620
A4 Saloon 1.6 manual	1265	1070	75	630
A4 Saloon 1.6 auto	1265	1070	75	630
A4 Saloon 1.8 manual	1265	1070	75	630
A4 Saloon 1.8 auto	1265	1070	75	630
A4 Saloon 1.8 T manual	1270	1080	75	635
A4 Saloon 1.8 T auto	1270	1080	75	635
A4 Saloon 2.6 manual	1300	1100	75	650
A4 Saloon 2.6 auto	1300	1100	75	650
A4 Saloon 2.8 manual	1320	1120	75	660
A4 Saloon 2.8 auto	1320	1120	75	660
A4 Saloon 2.6 quattro man	1320	1120	75	660
A4 Saloon 2.6 quattro auto	1320	1120	75	660
A4 Saloon 2.8 quattro man	1430	1210	75	715
A4 Saloon 2.8 quattro auto	1430	1210	75	715
A4 Saloon 1.9 TDI manual	1285	1090	75	640
A4 Saloon 1.9 TDI auto	1285	1090	75	640
A4 Saloon 1.9 TDI 110 man	1285	1090	75	641
A4 Saloon 1.9 TDI 110 auto	1285	1090	75	640
A6 Saloon 1.8 manual	1325	1125	50	660
A6 Saloon 1.8 auto	1325	1125	50	660
A6 Saloon 2.6 manual	1400	1190	50	700
A6 Saloon 2.6 auto	1400	1190	50	700
A6 Saloon 2.8 manual	1450	1230	50	725
A6 Saloon 2.8 auto	1450	1230	50	725
A6 Saloon 2.8 quattro man	1500	1275	75	750
A6 Saloon 2.8 quattro auto	1500	1275	75	750
A6 Saloon 1.9 TDI manual	1400	1190	50	700
A6 Saloon 1.9 TDI auto	1400	1190	50	700
A6 Saloon 2.5 TDI manual	1425	1210	50	710
A6 Saloon 2.5 TDI auto	1425	1210	50	710
A6 Saloon 2.5 TDI 140 man	1460	1240	50	730
A6 Saloon 2.5 TDI 140 auto	1460	1240	50	730
A6 Saloon TDI quattro	1500	1275	75	750
A6 Estate 1.8 manual	1375	1165	50	685
A6 Estate 1.8 auto	1375	1165	50	685

	Manufacturer & Model	Kerb Weight kg	Maxm. Bkd. kg	Nose Weight kg	Maxm. U/bkd kg
	A6 Estate 2.6 manual	1450	1230	50	725
	A6 Estate 2.6 auto	1450	1230	50	725
	A6 Estate 2.8 manual	1450	1230	50	725
	A6 Estate 2.8 auto	1450	1230	50	725
	A6 Estate 2.8 quattro, man	1550	1315	75	750
	A6 Estate 2.8 quattro auto	1550	1315	75	750
	A6 Estate 1.9 TDI manual	1400	1190	50	700
	A6 Estate 1.9 TDI auto	1400	1190	50	700
	A6 Estate 2.5 TDI manual	1475	1250	50	735
	A6 Estate 2.5 TDI auto	1475	1250	50	735
	A6 Estate 2.5 TDI 140 man	1460	1240	50	730
	A6 Estate 2.5 TDI 140 auto	1460	1240	50	730
	A6 Estate TDI Quattro	1550	1315	75	750
	BMW				
	Compact 316i	1215	1030	50	605
	Compact 3 18tds	1215	1030	50	605
	Compact 318ti	1255	1065	50	625
	316i	1125	955	50	560
	316i Coupe	1190	1010	50	595
	318i	1140	970	50	570
	318is Coupe	1240	1055	50	620
	320i/SE	1270	1080	50	635
	320i Coupe	1315	1120	50	655
	320i Convertible	1435	1220	50	715
	323i Coupe	1400	1190	50	700
	325i/SE	1295	1100	50	645
	325i Coupe	1330	1130	50	665
	316i Touring	1165	990	50	580
	318i Touring	1200	1020	50	600
	318i Convertible	1355	1150	50	675
	318 tds	1340	1139	50	670
	318 tds Touring	1405	1190	50	700
	320i Touring	1405	1190	50	700
	325i Touring	1270	1080	50	635
	325 tds	1350	1145	50	675
	325 tds Touring	1485	1260	50	740
	328i	1395	1185	50	695
	328i Touring	1440	1220	50	720
	328i Coupe	1395	1185	50	695
	328i Sport	1395	1185	50	695
	328i Convertible	1515	1285	50	750
	518i /SE	1330	1130	50	665
	518i Touring	1445	1225	50	720
	520i/SE	1440	1225	50	720
	523i	1495	1270	50	745
	525 tds	1555	1320	50	750
	525i/SE/Sport	1475	1250	50	730
	525ix/SE	1570	1335	50	750
	528iSE	1495	1270	50	745
	535i/SE/Sport	1525	1295	50	750
	520i/SE Touring	1530	1300	50	750
	525i/SE Touring	1575	1340	50	750
	525ix/SE Touring	1650	1400	50	750
	525 td/tds	1555	1320	50	750
	530i	1565	1330	50	750
	540i	1605	1360	50	750
	728i	1775	1505	50	750
	730i/SE	1600	1360	50	750
	730iV8	1700	1445	50	750
	735i	1865	1585	50	750
	740i Auto	1790	1520	50	750
	740iL Auto	1830	1555	50	750
	750iauto	2070	1760	50	750
	750iL auto	2070	1760	50	750
	8400	1830	1555	50	750
	M3 Evolution	NOT EQUIPPED FOR TOWING			
	CITROEN				
	C3 1.4i	1136	850	34	540
	C3 1.6i 16V	1177	850	34	566
	AX 14D Echo 3dr.	720	610	50	360
	AX 14D Echo 5dr/TZD	735	625	50	365
	AX 14 TZX	785	670	50	390
	AX GT 3dr.	790	670	50	395
	AX GTi	790	670	50	395
	ZX Reflex/Avantage/Aura	950	810	75	475
	ZX 1.6i Aura	995	845	75	495
	ZX 1.91D Reflex/Avan/Aura	1020	870	75	510

Manufacturer & Model	Kerb Weight kg	Maxm. Bkd. kg	Nose Weight kg	Maxm. U/bkd kg
ZX Funo	1005	855	75	500
ZX I.9TD Avan/AuraNolcane	1100	935	75	550
ZX 2.0 Volcane	1050	890	75	525
ZX 1.9i Volcane Auto,	1055	895	75	525
ZX 16V	1150	980	75	575
BX 16 TXi	965	820	70	480
BX 17 TGD	985	835	70	490
BX 19 TXDI	985	835	70	490
BX TXD Turbo	985	835	70	490
BX TZD Turbo,	1070	910	70	535
BX 19 GTi	1020	865	70	510
BX 16TXi Est.	1000	850	70	500
BX 19 TXD Est.	1030	875	70	515
BX TZD Turbo Est.	1075	915	70	535,
Xantia 1.9 D/TD	1312	1200	85	-
Xantia 2.0i Petrol	1320	1300	85	-
Xsara Picasso 2.0 HDi	1300	1300	80	-
XM .2.0i/Si/SEi	1310	1110	100	655
XM 2.0i/Si/SEi Turbo	1400	1190	100	700
XM Turbo D/SD/SED	1375	1165	100	685
XM V6 3.OSEi	1420	1205	100	710
XM V6 24V	1470	1250	100	735
XM 2.0i/Si Est.	1380	1170	100	690
XM 2 * Oi/Si Turbo Est.	1500	1275	100	750
XM Turbo SID Est.	1450	1230	100	725
XM V6 3.0& Est.	1500	1275	100	750
DAEWOO				
Espero 1.5 GLXi manual	1108	940	75	500
Espero, 1.5 GLXi auto	1108	940	75	500
Nexia GLi 3,-dr	1007	855	75	400
DAIHATSU				
Charade 1.3 CX	815	690	50	405
Charade 1.3 GXi	805	685	50	400
Applause 1.6 GXi/GLXi	930	790	50	465
Sportrak 1.6 STi	110	2400	50	550
Sportrak I.6ELi/ELXi	1170	2400	50	585
Fourtrak 2.2 ~GX	1475	3500	50	600
Fourtrak 2.8 DL	1485	3500	50	600
Fourtrak 2.8 TDL/TDX	1485	3500	50	600
FIAT				
Bravo I.4 S	1010	855	70	400
Bravo 1.4 SX	1010	855	70	400
Bravo 1.8 HLX	1100	935	70	400
Brava I.4 S	1040	880	70	400
Brava 1.4 SX	1040	880	70	400
Brava 1.6 SX	1090	925	70	400
Brava J.6 ELX	1090	925	70	400
Brava 1.8 ELX	1130	960	70	400
CinquecentoS/SX	710	400	20-35	350
Cinquecento Sporting	735	400	20-35	350
Coupe	1250	1060	80	500
Punto 55 S 3/5-dr	865	735	70	400
Punto IDS 3/5-dr	995	845	70	400
Punto 55 SX 3/5-dr	860/875	900	70	400
Punto 55 SX 6-speed	865	735	70	400
Punto 60 SX Selecta 5mclr	865	735	70	400
Punto 75 SX 3/5-dr	910	770	70	400
Punto TD SX 3/5-d'r.,	10215	870	70	400
Punto 75 ELX 3/5,-dr:	920.	780	70	400
Punto 90 ELX 5-dr	990	840	70	400
Punto Sporting,	975	825	70	400
Punto 90 ELX cabrio	1070	905	70	400
Punto GT 3-dr	1000	850	70	400
Uno 1.4ie S	840	710	50	420
Tipo 1.4 Formula/S	945	800	70	470
Tipo 1.6 S/SX	970	825	75	485
Tipo 1.9 TD SX	1105	940	80	550
Tipo 2.0ie, 16V	1175	995	80	585
Tempra 1.6 S/SX	1030	875	70	515
Tempra 1.6ie S SW	1160	1200	75	400
Tempra 1.6ie S	1100	935	75	400
Tempra 1.9 IDS	1170	1200	75	450
Tempra 1.9 IDS SW	1230	1045	75	450,
Tempra 1.9 TD SX	1210	1025	75	450
Tempra 2.0ie SX	1150	980	70	575
Tempra 1.9 Tcls	1150	980	70	575
Tempra 1.6 S Stat Wag	1095	930	70	545
Tempra 2.0ie SX Stat Wag	1250	1060	70	625
Tempra 1.9 Tcls Stat Wag	1220	1040	70	610
Ulysse 2.OS	1510	1280	60	750
Ulysse 1.9 TDS	1565	1330	60	750
Ulysse 2.0 EL	1510	1280	60	750
Ulysse 1.9 TD EL	1565	1330	60	750
FORD				
Fiesta 1.25i 16V	940	800	50	470
Fiesta 1.3 LX 3dr.	830	705	50	415
Fiesta 13 LX 5dr.	850	720	50	425
Fiesta 1.3 Ghia 5dr.	860	730	50	430
Fiesta 1.8 LID 3dr.	875	745	50	435
Fiesta 1.8 LID 5dr.	895	760	50	445
Fiesta XR2i.	965	820	50	480
Galaxy 1.9 TDAspen	1650	1400	85	750
Galaxy 1.9 TD.GLX/Ghia	1650	1400	85	750
Galaxy 2.0i man Aspen	1590	1285	85	750
Galaxy 2 * Oi man GLX/Ghia	1650	1285	85	750
Galaxy 2.0i auto GLX/Ghia	1680	1285	85	750
Galaxy 2.8iCD46 GLX/Ghia	1710	1450	85	750
Galaxy 2.8iCD-V6 auto GLX/Ghia	1740	1480	85	750
Escort 1.3 3dr.	990	840	50	495
Escort 1.3 5dr.	1010	860	50	505
Escort 1.4 L/LXIGhia	1080	920	50	540

Manufacturer & Model	Kerb Weight kg	Maxm. Bkd. kg	Nose Weight kg	Maxm. U/bkd kg
Escort 1.6i L/LX 16V.	1100	935	50	550
Escort 1.6i Ghia 16V	1140	970	50	570
Escort 1.8i LX 16V 3dr.	1050	890	50	525
Escort 1.8i LX 16V 5dr.	1070	910	50	535
Escort 1.8i Ghia 16V 5dr.	1090	925	50	545
Escort 1.8I D 3dr.	1010	860	50	505
Escort 1.8I D L/LX 5dr.	1025	870	50	510
Escort XR3i 16V	1080	920	50	540
Escort XR3i Cabriolet	1145	975	50	570
Escort 1. 3 Est.	1045	890	50	520
Escort 1.4 Est.	1085	920	50	540
Escort 1.4 L Est.	1095	930	50	545
Escort 1.4 LX Est.	1035	880	50	515
Escort 1.4 Ghia Est.	1130	960	50	565
Escort 1.6i L/LX 16V Est.	1135	965	50	565
Escort 1.6i Ghia 16V Est.	1175	1000	50	585
Escort 1.8i LX 16V Est.	1140	970	50	520
Escort 1.8i Ghia 16V Est.	1175	1000	50	585
Escort 1.8I D Est.	1140	970	50	570
Escort 1.8I D L Est.	1150	980	50	575
Escort 1.8I D LX Est.	1155	980	50	'575
Orion 1.4 LX/Ghia	1010	855	50	505
Orion 1.6 LX 16V	1105	940	50	550
Orion 1.6 Ghia 16V	1145	975	50	570
Orion 1.8I D L	1100	935	50	550,
Orion 1.8I D LX	1060	900	56	530
Orion 1.8 LX 16V	1070	910	50	535
Orion 1.8 Ghia 16V	1090	925	50	545
Orion 1.8 Ghia Si 16V	1105	940	50	550
Mondeo, 1.6/LX/GLX	1070	910	50	535
Mondeo 1.8 LX	1075	915	50	535
Mondeo 1.8 GLX	1095	930	50	545
Monoleo, 2.0 GLX	1140	970	50	570
Mondeo 2.0 Si	1155	980	50	575
Mondeo 2.0 Ghia	1190	1010	50	585
Mondeo 2.0 Si 4x4	1245	1055	50	620
Maverick 2.4i SWB	1620	2800	100	750
Maverick 2.7 TD SWB	1730	2800	100	750
Maverick 2.4i LWB	1750	2800	100	750
Maverick 2.7 TD LWB	1850	2800	100	750
Probe 2.0i 16V	1215	1030	75	605
Probe 2.5i 24V	1280	1090	75	640
Granada 2.0i LX	1260	1070	75	630
Granada 2.0i GLX	1270	1080	75	630
Granada 2.0i Ghia	1280	1085	75	640
Granada 2.9i GLX Auto	1335	1135	75	665
Granada 2.9i Ghia Auto	1350	1150	75	675
Scorpio 2.0i Auto	1305	1110	75	650
Scorpio 24V Auto	1425	1210	75	710
Granada 2.0i LX/GLX Est.	1320	1120	75	660
Granada 2.0i Ghia Est.	1340	1140	75	670
Granada 2.9i GLX Auto Est.	1390	1180	75	695
Granada 2.9i Ghia Auto Est.	1415	1205	75	705
Scorpio 2.0i 8V Exec man	1470	1250	75	735
Scorpio 2.0i Auto Est.	1365	1160	75	680
Scorpio 2.9i 24V Cosworth auto Ghia	1587	1350	75	750
Scorpio 2.9i Auto Est.	1455	1235	75	725
Scorpio 2.5 TD Ultima	1676	1425	75	750
KA NOT EQUIPPED FOR TOWING				
HONDA				
Civic 11.5 LSi 3dr	950	805	50	475
Civic 1.5 LSi 4dr.	995	845	50	495
Civic 1.5 VEi	935	795	50	465
Civic 1.6 ESi	1000	850	50	500
Civic 1.6 VTi 3dr.	1075	910	50	535
Civic 1.6 VTi 4dr.	1115	945	50	555
Concerto 1.5i	1035	880	50	515
Concerto 1.6i	1075	910	50	535
Concerto 1.6i- I 6/SE	1090	925	50	545
Accord 2.0/2.0i	1225	1040	50	610
Accord 2.2i 4WS	1325	1125	50	660
Accord Aerodeck/SE	1400	1190	50	700
Accord Coupe	1760	1200	50	750
Legend	1575	1335	50	750
Legend Coupe	1565	1330	50	750
Prelude 2.0	1235	1050	75	615
Prelude 2.3	1270	1080	75	635
CR-V 2.0 SE	1485	1500	60	600
CR-V 2.0 SE auto	1515	1200	48	600
CR-V 2.0 Sport	1493	1500	60	600
CR-V 2.0 Sport auto	1523	1200	48	600
HYUNDAI				
Accent 1.3	930	790	50	465
Accent 1.5	1010	860	50	505
X2 1.3 Sonnet/LS 3dr./4dr.	910	770	50	455
X2 1.3 LS 5 d r.	925	785	50	460
IX2 1.5 GSi 3dr.	910	770	50	455
X2 1.5 GSi 4dr./5dr.	925	785	50	460
Lantra 1.6 GI-Si	109S	930	50	545
Lantra 1.8 Cdi	1155	980	50	575
Lantra 2.0 Cdi 16V	1250	1065	50	625
Coupe MVi	1040	885	50	520
Coupe MVTi	1040	885	50	520
Sonata 2.0	1260	1070	50	630
Sonata 3.0 V6	1300	1105	50	650
ISUZU				
Trooper SWB 3.2 V6	1795	3000	120	750
Trooper LWB 3.2 V6	1880	3000	120	750
Trooper SWB 3. 1 TD	1900	3000	120	750
Trooper LWB 3.1 TD	1985	3000	120	750

Manufacturer & Model	Kerb Weight kg	Maxm. Bkd. kg	Nose Weight kg	Maxm. U/bkd kg
JAGUAR				
XJ6 3.2 Sovereign	1795	1495	50	750
XJ6 4.0 Sovereign/Daimler	1820	1495	50	750
XJS 4.0 Coupe	1705	1450	50	750
XJS V 12 Coupe	1820	1860	50	750
Xj 12/Daimler Double 6	1985	1685	50	750
JEEP				
Cherokee 2.5 Sport	1450	3300	90	725
Cherokee 4.0 Limited	1505	3300	90	750
Wrangler 2.5	1390	2500	80	695
Wrangler 4.0	1455	2500	80	725
KIA				
Pride 1.3 LX 3dr.	755	640	50	375
Pride 1.3 LX 5dr.	770	655	50	385
LADA				
Riva 1500 E/L	1025	870	45	510
Riva 1500 L Est.	1015	860	45	505
Samara 1300 E/L 3dr/5dr.	900	765	45	450
Samara 1300 L 4dr.	915	780	45	455
Samara 1500 GL 3dr/5dr.	900	765	45	450
Samara 1500 GL 4dr.	915	780	45	400
Niva 4WD	1149	1574	45	570
LANCIA				
Dedra 1.6ie	1055	895	75	525
Dedra 1.8ie	1140	970	75	570
Dedra 2.0ie	1160	985	75	580
Thema 2.0 16V/LE	1300	1105	75	650
Therna 2.0 Turbo 16V LS	1330	1130	75	665
LAND ROVER				
Defender 90 2.5 Tdi	1790	4000	75	750
Defender I 10 2.5 Tdi	2050	4000	75	750
Discovery Mpi 3dr.	1890	2750	75	750
Discovery Mpi/S 5dr.	1925	2750	75	750
Discovery V8i 3dr.	1920	4000	75	750
Discovery 200 Tdi 3dr.	2005	4000	75	750
Discovery 200 Tdi 5dr.	1990	4000	75	750
Discovery 200 Tdi S 5dr.	2050	4000	75	750
Classic Range Rover Vogue TDi	2050	4000	75	750
Classic Range Rover Vogue EFi	1955	4000	75	750
Classic Range Rover Vogue SE	2000	4000	75	750
Classic Range Rover Vogue LSE	2150	4000	75	750
MAHINDRA				
340 Classic/Sport	1285	1500	100	640
540 Classic/Sport	1335	1500	100	665
MM 740	1395	1500	100	695
MAZDA				
121 1.25 3-dr/5-dr	1057	900	50	310
121 1.3 3-dr/5-dr	1057	900	50	310
121 1.8 DXi	1105	900	50	310
121 GLX	830	700	50	400
323 1.3i LX 3dr.	945	800	50	400
323 1.5 Gl/GXi	1115	950	50	400
323 1.6i GLX 4dr.	985	835	50	400
323F 1.6i GLX	1000	850	50	400
323F 1.8i GT	1080	915	50	400
323F 2.0 ZXi	1210	1030	50	400
323 1.8 Executive	1155	980	50	400
323 1.6i GLX Est.	1025	870	50	400
626 1.8 4-dr	1160	990	50	550
626 1.8 5-dr	1192	1010	50	550
626 1.8i GLX 4dr.	1145	970	50	550
626 1.8i GLX 5dr.	1180	1000	50	550
626 2.0 5-dr	1192	1010	50	550
626 2.0i GLX 4dr.	1180	1000	50	550
626 2.0i GLX 4dr. Auto	1210	1025	50	550
626 2.0i GLX 5dr.	1280	1085	50	550
626 2.0i GLX 5dr. Auto	1250	1060	50	550
626 2.5i GT 5dr.	1280	1065	50	550
626 2.5i GT 5dr. Auto	1315	1115	50	550
MX3 1.6i Auto	1075	910	50	400
MX3 1.6	1128	960	50	400
MX3 1.8	1130	960	50	400
MX5 1.6	955		Towing NOT Recommended	
MX5 1.8	990		Towing NOT Recommended	
MX6	1195	1015	50	550
MX6 2.5	1245	1060	75	550
MX6 Auto	1225	1040	50	550
Xed- 1.6	1142	970	75	550
Xeclos 2.0	1238	1050	75	550
Xeclos 6 2.0i V6	1195	1015	50	550
Xed-6 2.0i V6 Auto	1230	1045	50	550
Xeclos 9	1455	1240	75	550
MERCEDES				
190 D	1175	995	75	585
190 D 2.5	1230	1045	75	615
190 E 1.8	1155	980	75	575
190 E	1165	990	75	580
190 E 2.6	1270	1080	75	635
220 CE	1385	1175	75	690
250 D	1385	1175	75	690
280 E	1490	1265	75	745
320 E/CE	1490	1265	75	745
300 D	1435	1220	75	715
500 E	1695	1440	75	750
300 TD Est.	1560	1325	75	750
200 TE 4V Est.	1470	1250	75	735
220 TE Est.	1480	1260	75	740
280 TE Est.	1590	1350	75	750
320 TE Est.	1590	1350	75	750
C 180 Saloon	1350	1150	75	675
C200 Saloon	1365	1160	75	680
C220 Saloon	1410	1200	75	705
C230 Saloon	1410	1200	75	705
C230 Compressor Saloon	1420	1210	75	710
C280 Saloon	1490	1270	75	745
C220D Saloon	1400	1190	75	700
C250D Saloon	1450	1230	75	725
C250 Turbo Diesel Saloon	1480	1260	75	740
C180 Estate	1410	1200	75	705
C200 Estate	1420	1210	75	710
C230 Estate	1450	1230	75	725
C220D Estate	1450	1230	75	725
C250 Turbo Diesel Estate	1520	1290	75	750
E200 Saloon	1440	1220	75	720
E230 Saloon	1450	1230	75	725
E280 Saloon	1570	1330	75	750
E320 Saloon	1530	1300	75	750
E250D Saloon	1510	1280	75	750
E300D Saloon	1560	1330	75	750
E200 Estate	1550	1320	75	750
E230 Estate	1560	1330	75	750
G-Wagen 300 GES 2dr.	2080	2620	75	750
G-Wagen 300 GEL 4dr.	2220	2950	75	750
G-Wagen 300 GDS 2dr.	2085	2620	75	750
G-Wagen 300 GDL 4dr.	2225	2950	75	750
S280 Saloon	1890	1610	75	750
S320 Saloon	1890	1610	75	750
S320 Limousine	1900	1615	75	750
S420 Saloon	1990	1690	75	750
S420 Limousine	2000	1700	75	750
S500 Saloon	2000	1700	75	750
S500 Limousine	2010	1700	75	750
S600 Limousine	2190	1860	75	750
MITSUBISHI				
Carisma 1.6 GL/GLX	1105	940	75	550
Carisma 1.8 GLX/GLS	1130	960	75	565
Colt 1300 GLi 12V	910	775	75	455
Colt 1.3 GLX	950	810	50	475
Colt 1600 GLXi 16V	945	805	75	470
Colt 1600 G LXi Auto	965	805	75	480
Colt 1.6 GLX/Mirage	975	830	50	485
Colt 1800 GTi 16V	995	845	75	495
Lancer 1600 GLXi 16V	1050	890	75	525
Lancer 1800 GTi 16V	1120	950	75	560
Galant 1.8 GLSi 16V	1180	1005	75	590
Galant 1.8 GLSi 16V Auto	1200	1020	75	600
Galant 2.0 GLSi 16V	1230	1045	75	615
Galant 2.0 GLSi 16V Auto	1250	1060	75	625
Galant 2.0 GLSi/Coupe	1230	1045	75	615
Galant 2.0 V6/Coupe	1330	1130	75	665
Galant 2.0 V6 24V	1330	1130	75	665
Galant 2.0 V6 24V Auto	1350	1145	75	675
Galant 1.8 GLSi 16 V 5dr.	1220	1035	75	610
Galant 1.8 GLSi 16V Auto 5dr.	1240	1055	75	620
Galant 2.0 GLSi 16V 5dr.	1270	1080	75	635
Galant 2.0 GLSi 16V Auto Sdr.	1290	1095	75	645
Galant 2.0 V6 24V 5dr.	1370	1165	75	685
Galant 2.5 V6 24V 4WD/4WS	1540	1310	75	750
Space Runner 1800-16V	1180	1000	75	590
Space Runner	1205	1020	75	600
Space Wagon 2000-16V	1295	1100	75	645
Space Wagon GLXi	1295	1100	75	645
Sigma	1560	1325	75	750
Sigma Est.	1540	1310	75	750
Shogun TD 3dr.	1750	2800	75	750
Shogun TD 5dr.	1945	3300	75	750
Shogun 2.5 TD 3-dr	1730	2800	100	750
Shogun 2.8 TD 5-dr	2010	3300	100	750
Shogun V6 3dr.	1735	2800	75	750
Shogun V6 5dr.	1915	3300	75	.750
Shogun 3.0 V6 3-dr	1760	2800	100	750
Shogun 3.0 V6 5-dr	1955	3300	100	750
Shogun 3.5 V6 3-dr	1810	2800	100	750
Shogun 3.5 V6 5-dr	1990	3300	100	750
MORGAN				
All models 2-str/4-str	920/1000	400	-	-
NISSAN				
Almera 1.4 Equation/GX/Si 3-dr	1035	880	75	450
Almera 1.4 Equation/GX/Si 5-dr	1045	890	75	450
Almera 1.6 GX/SLX/SRi 3-dr	1070	910	75	500
Almera 1.6 GX/SLX/SRi 5-dr man	1085	920	75	500
Almera 1.6 GX/SLX/SRi 5-dr auto	1110	940	75	500
Almera 2.0 D GX	1155	840	75	550
Almera 1.6 GX/SLX man 4-dr	1155	980	75	500
Almera 2.0D GX 4-dr	1120	840	75	550
Almera 1.6 GX/SLX auto 4-dr	11 85	1010	75	500
Almera 2.0 GTi	1155	980	75	575
Micra 1.0 Shape 3-dr man	775	600	50	310
Micra 1.0 Shape 3-dr auto	805	450	50	310
Micra 1.0 Shape 5-dr man	795	600	50	310
Micra 1.0 Shape 5-dr auto	825	450	50	310
Micra 1.0 S 3-dr man	785	600	50	310
Micra 1.0 GX 3-dr man	785	600	50	310
Micra 1.0 GX 3-dr auto	810	450	50	310
Micra 1.0 GX 5-dr man	805	600	50	310
Micra 1.0 GX 5-dr auto	830	450	50	310
Micra 1.3 GX 3-dr man	810	690	50	310
Micra 1.3 GX 3-dr auto	830	650	50	310
Micra 1.3 GX 5-dr man	835	710	50	310
Micra 1.3 GX 5-dr auto	850	650	50	310
Micra 1.3 SR 3-dr man	825	700	50	310
Micra 1.3 SLX 5-dr man	850	720	50	310

Manufacturer & Model	Kerb Weight kg	Maxm. Bkd. kg	Nose Weight kg	Maxm. U/bkd kg
Micra 1.3 SLX 5-dr auto	870	650	50	310
Sunny 1.4 L/LX 3dr.	1005	855	75	500
Sunny 1.4 L/LX 4dr.	1015	860	75	505
Sunny 1.4 L/LX 5dr.	1020	865	75	510
Sunny 1.6 LX 4dr/5dr.	1055	895	75	525
Sunny 1.6 SLX 4dr.	1040	885	75	520
Sunny 1.6 SLX 5dr.	1070	910	75	535
Sunny 1.6 SR	1025	870	75	510
Sunny 2.0 DL/DLX 4dr.	1090	925	75	545
Sunny 2.0 DL/DLX 5dr.	ills	950	75	555
Sunny 2.0 GTi	1125	955	75	560
Sunny 1.6 L Est.	1055	895	75	525
100 NX	940	800	75	470
Primera 1.61-	1065	905	75	530
Primera, 1.61- 5dr/SLX 4dr.	1085	920	75	540
Primera 1.6 LX	1075	910	75	535
Primera 1.6LX 5dr.	1095	930	75	545
Primera 1.6DLX 5dr.	1105	940	75	550
Primera 2.0 DLX	1155	980	75	575
Primera 2.0 DLX 5dr.	1175	995	7S	585
Primera 2.0i LX	1150	975	75	575
Primera 2.0i LX Auto	1175	995	75	585
Primera 2.0i LX 5dr.	1170	995	75	585
Primera 2.0i LX 5dr. Auto	1195	1015	75	595
Primera 2.0 DSLX	1165	990	75	580
Primera 2.0 DSLX Auto	1175	99S	75	585
Primera 2.0 DSLX 5dr.	1185	1005	75	590
Primera 2.0 DSLX 5dr. Auto	1195	1015	75	595
Primera 2.0i SLX	1160	985	75	580
Primera 2.0i SLX Auto	1185	1005	75	590
Primera 2.0i SLX 5dr.	1180	1000	75	590
Primera 2.0i SLX 5dr. Auto	120S	1025	75	600
Primera 2.0i SGX	1165	990	75	580
Primera 2.0i SGX Auto	1190	1010	75	595
Primera 2.0i SGX 5dr.	1185	1005	75	590
Primera 2.0i SGX 5dr. Auto	1210	1025	75	605
Primera 2.0e GT	1190	1010	75	595
Primera 2.0e GT 5dr.	1210	1025	75	605
Primera 1.6 LX Est.	1155	980	75	575
Primera 1.6 SLX Est.	1175	995	75	585
Primera 2.0i LX Est.	1190	1010	75	595
Primera 2.0i LX Est. Auto	1210	1025	75	605
Primera 2.0i SLX Est.	1215	1030	75	605
Primera 2.0i SLX Est. Auto	1235	1050	75	615
QX 2.0 V6 man	1335	1135	75	665
QX 2.0 V6 auto	1375	1170	75	685
QX 3.0 V6	1385	1180	75	690
200 SX	1200	1020	75	600
200 SX Auto	1220	1035	75	610
Serena 1.6 LX	1385	1180	75	690
Serena 2.0 SLX	1485	1200	75	740
Serena 2.0 SGX	1500	1200	75	750
Serena 2.01D LX	1465	1200	75	730
Serena 2.01D SLX	1490	1200	75	745
Serena 2.31D LX	1505	1200	75	500
Serena 2.31D SLX	1530	1200	75	500
Maxima V6/S	1380	1175	75	690
Maxima SE	1385	1180	75	690
Patrol GR SLX Dsl. 3dr.	2070	3500	100	750
Patrol GR SLX/SGX Pet. 5dr.	2115	3500	100	750
Patrol GR SGX Diesel 5dr.	2230	3500	100	750
Terrano	1730	2800	100	750
Terrano 11 S/SR/SE	1745	2800	115	750
Terrano 11 SR/SE/SE Touring	1875	2800	115	750
Terrano 11 SR/SR Sport	1630	2800	115	750
Terrano 11 SE	1760	2800	115	750
PEUGEOT				
106 1.1 3-dr	815	650	50	405
106 1.4 3-dr	815	700	50	405
106 1.5 diesel 3-dr	875	700	50	435
106 1.5 diesel 5-dr	895	700	50	445
106 1.1 5-dr	835	650	50	415
1061.4 5-dr	835	700	50	415
106 XT 1.4i	815	690	50	405
106 XSi 1.4i	855	495	50	425
1205 XR 1.4i	845	715	50	420
205 XL Auto 1.6	845	715	50	420
205 GR 1.4i	840	710	50	420
205 Auto 1.6	875	740	50	435
205 Style D/XLD/GLD/GRD	875	740	50	435
205 XRDT/GRDT	925	785	50	460
205 GTi 1.9	880	745	50	440
205 CT 1.4i Cabriolet	900	765	50	450
205 CTi 1.9 Cabriolet	935	795	50	465
206 1.6 (petrol)	1013	1100	50	485
206 2.0 HD1 (diesel)	1070	1100	50	485
306 1.4 XN/XL/XR	890	755	60	445
306 1.6 XL/XR/XT	910	770	60	455
306 1.8 XT	950	805	60	475
306 2.0 Cabriolet	1260	1000	50	600
306 Sedan	1040-1190	900	50	520
307 1.6 (petrol)	1176	1200	60	610
307 2.0 HDi (diesel)	1279	1340	60	-
307 Estate 1.6	1269	1100	60	670
307 Estate 2.0 HDi 90	1328	1500	70	745
307 Estate 2.0 HDi 110	1359	1500	70	745
405 Style/GL 1.4i	1030	875	60	515
405 Style GL/GR 1.6i	1075	915	60	535
405 GL/GR 1.8i	1095	930	60	545
405 Style/GLD/GRD 1.9	1120	950	60	560

Manufacturer & Model	Kerb Weight kg	Maxm. Bkd. kg	Nose Weight kg	Maxm. U/bkd kg
405 GLD/GRD/STD Turb 1.9	1150	980	60	575
405 GR/SR/ST 2.0i	1140	970	60	570
405 Mi 1.6	1180	1005	60	590
405 Style/GL 1.6i Est.	1085	920	80	540
405 Style/D/GLD/GRD 1.9 Est.	1165	990	80	580
405 GL/GR 1.8i Est.	1140	970	80	570
405 GLD/GRD/STD T. Est.	1210	1030	80	605
405 GR/ST 2.0i Est.	1170	995	80	585
406 1.8	1275	1080	80	635
4062.0	1315	1120	80	655
406 1.91DT	1335	1135	80	665
406 2.1 DT	1415	1200	80	705
605 2.0 SLi/SRi/SVi	1325	1125	80	660
605 3.0 SV	1415	1200	80	705
605 3.0 SVE	1460	1240	80	730
605 SVE 24	1460	1240	80	730
605 SRDT/SLD/SVDT	1430	1215	80	715
806 SL 5-seat	1510	1300	60	-
806 SL 7/8-seat	1545	1300	60	
806 SR S-seat	1510	1300	60	
806 SR 7/8-seat	1545	1300	60	
806 SV 7-seat	1545	1300	60	
806 SV 6-seat	1545	1300	60	
806 SLDT 5-seat	1565	1300	60	
806 SLDT 7/8-seat	1600	1300	60	
806 SRDT 5-seat	1565	1300	60	
806 SRDT 7/8-seat	1600	1300	60	
806 SVDT 7-seat	1600	1300	60	
806 SVDT 6-seat	1600,	1300	60	
PROTON				
1.3 GE/GL/GLS	950	810	75	475
1.5 GL/GLS	980	835	75	490
1.5 SE	990	840	75	495
RANGE-ROVER				
4.0 V8 auto	2100	3500	75	750
4.0 V8 manual	2090	3500	75	750
4.6 V8	2220	3500	75	750
2.5 diesel	2115	3500	75	750
RENAULT				
Clio 1.2 RL/RN	855	650	50	425
Clio 1.4 RN	830	650	50	415
Clio 1.4 RT 3dr.	845	715	50	420
Clio 1.4 RT 5dr.	855	725	50	425
Clio 1.4 RT	885	750	50	440
Clio 1.4 RT auto	885	750	50	440
Clio 1.4S	840	715	50	420
Clio 1.9 RL/RN	900	765	50	450
Clio 1.91D RL/RN/RT	935	800	50	465
Clio 1.8 RT	865	735	50	430
Clio 16V	980	795	50	490
Clio Baccara 1.4 Auto	895	750	50	445
Clio 1.8 RSi	950	800	50	475
19 RL 1.4 3dr.	885	750	50	440
19 RL/RN/RT 1.4 4/5dr.	960	815	50	480
19 RL/RN 1.91D	1030	875	50	515
19 RT 1.8	1045	890	50	520
19 1.8 Cabriolet	1125	955	50	562
19 RN/RT 1.9 TID	1080	920	50	540
19 16V 1.8	1125	955	50	560
19 Cabriolet 16V	1190	1000	50	595
21 TS Prima/GTS	990	840	50	495
21 GTX	1085	920	50	540
21 GTD	1040	880	50	520
21 2L Turbo	1190	1010	50	595
21 Savanna TS/GTS	1035	880	50	515
21 Savanna GTX	1155	980	50	575
21 Savanna GTD	1145	975	50	570
Laguna 1.8 RN/RT	1225	1040	-	510
Laguna 2.0 RN/RT/Exec	1245	1100		620
Laguna 2.0 16V RTi	1280	1090		635
Laguna 2.0 auto RT/RXE/Ex-	1245	1060		620
Laguna 2.2 diesel RN/RT/RXE	1335	1130		665
Laguna 2.2 DT RT/RXE/Exec	1405	1200		700
Laguna 1.8 RN Estate	1305	1000		650
Laguna 1.8 RN Family Estate	1375	1000		650
Laguna 2.0 RT Estate	1315	1000		650
Laguna 2.0 RT Family Estate	1335	1000		650
Laguna 2.0 16V RXE Estate	1355	1000		675
Laguna 2.0 16V RXE Family Est	1375	1000		675
Laguna 2.0 RT Estate auto	1325	1000		660
Laguna 2.2 RN Estate	1410	1000		700
Laguna 2.2 RN Family Estate	1430	1000		700
Laguna Baccara V6	1390	1190		690
Megane 1.4 RN/RT	1015	860		505
Megane 1.91D RN/RT	1110	925		550
Megane 1.91D T RT/RXE	1130	960		550
Megane 1.6 RT/RXE	1055	900		525
Megane 1.6 RT/RXE auto	1085	900		540
Megane 2.0 RXE	1085	900		S40
Megane 2.0 RXE auto	1115	950		550
Megane 1.6	1010	860		500
Megane, Coupe 1.6 auto	1045	890		520
Megane Coupe 2.0	1045	890		520
Megane Coupe 2.0 auto	1075	910		535
Megane Coupe 16V	1095	930		545
Safrane RT 2.0	1395	1185		695
Safrane RXE V6	1495	1270		745
Safrane, 2.0i	1367	1160		680
Safrane 2.5dT Exec	1593	1300		750
Safrane 2.2vi	1437	1220		715

Manufacturer & Model	Kerb Weight kg	Maxm. Bkd. kg	Nose Weight kg	Maxm. U/bkd kg
Safrane 3.0 V6 auto	1491	1270	-	745
Espace 2.0 RN/RT/RXE	1320	1120	75	660
Espace 2.9 RT/RXE	1390	1180	75	695
Espace 2.0 RT Helios/RTAlize,	1330	1130	-	600
Espace 2.1 dT RN Helios	1370	1160		600
Espace 2.1 dT RT Alize/Exec	1370	1160		600
Espace 2.2 auto RT Alize/Exec	1370	1160		600
Espace Executive V6 auto	1430	1215		650
ROVER				
Metro 1.4 S 3dr.	825	700	55	410
Metro 1.4 S 5dr.	840	715	55	420
Metro 1.4 L 3dr.	840	715	55	420
Metro 1.4 USL Sdr.	855	725	55	425
Metro 1.4 GS	865	735	55	430
Metro 1.4 LID 3dr.	840	460	55	420
Metro 1.4 LID 5dr.	855	460	55	425
Metro 1.4 SID 3dr.	845	460	55	420
Metro 1.4 SID Sdr.	860	460	55	430
Metro GTa 16V cat 3dr.	860	730	55	430
Metro GTa 16V cat Sdr.	875	745	55	435
Metro GTi 16V cat	880	750	55	440
Maestro Clubman 2.0D/DLX	1090	925	45	545
Maestro 1.3 Clubman	945	805	45	470
Montego 2.01D Clubman Est.	1210	1030	45	605
Montego 2.01D Country Est.	1240	1055	45	620
Montego 2.0 LXi/SLXi Est.	1185	1010	45	590
Montego 2.0 DLX/DSLX Est.	1220	1035	45	610
Montego 2.0 Country Est.	1195	1015	45	595
214 Si 16V 3dr.	1020	865	50	510
214 Si 16V 5dr.	1030	875	50	515
214 SU 16V	1050	890	50	525
214 GSil6V	1065	905	50	530
214 Cabriolet,	1075	915	50	535
216 GTi 16V 3dr.	1095	930	50	545
216 SLi	1065	905	50	530
216 GSi	1075	915	50	535
216 GTi 16V 5dr.	1120	950	50	560
216 Coupe	1075	915	50	535
216 Cabriolet 16V	1135	965	50	565
218 SID	1145	975	50	570
218 SLID Turbo	1185	1000	50	590
220 GTi 16V	1195	1000	50	595
220 Coupe	1155	980	50	575
220 Turbo Coupe	1185	1005	50	590
220 GTi Turbo	1210	1000	50	605
414 Si/SLi 16V	1025	870	50	510
416 Si/SLi/GSi 16V	1075	915	50	535
418 SLID	1145	975	50	570
418 SLID Turbo	1160	985	50	580
418 GSD Turbo	1170	995	50	585
420 SLi 16V	1165	990	50	580
420 GSi/Exec 16V	1175	1000	50	585
420 GSi Sport	1185	1000	50	590
420 GSi Sport Turbo	1220	1000	50	610
620i	1255	1065	50	625
620Si	1270,	1080	50	636
620 SLi/GSi	1310	1 [15	50	655
623iS	1320	1120	50	660
623 GSi	1370	1165	50	685
820i 4dr.	1350	1135	70	665
820i Sdr.	1365	1160	70	680
820 Si 4dr.	1350	1150	70	675
820 Si 5dr.	1380	1175	70	690
820 SLi 4dr.	1385	1180	70	690
820 SLi 5dr.	1415	1205	70	705
825 D 4dr.	1440	1225	70	720
825 D 5dr.	1470	1250	70	735
825 SID 4dr.	1450	1235	70	725
825 SID 5dr.	1480	1260	70	740
825 SLID 4dr.	1485	1025	70	740
825 SLID 5dr.	1515	1025	70	750
827 Si 4dr.	1390	1180	70	695
827 Si 5dr.	1420	1205	70	710
827 SLi 4dr.	1425	1210	70	710
827 SLi 5dr.	1455	1235	70	725
Vitesse	1500	1275	70	750
Sterling 4dr.	1460	1240	70	730
Sterling 5dr.	1500	1275	70	750
800 Coupe	1440	1225	70	720
SAAB				
900i/SE	1285	1090	90	640
900i Convertible	1310	1110	90	655
900SE/Aero, LPT	1285	1090	90	640
900S Convertible LPT	1330	1130	90	665
900 Turbo S	1285	1090	90	640
900 Convertible S	1310	1115	90	655
9000 2.0i CS/CSE	1305	1110	90	650
9000 2.0i LPT CS/CSE	1425	1210	90	710
9000 2.3i CSE	1325	1125	90	660
9000 23T CS/CSE	1370	1165	90	685
9000 2.0i CD/CDE	1425	1210	90	710
9000 2.0i LPT CD/CDE	1425	1210	90	710
9000 2.3i CDE	1445	1225	90	720
9000 23T CD/CDE/Griffin	1465	1245	90	730
SEAT				
Cordoba 1.4	1020	870	70	400
Cordoba 1.6/1.6 CLX	1030	880	70	450
Cordoba 2.0	1130	960	70	500
Corcloba 1.9D/1.9 TD	1100/1130	935	70	480
Ibiza 1.5 SX	915	775	70	455

Manufacturer & Model	Kerb Weight kg	Maxm. Bkd. kg	Nose Weight kg	Maxm. U/bkd kg
Ibiza IM SL/SLX 3dr.	950	805	70	475
Ibiza 1.7D SL/SLX 5dr.	970	825	70	485
Ibiza 1.7i Sportline	915	775	70	455
Toledo 1.6i CL	985	835	70	490
Toledo 1.8 GLi/GLXi	1015	860	70	505
Toledo 1.8 16V GTi	1055	895	70	525
Toledo 2.0 GTi	1030	875	70	515
Toledo 1.9 D CL	1030	875	70	515
Toledo 1.9 TD GLX	1120	950	70	560
SKODA				
Favorit LX/Plus	875	745	*50*	435
Favorit Gl-Xi	895	750	50	445
Favorit l-Xi Est.	920	750	50	460
Favorit GLXi Est.	930	750	50	465
Felicia LX	985	840	50	400
Felicia LXi/LXi Plus/GLXi	985	840	*50*	400
SSANGYONG				
Musso 2.9D S	1780	2300	75	750
Musso 2.9D SE	1810	2300	75	750
Musso 2.9D GSE manual	1875	2300	75	750
Musso 2.9D GSE auto	1875	2300	75	750
Musso GX220 manual	1810	3500	75	750
Musso GX220 auto	1875	3500	75	750
SUBARU				
Impreza 1.6 5-dr manual	1160	990	75	500
Impreza 2.0 4-dr manual	1130	960	75	500
Impreza 2.0 5-dr manual	1165	990	75	500
Impreza 2.0 4-dr auto	1165	990	75	500
Impreza 2.0 5-dr auto	1195	1015	75	500
ImPreza 2.0 Turbo 4WD 4-door	1235	1000	75	500
Impreza 2.0 Turbo 4WD 5-door	1270	1000	75	500
Impreza 1.6 LX 4-dr	1025	870	75	500
Impreza 1.6 GL 4-dr	1050	890	75	500
Impreza 1.6 GL 5-dr	1080	920	75	500
Justy 1.3 GX 4WD 3-dr	865	735	50	430
Justy 1.3 GX 4WD 5-dr	910	780	50	455
Legacy 2.0 Saloon manual	1240	1050	75	500
Legacy 2.0 Saloon auto	1270	1080	75	500
Legacy 2.2 Saloon manual	1240	1050	75	500
Legacy 2.2 Saloon auto	1275	1080	75	500
Legacy 2.0 Estate manual	1290	1100	75	500
Legacy 2.0 Estate auto	1315	1120	75	500
Legacy 2.2 Estate manual	1295	1100	75	500
Legacy 2.2 Estate auto	1325	1130	75	500
Legacy 2.0i GL 4WD	1275	1080	70	500
Legacy 2.0 Turbo 4WD	1375	1000	70	450
Legacy 2.2 GX 4WD	1280	1085	70	500
Legacy 2.0i GL 4WD Est.	1385	1140	70	500
Legacy 2.0 Turbo 4WD Est.	1425	1000	70	450
Legacy 2.2 GX 4WD Est.	1375	1165	70	500
SVX	1610	1200	75	500
Forester 2.0	1360	1500	75	715
Forester 2.0 Auto	1375	1500	75	725
Forester 2.0 Sport	1365	1500	75	-
Forester 2.0 All-Weather	1365	1500	75	715
Forester 2.0 S turbo	1435	1800	75	740
Forester 2.0 S turbo Auto	1435	1800	75	750
SUZUKI				
Swift 1.3 GS	775	660	50	385
Swift 1.3 GLX	805	685	50	400
Swift 1.3 GTi	835	710	50	415
Samuri Sport Soft Top	930	1000	50	465
Samuri LWB Est.	970	1000	50	485
Vitara Est. Soft Top	1010	1000	50	505
Vitara j LX SE Est. S/T	1075	1000	50	535
Vitara JLX Est. 5dr.	1190	1500	50	595
TOYOTA				
Starlet 1.3 GLi	840	715	75	420
Corolla 1.3 XLi 3dr.	995	845	75	495
Corolla 1.3 XLi 5dr.	1000	850	75	500
Corolla 1.3 GLi 3dr.	1000	850	75	500
Corolla 1.3 GLi 4dr.	990	840	75	495
Corolla I.3 GLi Est.	1030	875	75	515
Corolla 1.6 GLi 4dr.	1015	865	75	505
Corolla 1.6 GLi/Exec 5dr.	1020	865	75	510
Corolla 1.8 GXi 3dr.	1060	900	75	530
Carina E 1.6 XLi 4dr.	1070	910	75	535
Carina E 1.6 XLi 5dr.	1175	1000	75	585
Carina E 1.6 GLi 4dr./Sdr.	1180	1005	75	590
Carina E 2.0 XLD 4dr.	1190	1010	75	595
Carina E 2.0 XLD 5dr.	1250	1060	7S	625
Carina E 2.0 GLi 4dr.	1270	1080	75	635
Carina E 2.0 GLi 5dr.	1225	1040	75	610
Carina E 2.0 Exec 4dr.	1245	1060	75	620
Carina E 2.0 Exec 5dr.	1250	1060	75	625
Carina E 2.0 GTi 4dr.	1270	1080	75	635
Carina E 2.0 GTi 5dr.	1280	1090	75	640
Camry GLi	1300	1105	75	650
Camry V6 GX	13-95	1185	75,	695
Camry GLi Est.	1510	1280	75	750
Camry V6 GX Est.	1415	1205	75	705
Celica GT	1565	1330	75	750
Celica GT-Four	1260	1070	75	630
Supra 3.0i	I 530	1200	75	750
Supra Turbo	1540	1310	75	750
Landcruiser 11	1600	1360	75	750
Landcruiser VX	1800	3500	150	750
Previa	2410	3500	150	750
	1800	1530	75	750

Manufacturer & Model	Kerb Weight kg	Maxm. Bkd. kg	Nose Weight kg	Maxm. U/bkd kg
Rav4 to 2002 3 door	1640	1500	75	640
Rav4 to 2002 5 door	1770	1500	75	640
Rav 2002-on				
1.8 VVT-i	1125	1000	-	-
Rav4 3 door				
2.0 VVT-i	120	1500	-	640
2.0 VVT-i Auto	1355	1500	-	640
Rav4 5 door				
2.0 VVT-i	1275	1500	-	640
2.0 VVT-i Auto	1310	1500	-	640
2.0 D-4D	1370	1500	-	640
Avensis 4-door				
1.6 VVT-i	1280	1300	-	500
1.8 VVT-i	1280	1300	-	500
1.8 VVT-i Auto	1315	1300	-	500
2.0 VVT-i	1320	1400	-	500
2.0 VVT-i Auto	1345	1400	-	500
2.0 D-4D	1395	1300	-	500
Avensis 5 door				
1.6 VVT-i	1300	1300	-	500
1.8 VVT-i	1305	1300	-	500
1.8 VVT-i Auto	1335	1300	-	500
2.0 VVT-i	1340	1400	-	500
2.0 VVT-i Auto	1365	1400	-	500
2.0 D-4D	1430	1300	-	500
Avensis Estate				
1.8 VVT-i	1320	1300	-	500
2.0 VVT-i	1355	1400	-	500
2.0 VVT-i Auto	1380	1400	-	500
2.0 D-4D	1430	1300	-	500
VAUXHALL				
Corsa 1.2i Merit	865	550	75	400
Corsa 1.2i LS	873	500	75,	400
Corsa IA LS 3dr.	850	720	75	425
Corsa 1.4i LS Sdr.	875	740:	75	435
Corsa IA Flair 3dr,	865	735	75	430
Corsa 1.4i SRi	875	740	7S	435
Corsa IA GLS	905	770	75	450
Corsa 1.4 (Hi-torq) Merit	915	1000	75	450
Corsa 1.4 16V Sport	936	900	75	450
Corsa 1.5D Merit 3dr.	890	755	75	445
Corsa 1.5D Merit 5dr.	915	780	75	455
Corsa 1.5TD LS 3,dr	905	770	75	450
Corsal.55TD,.LS/GLS Sdr.	930	790	75	465
Corsa 1.6i GSi 16Y	960	815	75	480
Corsa, 1.7D Merit	920	780	75	450
Astra 1.4 Merit 3,dr.	930	790	75	465
Astra 1.4i Merit 5dr.	950	80$	75	475,
Astra 1.4i Merit 4dr.	960	815	75	480
Astra 1.4, L/LS 4dr.	980	835	75	490
Astra1.4 L/LS Mr.	950	805	75	475
Astra 1.4 L/LS 5dr.	965	820	75	480
Astra 1.4 LS 4dr.	990	840	75	495
Astra 1.4 LS 3dr.	955	810	75	475
Astra 1.4 LS 5dr.	975	825	75	485
Astra 1.4i GLS	1015,	860	75	505
Astra 1.4 SJ 4dr.	1010	860,	75	505
Astra 1.4 Si 3dr.	975	825	75	485
Astra 1.4 Si 5dr.	995	845	75	495
Asira 1.4l CID 4dr.	1030	875	75	515
Astra 1.4 CID Sclr.	1020	865	75	510
Astra 1.6i GLS 4dr.	1035	880	75	515
Astra 1.6i GLS 5dr.	1020	865	75	510
Astra 1.6i Si 4dr.	1030	875	75	515
Astra 1.6i Si 3dr.	995	845	75	515
Astra 1.6i Si Sdr.	1015	875	75	505
Astra 1.6i CID 4dr.	1040	885	75	520
Astra 1.6i CID 5dr.	1030	875	75	515
Astra 1.7D Merit 3dr.	1005	845	75	500
Astra 1.7D Merit 5dr	1025	845	75	510
Astra 1.7D LS 4dr.	1055	850	75	525
Astra 1.7D LS 5dr.	1040	845	75	520
Astra 1.7D GLS 4dr.	1080	850	75	540
Astra 1.7D GLS 5dr.	1065	845	75	530
Astra 1.7TD LS 4dr.	1115	950	75	555
Astra1.7TD LS 5dr.	1040	845	75	520
Astra 1.7TD GLS 4dr.	1140	970	75	570
Astra 1.7TD GLS 5dr.	1130	960	75	565
Astra 2.0i SRi 4dr.	1090,	925	75	545
Astra, 2.0i SRi 3dr-	1060	900	75	530
Astra 2.0i SRi 5dr	1075	910	75	535
Astra 2.0i CID 4dr.	1120	950	75	560
Astra 2.0i CID 5dr.	1110	940	75	555
Astra 2.0i GSi 16V	1130	960	75	565
Astra 1.6i 16V Sport	1167	990	75	500
Astra, IA 16.V CDX.	1157	980	75	500
Astra 2.0i 116V CDX	1233	1050	75	500
Astra 1.6l Convertible	1000	850	75	5 00
Astra 2.0i Convertible	1050	890	75	525
Astra IA Merit Est.	995	795	75	495
Astra IA Merit Est.	1005	855	75	500
Astra 1.4i L Est.	1010	795	75	505
Astra IA LS Est.	1020	865	75	510
Astra 1.4i GLS Est.	1070	910	75	535
Astra 1.6i Si Est.	1055	895	75	525
Astra 1.6i GLS Est.	107S	910	75	535
Astra IYD Merit Est.	1070	795	75	535
Astra 1.71D LSEst.	1085	795	75	540
Astra 1.71D GLS Est.	1120	79S	75	560
Astra 1.7TD LS Est.	1150	980	75	575

Manufacturer & Model	Kerb Weight kg	Maxm. Bkd. kg	Nose Weight kg	Maxm. U/bkd kg
Astra IYTD GLS Est.	1175	1000	75	585
Astra 2,Oi SRi E st.	1125	795	75	560
Cavalier 1.6 i Envoy 4dr.	1090	925	75	545
Cavalier 1.6i Envoy 5dr.	1105	940	75	550
Cavalier 1.6i LS 4dr.	1105	940	75	550
Cavalier 1.6i LS 5dr.	1125	955	75	560
Cavalier 1.6i GLS 4dr	1120	950	75	560
Cavalier 1.6i GLS 5dr.	1140	970	75	570
Cavalier 1.7 DLS 4dr.	1145	850	75,	570
Cavalier 1.7 DLS 5dr.	1160	850	75	580
Cavalier 1.7 LS TD 4dr.	1185	965	75	590
Cavalier 1.7 LS TD Sdr.	1200	1000	75	600
Cavalier 1.7 GLS TD 4dr.	1195	1000	75	595
Cavalier 1.7 GLS TD 5dr.	1215	1000	75	605
Cavalier 1.7 CD TD 4dr.	1215	1000	75	605
Cavalier 1.7 CD TD 5dr.	1235	1000	75	615
Cavalier 1.8i LS 4dr.	1125	955	75	560
Cavalier 1.8i LS 5dr.	1140	970	75	570
Cavalier 1.8i GLS 4dr.	1135	965	75	565
Cavalier 1.8i GLS 5dr.	1155	980	75	575
Cavalier 2.0i ILS 4dr.	1160	985	75	580:
Cavalier 2.0i ILS 5dr.	1 M	990	75	585
Cavalier 2.0i 4WD 4dr.	1300	1105	75	650
Cavalier 2.0i GLS 4dr.	1170	995	75	585
Cavalier 2.0i GILS Sdr.	1190	1010	75	595
Cavalier 2.0 SRi/CD 4dr.	1190	1010	75:	595
Cavalier 2.0 SRi/CD 5dr.	1205	1025	75	600
Cavalier 2.0 SRi 16V 4d r.	1225	1040	75	610
Cavalier 20 SKi 16V 5 d r.	1240	1055	75	620
Cavalier 2.0 Dip: 4dr.	1220	1035	75	610
Cavalier 2.0 Dip 5dr.	1250	1060	75	625
Cavalier Turbo 4A	1225	1040	75	610
Calibra 2.0i	1195	1015	75	595
Calibra 2.0i auto	1260	1070	75	630
Calibra 2.0i 16V	1215	1035	75	605
Calibra 2.0i 16V auto	1295	1100	75	645
Calibra 2.5i V6 24V	1340	1140	75	660
Calibra 2.5i V6 24Y Auto	1360	1160	75	660
Calibra 2.0i Turbo 4A	1390	1180	75	695
Carlton 1.0i. Plaza	1295	1100	75	645
Carlton 2.0i L	1225	1040	75	610
Carlton 2.0i GL	1310	1115	75	6SS
Carlton 2.0i CD/CDX	1315	1115	75	655
Carlton 2.0i Diplomat.	1340	1140	75	670
Carlton 2.3 L TD	1395	1185	75	695
Carlton 2.3 GIL TD	1410	1195	75	705
Carlton 2.3 CID TD	1420	1205	75	710
Carlton 2i6i CDX	1410	1195	75	705
Carlto2.6i Dip	1435	1220	75	715
Carlton 3.0 GSi 24V	1435	1220	75	715
Carlton 10i Club/L Est.	1275	1080	75	635
Carlton 2.0i Plaza Est.	1330	1130	75	675
Carlton 2.0i GL Est.	1355	1150	75	675
Carlton CD/Diam/CDX Est.	1360	1155	75-	680
Carlton 2.3 L TD Est.	1415	1100:	75	71S
Carlton 2.3 GL TD Est.	1460	1150	75	730
Carlton 2.3 CID TD Est.	1475	1150	75	735
Carlton 2.6i CDX Est.	1455	1235	75	725
Senator 2.6i CID	1400	1190	75	700
Senator 3.0i CD 24V	1540	1310	75	750
Frontera 2.0i Sport	1560	2000	75	750
Frontera 2.8 TD Sport	1828	2000	75	750.
Frontera 2.2 16V	1811	2400	75	750
Frontera 2.4i 5dr.	1720	2000	75	750
Frontera 2.3 TD	1785	2000	75-	750
Frontera 2.8 TD	1928	2500	75	750
Monterey	1795,	3000	120	750;
Omega 2.0i Select 4-d,r man	1450	1230	-	725
Omega 2.0i Select-4-dr auto	1250	1250		735
Omega, 24 TD, Select 4~dr man	1560	1330		750
Omega, 2.5 TP Select 4-dr auto	1580	1340		750
Omega 2.5i 24V Select 4-dr man	1550	1320		750
Omega 2.5i 24V Select 4-dr auto	1570	1330		750
Omega 2.0i 16V GLS 4-dr man	1475	1250		735
Omega 2.0i 16V GLS 4-dr auto	1495	1270		745
Omega 2.5i 24V GLS 4-dr man	1560	1326		750
Omega 2.5i 24V GLS 4-dr auto	1580	1340		750
Omega 2.5 TD GLS 4-dr man	1570	1335		750
Omega 2.5 TD GLS 4-dr auto	1590	1350		750
Omega 2.0i 16V CD 4-dr man	1514	1290		750
Omega 2.0i 16V~C/d. 4,dr auto	1534	1300		750
Omega 2.5i 24V CD 4dr man	1599	1360:		750
Omega 2.5i 24V CD 4-dr auto	1619	1380		750
Omega 2.5 TD CD 4-dr man	1609	1370		750
Omega 2.5 TD CD 4-dr auto	1629	1385		750
Omega 2.0i 16V CDX 4-dr man	1514	1290		750
Omega 2.0i 16V CDX 4-dr auto	1534	1300		750
Omega 2.5i 24V CDX 4-dr man	1599	1360		750
Omega 2.5i 24V CDX 4-dr auto	1619	1380		750
Omega 2.5 TD CDX 4-dr man	1609	1370		750
Omega 2.5 TD CDX 4-dr auto	1629.	1385		750
Omega 2.0i Select 5-dr	1520	1290		750
Omega 2.5TD Select 5-dr man	1610	1370		750
Omega 2.5 TD, Select 5-dr auto	1630	1385		750
Omega 2.5i 24V SeLect 5-dr man	1600	1360		750
Omega 2.5i 24V Select 5-dr auto	1620	1380		750
Omega 2.0i 16V GLS 5-dr man	1525	1300		750
Omega 2.0t 16V GLS 5-dr auto	1545	1310		750
Omega 2.5i 24V GLS 5-dr man	1610	1370		750
Ornega 2.5i 24V GLS 5-d:r auto	1630	1385		750

Manufacturer & Model	Kerb Weight kg	Maxm. Bkd. kg	Nose Weight kg	Maxm. U/bkd kg
Omega 2.5 TD GLS,5-dr man	1620	1380		750
Omega 2.5TD, LS S-dr auto	1640	1390		750
Omega 2.0i 16V CD.SAr man	1568	1330		750
Omega 2.0i 16V CD 5-dr auto	1588	1350		750
Omega 2Si 24V CD 5-dr man	1653	1405		750
Omega 2.5i 24V CD 5-dr man	1673	1420		750
Omega 2.5 TI) CD 5-dr man	1663	1410		750
Omega 2.5 TD CD 5-dr auto	1683	1430		750
Omega 2.0i 16V CDX 5-dr man	1568	1330		750
Omega 2.0i 16V CDX 5-dr auto	1588	1350		750
Omega 2.5i 24V CDX 5-dr man	1653	1405		750
Omega 2.5i 24V CDX 5-dr auto	1673	1420		750
Omega 2.5 TD CDX 5-dr man	1663	1410		750
Omega 2.5 TD CDX 5-dr auto	1683	1430		750
Tigra 1.4i man/auto	TOWING NOT RECOMMENDED			
Tigra 1.6i man/auto	TOWING NOT RECOMMENDED			
Vectra Envoy 1.6i	1185	1000		590
Vectra Envoy 1.7 TDS	1275	1080		635
Vectra 1.6i LS hatch	1232	1050		615
Vectra 1.6i LS saloon	1217	1030		605
Vectra 1.6i LS auto hatch	1262	1075		630
Vectra 1.6i LS auto saloon	1247	1060		620
Vectra 1.7 TDS hatch	1292	1100		645
Vectra 1.7 TDS saloon	1277	1085		635
Vectra 1.8i LS hatch	1277	1085		635
Vectra 1.8i LS saloon	1262	1075		630
Vectra 1.8i LS auto hatch	1307	1110		650
Vectra 1.8i LS auto saloon	1292	1100		645
Vectra 1.6i GLS hatch	1250	1060		625
Vectra 1.6i GLS saloon	1236	1050		615
Vectra 1.6i GLS auto hatch	1280	1090		640
Vectra 1.6i GLS auto saloon	1266	1080		630
Vectra 1.7 TDS GLS hatch	1319	1100		655
Vectra 1.7 TDS GILS saloon	1305	1100		665
Vectra 1.8i GLS hatch	1295	1100		645
Vectra 1.8i GLS saloon	1281	1090		640
Vectra 1.8i GLS auto hatch	1325	1130		660
Vectra 1.8i GLS auto saloon	1311	1110		655
Vectra 2.0i GLS hatch	1317	1120		655
Vectra 2.0i GLS saloon	1302	1100		650
Vectra 2.0i GLS auto hatch	1347	1145		670
Vectra 2.0i GLS auto saloon	1332	1130		665
Vectra 2.5i V6 GLS hatch	1372	1165		685
Vectra 2.5i V6 GLS saloon	1357	1150		675
Vectra 2.5i V6 GLS auto hatch	1392	1180		695
Vectra 2.5i V6 GLS auto saloon	1377	1170		685
Vectra 2.0i SRi hatch	1347	1145		670
Vectra 2.0i SRi saloon	1332	1130		665
Vectra 1.7 TDS CDX hatch	1363	900		665
Vectra 1.7 TDS CDX saloon	1348	900		665
Vectra 2.0i CDX hatch	1353	1150		675
Vectra 2.0i CDX saloon	1338	1140		665
Vectra 2.0i CDX auto hatch	1383	1175		680
Vectra 2.0i CDX auto saloon	1368	1160		680
Vectra 2.5i V6 CDX hatch	1408	1195		700
Vectra 2.5i V6 CDX saloon	1393	1180		695
Vectra 2.5i V6 CDX auto hatch	1428	1210		700
Vectra 2.5i V6 CDX auto saloon	1413	1200		700
Zafira				
1.6	1338	1100	75	600
1.8	1390	1300	75	600
1.8 Auto	1410	1200	75	600
2.0 DTi	1505	1050	75	600
2.2	1430	1400	75	600
2.2 Auto	1450	1400	75	600
VOLVO				
440 1.6 Li	1025	870	75	510
440 Li/Si/SE	1030	865	75	510
440 SE/GLT 2.0i	1055	895	75	525
440 Turbo	1090	925	75	545
460 Li/Si/SE	1020	865	75	510
460 SE/GLE/CD 2.0i	1055	895	75	525
480S	1045	890	75	520
480 ES 2.0i	1055	895	75	525
480 Turbo	1090	925	75	545
240 Torslanda/SE Est.	1430	1215	75	715
240 SE 2.3 Est.	1430	1215	75	715
850 SE/GLT 2.0	1455	1235	75	725
850 SE/GLT 2.5	1480	1255	75	740
850 SE/GLT 2.0 Est.	1455	1235	75	725
850 GILT 2.5 Est.	1460	1240	75	730
940 S/SE	1460	1240	75	730
940 S/SE/GLE 2.3	1460	1240	75	730
940 S/SE/Went/GLE Turbo	1495	1270	75	745
940 SE/GLE TID	1530	1300	75	750
940 2.3 Turbo	1500	1275	75	750
940 S/SE Est.	1460	1240	75	730
940 S/SE/GLE 2.3 Est.	1460	1240	75	730
940 S/SE/Went/GLE Tur. Est.	1495	1270	75	745
940 SE/GLE TID Est.	1530	1300	75	750
940 2.3 Turbo Est.	1500	1275	75	750
960 24V	1570	1295	75	750
960 24V Est.	1525	1295	75	750
S40/V40 1.8i	1240	1020	75	620
S40N40 2.0i	1240	1020	75	620
VOLKSWAGEN				
Polo 1.3 CL/Genesis	775	650	50	385
Polo Coupe 1.3 CUGenesis	780	650	50	39G
Polo Coupe 1.3 GT	780	650	50	390
Polo G40 1.3	830	650	50	415
Golf. 1.4 CL 3dr.	960	795	50	480
Golf 1.4 CL 5dr.	985	795	50	490
Golf 1.8 CL	1030	875	50	500
Golf 1.9 CL/GL/ TD	1080	920	50	500
Golf GTi 3dr.	1035	880	50	500
Golf GTi 5dr.	1060	900	50	500
Golf VR6 3dr.	1155	980	50	575
Golf VR6 5dr.	1180	1005	50	590
Golf GTi Sportline/Rivage	965	820	50	480
Vento 1.8 CL/GL	1075	915	50	500
Vento 1.9 CLD/GLD	1105	940	50	500
Vento 2.0 GL	1085	920	50	500
Vento 2.8 VR6	1210	1030	50	600
Passat L	1125	955	85	560
Passat L TD	1150	975	85	575
Passat CL/GL	1155	980	85	575
Passat CL/GL TD	1225	1040	85	610
Passat GL 16V	1210	1030	85	605
Passat VR6	1300	1105	85	650
Passat L Est.	1150	975	85	575
Passat L TD Est.	1215	1000	85	605
Pasiat CL/GL Est.	1180	1000	85	590
Passat CL/GL TID Est.	1250	1060	85	625
Passat GL 16V Est.	1235	1050	85	615
Passat VR6 Est.	1325	1125	85	660
Corrado 16V	1095	930	50	520
Corrado VR6	1210	1030	50	600
Caravelle 2.0 GL/CL	1485	1260	100	740
Caravelle 2.4 GLD/CLD	1565	1330	100	750
Caravelle 2.5 GL	1565	1330	100	750
Sharan - see Ford Galaxy				

COMMERCIALS

Commercial vehicles are measured according to two important weights: 'gross train weight', and 'towing limit'.
'Gross Train Weight' is the maximum weight, of trailer and payload combined, which a particular model of vehicle can tow.
'Towing limit' is the maximum towing limit for a trailer with over-run brakes.
The regulations covering unbraked trailers apply to commercials too.'

MAKE/MODEL	GROSS PAYLOAD	GROSS VEHICLE WEIGHT	KERB WEIGHT	TOWING LIMIT
CITROEN				
C15 Champ 1.9 600D	600	1545	945	620
C15 Champ 1.9 765D	765	1710	945	620
Berlingo 1.9D 600X	600	1755	1155	1100
Berlingo 1.9D 600LX	600	1755	1155	1100
Berlingo 1.9D 800LX	800	1955	1155	1100
Berlingo 2.0 HDi 600LX	600	1790	1190	1100
Berlingo 2.0 HDi 800LX	779	1990	1211	1100
Xsara 2.0 HDi Enterprise	511	1740	1229	1100
Xsara 3.0 HDi Enterprise	511	1740	1229	1100
Dispatch 1.9D 815	815	2205	1390	1100
Dispatch 2.0 HDi 815	815	2215	1400	1300
Dispatch 2.0 HDi 900	900	2315	1415	1300
Relay 2.0 HDi 1100 SWB	1145	2900	1755	2000
Relay 2.0 HDi 1100 MWB	1105	2900	1795	2000
Relay 2.0 HDi 1500 SWB	1545	3300	1755	1600
Relay 2.0 HDi 1500 MWB	1505	3300	1795	1600
Relay 2.2 HDi 1500 h/r	1425	3200	1775	2000
Relay 2.8 HDi 1500 LWB	1330	3300	1970	2000
Relay 2.2 HDi 1800 SWB	1605	3500	1895	2000
Relay 2.8 HDi 1800 SWB	1550	3500	1950	2000
Relay 2.2 HDi 1800 MWB	1585	3500	1915	2000
Relay 2.8 HDi 1800 MWB	1565	3500	1935	2000
DAIHATSU				
Hijet 1.3 EFI	635	1550	915	600
Hijet 1.3 EFI Pick-Up	850	1550	700	600
FIAT				
Punto 1.9D 60	510	1430	920	1000
Doblo Cargo 1.2P	625	1835	1210	1100
Doblo Cargo 1.9D	625	1905	1280	1100
Doblo Cargo 1.9 JTD	625	1935	1310	1100
Doblo Cargo 1.9D SX	625	1905	1280	1100
Scudo 1.9D EL	815	2190	1375	1100
Scudo 2.0 JTD 8v 900	900	2315	1415	1300
Scudo 2.0 JTD 16v 815	815	2215	1400	1300
Ducato 9 MWB 2.0 JTD	1145	2900	1755	1600
Ducato 11 SWB 2.0 JTD	1145	2900	1755	2000
Ducato 11 SWB 2.3 JTD	1185	2900	1715	2000
Ducato 11 MWB 2.0 JTD	1105	2900	1795	1600
Ducato 11 MWB 2.3 JTD	1535	3300	1765	2000
Ducato 15 SWB 2.0 JTD	1545	3300	1755	1600
Ducato 15 MWB 2.8 JTD h/r	1425	3500	2075	2000
Ducato 15 LWB 2.3 JTD	1355	3300	1945	2000
Ducato 15 LWB 2.8 JTD	1330	3300	1970	2000
Ducato Maxi 2.3 JTD LWB h/r	1505	3500	1995	2000
Ducato Maxi 2.8 JTD LWB h/r	1480	3500	2020	2000
FORD				
Ka Van 1.3i	394	1265	871	TBA
Connect 1.8 TDi T200 SWB	625	2025	1400	800
Connect 1.8 TDCi T200 SWB	625	2035	1410	800
Connect 1.8 TDCi T220 SWB	825	2240	1415	800
Connect 1.8 TDdi T220 LWB	825	2260	1435	800
Connect 1.8 TDCi T230 LWB	900	2340	1440	800
Transit 260 2.0 TD SWB l/r	843	2455	1612	1800
Transit 260 2.0 TDi SWB l/r	843	2455	1612	1800
Transit 280 2.0 TDi SWB l/r	1028	2640	1612	2000
Transit 280 2.0 TDCi SWB l/r	1028	2640	1612	2000
Transit 280 2.0 TDCi MWB m/r	1017	2710	1693	2000
Transit 330 2.4 TDI LWB m/r	1027	2900	1873	2250

Manufacturer & Model	Kerb	U/bkd Towing	Limits Towing	Train
Transit 300 2.0 TD/TDCi SWB l/r	1268	2880	1612	1800
Transit 300 2.0 TDI MWB m/r	1257	2950	1693	2000
Transit 300 2.0 TDCi MWB m/r	1257	2950	1693	2000
Transit 300 2.0 TDCi LWB m/r	1257	3000	1743	2000
Transit 330 2.4 TDI SWB l/r	1468	3210	1742	2250
Transit 330 2.4 TDI MWB m/r	1457	3280	1823	2250
Transit 330 2.4 TDI LWB m/r	1417	3290	1873	2250
Transit 330 2.4 TDI LWB h/r	1394	3290	1896	2000
Transit 330 2.4 TDI MWB h/r	1439	3280	1841	2000
Transit 350 2.4 TDI MWB m/r	1677	3500	1823	2000
Transit 350 2.4 TDI LWB m/r	1559	3500	1941	2250
Transit 350 2.4 TDI LWB h/r	1529	3500	1971	2250
Transit 350 2.4 TDI EL Jumbo	1424	3500	2076	2250
Transit 2.5 TD Single Cab 4x4	1180	2845	1665	2800
Transit 2.5 TD Super Cab 4x4	1210	2930	1720	2800
Transit 2.5 TD Double Cab 4x5	1135	2845	1710	2800
ISUZU				
TF Pickup 2.5 TDi Single Cab 4x2	1075	2550	1475	2000
TF Pickup 2.5 TDi Crew Cab 4x2	1015	2550	1535	2000
TF Pickup 2.5 TDi Single Cab 4x4	1075	2750	1675	2000
TF Pickup 2.5 TDi Crew Cab 4x4	1015	2750	1735	2000
TF P'Up 2.5 TDi 4Sport C'Cab 4x4	1018	2750	1732	2000
Trooper 3.0 DT Commercial SWB 4x4	685	2600	1915	3300
ISUZU TRUCK				
NKR-S Grafter Dropside	1400	3500	2100	2000
Daily 29L9 SWB l/r	1230	3200	1970	2000
Daily 35S11 SWB L m/r	1430	3500	2070	2000
Daily 35S11 MWB m/r	1365	3500	2135	2000
Daily 35S13 LWB m/r	1225	3500	2275	2000
Daily 45C11 LWB m/r	2100	4600	2500	3000
Daily 50C13 LWB h/r	2660	5200	2540	3500
Daily 65C15 LWB h/r	3815	6500	2685	3500
LAND ROVER				
Defender 90 Td5 Pick-Up	780	2400	1620	4000
Defender 90 Td5 Hard Top	735	2400	1665	4000
Defender 110 Td5 Hard Top	1205	3050	1845	4000
Defender 110 Td5 County D/cab	1205	3050	1845	4000
Freelander 2.0 Td4 Commercial	525	2050	1525	2000
Freelander Petrol	535	2040	1505	2000
Discovery 2.5 Td5 Commercial	680	2750	2070	2495
LDV				
Pilot 2.2t 1.9D	789	2175	1386	1325
Pilot 2.4t 1.9D	964	2350	1386	1150
Pilot 2.6t 1.9D	1150	2550	1400	950
Convoy 2.4dt75 2.8t SWB	1047	2850	1803	1500
Convoy 2.4dt90 2.8t SWB	1041	2850	1809	2000
Convoy 2.4dt75 3.1t LWB L/R	1245	3100	1855	1500
Convoy 2.4dt90 3.1t LWB Hi	1207	3100	1893	2000
Convoy 2.4dt75 3.5t Hi	1588	3500	1912	2000
Convoy 2.4dt90 3.5t XLWB Hi	1570	3500	1930	2000
MAZDA				
B2500 2.5 TD Single Cab 4x2	1160	2650	1490	2000
B2500 2.5 TD Single Cab 4x4	1180	2845	1665	2800
B2500 2.5 TD Double Cab 4x4	1135	2845	1710	2800
B2500TD RAP 4x4 4-Action	1210	2930	1720	2800
MERCEDES-BENZ				
Vito 108 CDI	995	2700	1705	1900
Vito 110 CDI	1060	2700	1640	1900
Vito 110 CDI	1055	2700	1645	1900
Vito 112 CDI	1055	2700	1645	1900
Vito 113 Petrol	1030	2700	1670	1900
Sprinter 208 CDI SWB 2.6t	795	2590	1795	2000
Sprinter 211 CDI SWB 2.8t	1000	2800	1800	2000
Sprinter 208 CDI MWB 2.8t	910	2800	1890	2000
Sprinter 213 CDI SWB 2.8t	1000	2800	1800	2000
Sprinter 311 CDI MWB 3.5t	1555	3500	1945	2000
Sprinter 308 CDI LWB 3.5t	1410	3500	2090	2000
Sprinter 313 CDI MWB 3.5t	1555	3500	1945	2000
Sprinter 316 CDI LWB 3.5t	1375	3500	2125	2000
Sprinter 416 CDI LWB 4.6t	2315	4600	2285	2000
MITSUBISHI				
Shogun Pinin 1.8 MPI SWB 4Work 1500	425	1680		1255
Shogun Pinin 2.0 GDI LWB 4Work 1500	500	1890		1390
Shogun 3.2 DI-D SWB 4Work	530	2510	1980	2800
Shogun 3.2 DI-D LWB 4Work	685	2810	2125	3300
L200 Single Cab 4x2	1205	2570	1365	1500
L200 Single Cab 4x4	1200	2830	1630	2200
L200 Double Cab 4x4	1025	2830	1805	2700
Canter 3.5t SWB	1700	3500	1800	3500
NISSAN				
Kubistar 1.5dCi 60E	620	1660	1040	820
Kubistar 1.5dCi 70E	620	1675	1055	810
Kubistar 1.5dCi 80SE 800	800	1885	1085	795
Primstar 1.9dCi 2700 E	1023	2700	1677	2000
Primstar 1.9dCi 2.7t SE 82	1023	2700	1677	2000
Primstar 1.9dCi 2.7t Access 82	1023	2700	1677	2000
Primstar 1.9dCi 2.7t SE 100	1023	2700	1677	2000
Primstar 1.9dCi 2.9t SE	1212	2900	1688	2000
Primstar 1.9dCi 2.9t SE LWB	1216	2940	1684	2000
Interstar 1.9dCi 2800 SWB l/r	1053	2800	1747	1900
Interstar 2.2dCi 3300 SWB m/r	1522	3300	1778	1900
Interstar 2.2dCi 3300 MWB m/r	1482	3300	1818	1900
Interstar 2.5dCi 3500 LWB h/r	1585	3500	1915	2000
Terrano II 2.7 TD Van	785	2510	1725	2800
Cabstar E 95L SWB Dropside	1415	3200	1785	2000
Cabstar E 120SL MWB Dropside	1600	3500	1900	2000
Cabstar E 120SL LWB Dropside	1600	3500	1900	2000
Navara 2.5Di Single Cab 4x4	1115	2860	1745	2800
Navara 2.5Di King Cab 4x4	1095	2860	1765	3000
Navara 2.5Di Double Cab 4x4	1065	2860	1795	3000
PEUGEOT				
206 1.4 HDi Van	526	1562	1036	1100
Partner 1.9D 600L	600	1755	1155	1100
Partner 1.9D 600LX	600	1755	1155	1100
Partner 2.0 HDi 600LX	600	1790	1190	1100
Expert 1.9D	815	2195	1380	1100
Expert 1.9 TD	815	2220	1405	1300
Expert 2.0 HDi 900	900	2315	1415	1300
Boxer 250S 2.0 HDi	660	2490	1830	1600
Boxer 330S 2.2 HDi	1000	2900	1900	2000
Boxer 330M 2.2 HDi	1360	3300	1940	2000
Boxer 330S 2.8 HDi	1340	3300	1960	2000
Boxer 330L 2.8 HDi h/r	1255	3300	2045	2000
Boxer 350L 2.8 HDi h/r	1405	3500	2095	2000
PIAGGIO				
Porter 1.4D	635	1550	915	600
PROTON				
Jumbuck 1.5GL	645	1680	1035	1000
Jumbuck 1.5GLS	635	1680	1045	1000
RENAULT				
Clio 1.5dCi	535	1515	980	900
Kangoo SL17 1.5dCi 60	620	1660	1040	820
Kangoo SL17 1.5dCi 70	620	1675	1055	810
Kangoo SL19 1.5dCi 80	800	1885	1085	795
Trafic SL27dCi 80	1023	2700	1677	2000
Trafic SL29dCi 80	1216	2900	1684	2000
Trafic SL27dCi 100	1023	2700	1677	2000
Trafic SL27P 120	1024	2685	1661	2000
Trafic SL29dCi 100	1216	2900	1684	2000
Master 2.8t 1.9dCi SWB l/r	1053	2800	1747	1900
Master 3.3t 2.2dCi SWB m/r	1522	3300	1778	1900
Master 3.3t 2.8tD SWB m/r	1500	3300	1800	2000
Master 3.3t 2.2dCi MWB m/r	1482	3300	1818	1900
Master 3.5t 2.2dCi MWB h/r	1650	3500	1850	2000
Master 3.5t 2.2dCi LWB m/r	1631	3500	1869	1900
Master 3.5t 2.5dCi LWB h/r	1585	3500	1915	2000
ROVER				
Rover CDV 2.0 TD	485	1600	1115	TBA
MG Express 2.0 TD	485	1600	1115	1000
MG Express 1.8VVC	480	1550	1070	1000
SEAT				
Inca 1.9D	625	1730	1105	1000
SUZUKI				
Carry 1.3i	577	1450	873	1100
Carry 1.3i Pick-Up	665	1450	785	1100
TATA				
TL Single Cab 4x2	1140	2780	1640	3065
TL Single Cab 4x4	1000	2780	1780	2925
TL Double Cab 4x2	1080	2780	1700	3005
TL Double Cab 4x4	1010	2930	1920	2785
TOYOTA				
Hiace 2.5D-4D 280S 88	1210	2800	1590	2000
Hiace 2.5D-4D 280GS 88	1210	2800	1590	2000
Hiace 2.5D-4D 300GS 88	1340	3000	1660	2000
Hilux 2.5D-4D 240SC 4x2	1110	2415	1305	1800
Hilux 2.5D 240FX EC 4x2	1005	2415	1410	1800
Hilux 2.5D 250EX SC 4x4	900	2515	1615	2250
Hilux 2.5 270GX DC 4x4	1055	2780	1725	2250
Dyna 300 2.5D Dropside	1340	3000	1660	2000
VAUXHALL				
Corsavan 1.7 Di 16v	455	1505	1050	1000
Corsavan 1.7 DTi 16v	495	1555	1060	1000
Combo 1.7 Di 1700	595	1805	1210	1200
Combo 1.7 DTi 1700	595	1805	1210	1200
Combo 1.7 DTi 2000	810	2020	1210	1200
Astravan 1.7 DTi 16v Envoy	615	1780	1165	1100
Astravan 1.6i LS	626	1690	1064	1100
Astravan 2.0 Di LS	626	1830	1204	1300
Vivaro 1.9 Di SWB	1023	2700	1677	2000
Vivaro 1.9 DTi SWB	1023	2700	1677	2000
Movano 2.8t 2.2 DTi SWB l/r	1050	2800	1750	2000
Movano 3.3t 2.2 DTi SWB h/r	1510	3300	1790	2000
Movano 3.3t 2.2 DTi MWB h/r	1470	3300	1830	2000
Movano 3.3t 2.5 DTi SWB h/r	1500	3300	1800	2000
Movano 3.5t 2.2 DTi LWB h/r	1625	3500	1875	1900
Movano 3.5t 2.5 DTi MWB Maxi	1630	3500	1870	2000
Movano 3.5t 2.5 DTi LWB Maxi	1585	3500	1915	2000
VOLKSWAGEN				
Caddy 1.9S Di	625	1730	1105	1000
Caddy 1.4i	625	1680	1055	1000
Caddy 1.9 TDI	625	1770	1145	1000
Transporter 1.9 TDI T28 SWB 85	1000	2800	1800	2200
Transporter 1.9 TDI T28 SWB 104 2200	995	2800	1805	
Transporter 2.5 TDI T28 SWB 130 2500	925	2800	1875	
Transporter 1.9 TDI T30 SWB 85	1200	3000	1800	2200
Transporter 1.9 TDI T30 SWB 104	1195	3000	1805	2200
Transporter 2.5 TDI T30 SWB 130	1125	3000	1875	2500
Transporter 2.5 TDI T30 SWB 174	1125	3000	1875	2500
LT 28 2.5 TDI SWB 83	1045	2800	1755	2000
LT 32 2.5 TDI MWB h/r	1298	3200	1902	2000
LT 35 2.5 TDI MWB h/r	1560	3500	1940	2000
LT 35 2.5 TDI LWB h/r 95	1433	3500	2067	2000
LT 46 2.8 TDI MWB 130	2543	4600	2057	2000

* Information obtained from a variety of sources. Indespension Ltd disclaims any responsibility for any errors in the above. If in any doubt you should contact the vehicle manufacturer.

APPENDIX 4 - WHAT THINGS WEIGH

When calculating the eventual weight of your home-built trailer, you will need to know the weights of the materials which you have used to build it. The following table gives the weights of varying sizes and shapes of steel sections.
IMPORTANT NOTE: Aluminium members of the same dimensions weigh about 35% of the figures given here for steel.

MATERIAL	WEIGHT
Chipboard (16mm thick)	11.72 kg/m^2
Hardboard (3mm thick)	2.03 kg/m^2
Plasterboard (9.5mm thick)	9.77 kg/m^2
Blockboard (25.4mm thick)	12.21 kg/m^2
Plywood (12.7mm thick)	8.24 kg/m^2 Asphalt (25.4 mm
thick)	58.5 kg/m^2
Bituminous roof felt	4.88 kg/m^2
Rubber (6.4mm thick)	13.2 kg/m^2
Glass (6.4mm thick)	17 kg/m^2
Slate (25.4mm thick)	73 kg/m^2
Ballast	1794 kg/m^2
Dry earth	1185 kg/m^2
Dry sand	1601 kg/m^2
Damp sand	1986 kg/m^2
Limestone/sandstone	2240 kg/m^2
Granite	2640 kg/m^2
Hay/straw	352 kg/m^2
Bricks (average)	3.13 kg each
3" solid breeze blocks (average)	8.9 kg each
Water	1.0 kg/litre
Petrol	0.7 kg/litre

CONVERSION CHART

1 kilogramme (kg) = 2.2046 pounds (Lb)
1 pound = 0.4536 kilogrammes
1 square metre = 1.176 square yards
1 square yard = 0.8361 square metres
1Lb/cu.ft = 16 kg/m^3
1 Lb/sq.ft = 4.9 kg/m^3
1Lb/gallon = 0.1 kg/litre

CIRCULAR HOLLOW SECTION

21.3 x 3.2	1.43
26.9 x 3.2	1.87
33.7 x 2.6	1.99
33.7 x 3.2	2.41
33.7 x 4.0	2.93
42.4 x 2.6	2.55
42.4 x 3.2	3.09
42.4 x 4.0	3.79
48.3 x 3.2	3.56
48.3 x 4.0	4.37
48.3 x 5.0	5.34
60.3 x 3.2	4.51
60.3 x 4.0	5.55
60.3 x 5.0	6.82

ROLLED STEEL JOISTS

76 x 38	6.25
76 x 76	12.65
102 x 44	7.44
102 x 64	9.65
102 x 102	23.06
127 x 76	13.36
127 x 114	29.76
152 x 76	17.86
152 x 89	17.09
152 x 127	37.20
178 x 102	21.54
203 x 102	25.33
203 x 152	52.03
254 x 114	37.20
254 x 203	81.84
305 x 203	98.72

MILD STEEL FLATS

10 x 3	0.24
13 x 3	0.31
13 x 5	0.51
13 x 6	0.61
13 x 10	1.02
15 x 3	0.36
15 x 5	0.59
16 x 3	0.38
16 x 5	0.63
16 x 6	0.75
16 x 8	1.00
16 x 10	1.26
20 x 3	0.47
20 x 5	0.79
20 x 6	0.94
20 x 8	1.26
20 x 10	1.57
20 x 12	1.88

CHANNELS

13 x 13 x 3	0.55
16 x 16 x 3	0.71
20 x 20 x 3	0.88
20 x 20 x 4	1.14
25 x 25 x 3	1.11
25 x 25 x 4	1.45
25 x 25 x 5	1.77
30 x 30 x 3	1.36
30 x 30 x 4	1.78
30 x 30 x 5	2.18
30 x 30 x 6	2.56
40 x 40 x 3	1.82
40 x 40 x 4	2.42
40 x 40 x 5	2.97
40 x 40 x 6	3.52
40 x 40 x 8	4.55
40 x 40 x 10	5.52
45 x 45 x 3	2.06
45 x 45 x 5	3.38
45 x 45 x 6	4.00

MILD STEEL SHEETS

THICKNESS (mm)	Kg/M²	THICKNESS (mm)	Kg/M²
3.00	23.55	1.20	9.42
2.50	19.65	1.00	7.85
2.00	15.70	0.90	7.07
1.60	12.56	0.80	6.28
1.50	11.78	0.60	4.71
1.25	9.81	0.50	3.93

MILD STEEL EQUAL ANGLES

32 x 27 x 5	2.80
38 x 19 x 5	2.49
51 x 25 x 5	3.44
51 x 25 x 6	4.46
51 x 38 x 6	5.80
64 x 25 x 8	6.70
76 x 38	7.46
76 x 51	9.45
102 x 51	10.42
127 x 64	14.90
152 x 76	17.88
152 x 89	23.84
178 x 76	20.84
178 x 89	26.81
203 x 76	23.82
203 x 89	29.78
229 x 76	26.06
229 x 89	32.76
254 x 76	28.29
254 x 89	35.74
305 x 89	41.67
305 x 102	46.18
381 x 102	55.10
432 x 102	65.54

SQUARE HOLLOW SECTION

20 x 20 x 2.0	1.12
20 x 20 x 2.6	1.39
30 x 30 x 2.6	2.21
30 x 30 x 3.2	2.65
40 x 40 x 2.6	3.03
40 x 40 x 3.2	3.66
40 x 40 x 4.0	4.46
50 x 50 x 3.2	4.66
50 x 50 x 4.0	5.72
50 x 50 x 5.0	6.97

APPENDIX 5 - THE PLANS

The following eight plans are all from Indespension's library, and include:

A. A 4'x 3' unbraked goods or camping trailer (350 kg* Gross Capacity).

B. A 5'x 3' unbraked goods or camping trailer (500 kg* Gross Capacity).

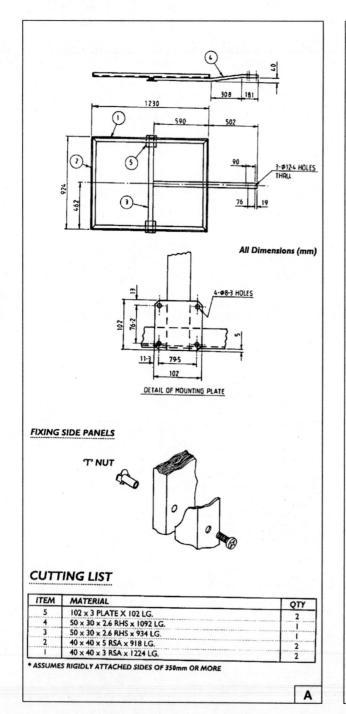

FIXING SIDE PANELS

'T' NUT

CUTTING LIST

ITEM	MATERIAL	QTY
5	102 x 3 PLATE X 102 LG.	2
4	50 x 30 x 2.6 RHS x 1092 LG.	1
3	50 x 30 x 2.6 RHS x 934 LG.	1
2	40 x 40 x 5 RSA x 918 LG.	2
1	40 x 40 x 3 RSA x 1224 LG.	2

* ASSUMES RIGIDLY ATTACHED SIDES OF 350mm OR MORE

A

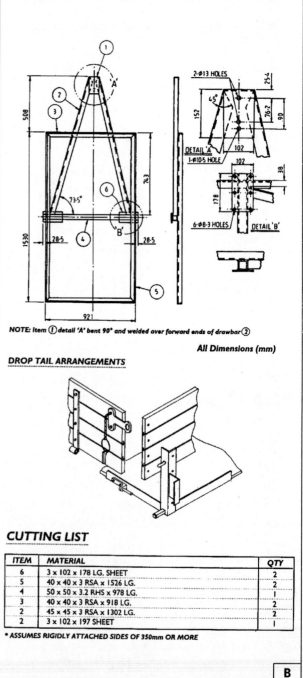

NOTE: Item ① detail 'A' bent 90° and welded over forward ends of drawbar ②

All Dimensions (mm)

DROP TAIL ARRANGEMENTS

CUTTING LIST

ITEM	MATERIAL	QTY
6	3 x 102 x 178 LG. SHEET	2
5	40 x 40 x 3 RSA x 1526 LG.	2
4	50 x 50 x 3.2 RHS x 978 LG.	1
3	40 x 40 x 3 RSA x 918 LG.	2
2	45 x 45 x 3 RSA x 1302 LG.	2
2	3 x 102 x 197 SHEET	1

* ASSUMES RIGIDLY ATTACHED SIDES OF 350mm OR MORE

B

C. A 5'x 4' unbraked goods or camping trailer (500 kg* Gross Capaicty).

D. An 8'6" x 4'6" braked goods trailer (1000 kg* Gross Capacity).

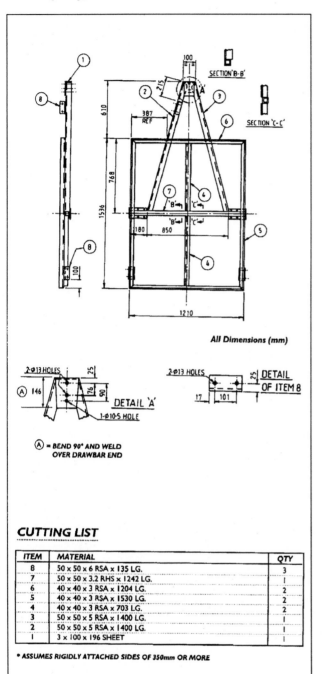

All Dimensions (mm)

Ⓐ = BEND 90° AND WELD OVER DRAWBAR END

CUTTING LIST

ITEM	MATERIAL	QTY
8	50 x 50 x 6 RSA x 135 LG.	3
7	50 x 50 x 3.2 RHS x 1242 LG.	1
6	40 x 40 x 3 RSA x 1204 LG.	2
5	40 x 40 x 3 RSA x 1530 LG.	2
4	40 x 40 x 3 RSA x 703 LG.	2
3	50 x 50 x 5 RSA x 1400 LG.	1
2	50 x 50 x 5 RSA x 1400 LG.	1
1	3 x 100 x 196 SHEET	1

* ASSUMES RIGIDLY ATTACHED SIDES OF 350mm OR MORE

C

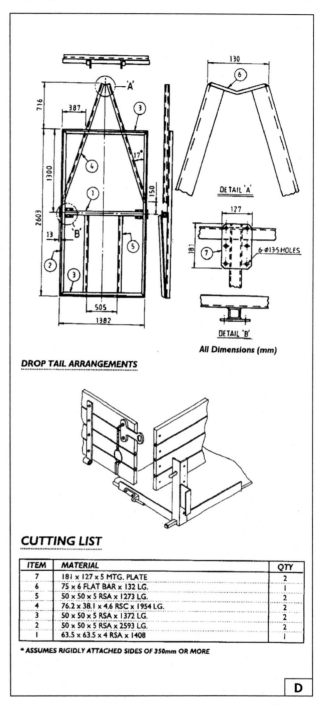

All Dimensions (mm)

DROP TAIL ARRANGEMENTS

CUTTING LIST

ITEM	MATERIAL	QTY
7	181 x 127 x 5 MTG. PLATE	2
6	75 x 6 FLAT BAR x 132 LG.	1
5	50 x 50 x 5 RSA x 1273 LG.	2
4	76.2 x 38.1 x 4.6 RSC x 1954 LG.	2
3	50 x 50 x 5 RSA x 1372 LG.	2
2	50 x 50 x 5 RSA x 2593 LG.	2
1	63.5 x 63.5 x 4 RSA x 1408	1

* ASSUMES RIGIDLY ATTACHED SIDES OF 350mm OR MORE

D

Each plan is accompanied by a list of the materials you will need, and the sizes they must be cut to. The following shorthand terms apply:

FLAT -A strip of steel in the dimensions given.
RSA - Rolled steel angle, or 'angle iron'.
RHS - Rolled Hollow Section, or 'box section'.
CHS - Circular Hollow Section, ie. a tube.
RSC - Rolled Steel Channel Section.
LG - Is an abbreviation for length.

See *Chapter 3, Building A Trailer*, for more information.

E. A triple motorcycle trailer (750 kg Gross Capacity).

F. A canoe trailer to carry fourteen canoes (500 kg Gross Capacity - 14 Canoes).

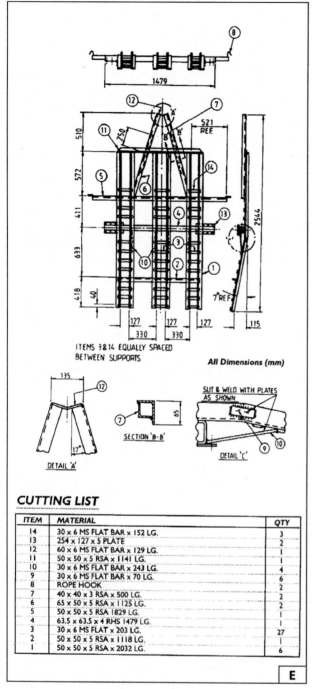

ITEMS 3 & 14 EQUALLY SPACED BETWEEN SUPPORTS

All Dimensions (mm)

SECTION 'B-B'

SLIT & WELD WITH PLATES AS SHOWN

DETAIL 'A'

DETAIL 'C'

E

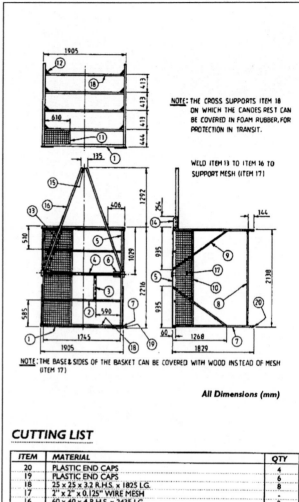

NOTE: THE CROSS SUPPORTS ITEM 18 ON WHICH THE CANOES REST CAN BE COVERED IN FOAM RUBBER, FOR PROTECTION IN TRANSIT.

WELD ITEM 13 TO ITEM 16 TO SUPPORT MESH (ITEM 17)

NOTE: THE BASE & SIDES OF THE BASKET CAN BE COVERED WITH WOOD INSTEAD OF MESH (ITEM 17)

All Dimensions (mm)

F

CUTTING LIST (E)

ITEM	MATERIAL	QTY
14	30 x 6 MS FLAT BAR x 152 LG.	3
13	254 x 127 x 5 PLATE	2
12	60 x 6 MS FLAT BAR x 129 LG.	1
11	50 x 50 x 5 RSA 1141 LG.	1
10	30 x 6 MS FLAT BAR x 243 LG.	4
9	30 x 6 MS FLAT BAR x 70 LG.	2
8	ROPE HOOK	6
7	40 x 40 x 3 RSA x 500 LG.	2
6	65 x 50 x 5 RSA x 1125 LG.	2
5	50 x 50 x 5 RSA 1829 LG.	1
4	63.5 x 63.5 x 4 RHS 1479 LG.	1
3	30 x 6 MS FLAT x 203 LG.	27
2	50 x 50 x 5 RSA x 1118 LG.	1
1	50 x 50 x 5 RSA x 2032 LG.	6

CUTTING LIST (F)

ITEM	MATERIAL	QTY
20	PLASTIC END CAPS	4
19	PLASTIC END CAPS	6
18	25 x 25 x 3.2 R.H.S. x 1825 LG.	8
17	2" x 2" x 0.125" WIRE MESH	-
16	60 x 40 x 4 R.H.S. x 2435 LG.	2
15	60 x 6 x 129 LG. FLAT BAR	1
14	254 x 92 x 3 PLATE	2
13	75 x 6 FLAT BAR	2
12	25 x 25 x 3.2 R.H.S. x 125 LG.	16
11	30 x 30 x 3 R.S.A. x 381 LG.	2
10	30 x 30 x 3 R.H.S. x 2058 LG.	2
9	25 x 25 x 3.2 R.H.S. x 1524 LG.	4
8	25 x 25 x 3.2 R.H.S. x 2058 LG.	2
7	40 x 40 x 2.6 R.H.S. x 1829 LG.	4
6	254 x 101.6 x 3 PLATE	2
5	60 x 40 x 4 R.H.S. x 2138 LG.	2
4	60 x 40 x 4 R.H.S. x 1745 LG.	1
3	30 x 30 x 3 R.S.A. x 557 LG.	1
2	25 x 25 x 3.2 R.H.S. x 1745 LG.	2
1	60 x 40 x 4 R.H.S. x 1905 LG.	2

Each plan is accompanied by a list of the materials you will need, and the sizes they must be cut to. The following shorthand terms apply:

FLAT - A strip of steel in the dimensions given.
RSA - Rolled steel angle, or 'angle iron'.
RHS - Rolled Hollow Section, or 'box section'.
CHS - Circular Hollow Section, ie. a tube.
RSC - Rolled Steel Channel Section.
LG - Is an abbreviation for length.

See *Chapter 3, Building A Trailer*, for more information.

G. A single-axle boat trailer (100 kg Gross Capacity).

H. A single-axle car transporter or flat bed (1300 kg Gross Capacity).

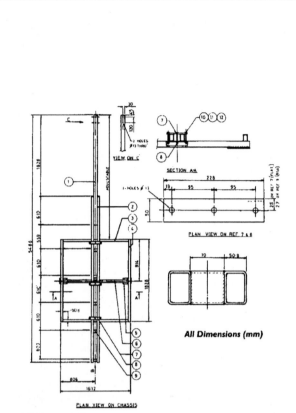

All Dimensions (mm)

CUTTING LIST

ITEM	MATERIAL	QTY
12	NUT. M12. SELF LOCKING.	9
11	WASHER. PLAIN. M12.	9
10	BOLT M12 x 130 LG.	9
9	76.2 x 50.8 x 3.2 R.H.S. x 70 LG.	5
8	50 x 50 x 5 R.S.A. x 228 LG.	3
7	50 x 10 FLAT x 228 LG.	3
6	63.5 x 63.5 x 4 R.H.S. x 1664 LG.	1
5	SUSPENSION PLATE 127 x 5 x 181	2
4	76.2 x 50.8 x 3.2 R.H.S. x 1828 LG.	2
3	76.2 x 50.8 x 3.2 R.H.S. x 1612 LG.	2
2	76.2 x 50.8 x 3.2 R.H.S. x 3658 LG.	2
1	70 x 70 x 3.6 R.H.S. x 2438 LG.	1

G

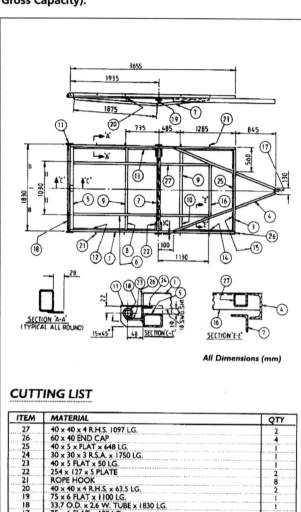

All Dimensions (mm)

CUTTING LIST

ITEM	MATERIAL	QTY
27	40 x 40 x 4 R.H.S. 1097 LG.	2
26	60 x 40 END CAP	4
25	40 x 5 x FLAT x 648 LG.	1
24	30 x 30 x 3 R.S.A. x 1750 LG.	1
23	40 x 5 FLAT x 50 LG.	1
22	254 x 127 x 5 PLATE	2
21	ROPE HOOK	8
20	40 x 40 x 4 R.H.S. x 63.5 LG.	2
19	75 x 6 FLAT x 1100 LG.	1
18	33.7 O.D. x 2.6 W. TUBE x 1830 LG.	1
17	75 x 6 FLAT x 120 LG.	1
16	50 x 50 x 5 R.S.A. x 1100 LG.	1
15	40 x 5 FLAT x 465 LG.	2
14	40 x 5 FLAT x 1385 LG.	2
13	40 x 5 FLAT x 650 LG.	2
12	40 x 5 FLAT x 1137 LG.	2
11	60 x 6 FLAT x 130 LG.	2
10	50 x 50 x 5 R.S.A. x 220 LG.	2
9	50 x 50 x 5 R.S.A. x 950 LG.	2
8	50 x 50 x 5 R.S.A. x 380 LG.	2
7	50 x 50 x 5 R.S.A. x 3010 LG.	2
6	40 x 40 x 4 R.H.S. x 1843 LG.	2
5	60 x 40 x 4 R.H.S. x 1830 LG.	1
4	76 x 38 R.S.C. x 2606 LG.	2
3	60 x 40 x 4 R.H.S. x 1750 LG.	1
2	63.5 x 63.5 x 4 R.H.S. x 1880 LG.	1
1	60 x 40 x 4 R.H.S. x 3655 LG.	2

H

Each plan is accompanied by a list of the materials you will need, and the sizes they must be cut to. The following shorthand terms apply:

FLAT -A strip of steel in the dimensions given.
RSA - Rolled steel angle, or 'angle iron'.
RHS - Rolled Hollow Section, or 'box section'.
CHS - Circular Hollow Section, ie. a tube.
RSC - Rolled Steel Channel Section.
LG - Is an abbreviation for length.

See *Chapter 3, Building A Trailer*, for more information.

APPENDIX 6 - WHEELS & TYRES

By far the most important components on your trailer are its wheels and tyres, and there are certain facts and figures which you will have to know in order to make sure that you choose the right wheels and tyres to fit your trailer.

Wheel Rims

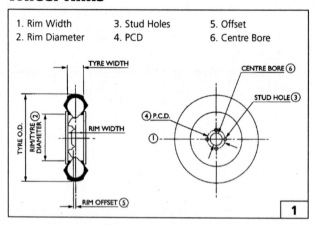

1. There are many different sizes and shapes of trailer wheels available, and when ordering replacements for your own trailer, you will have to give the following information: (Illustration, courtesy Indespension)

RIM WIDTH

This is the width inside the wheel flanges. This measurement should be given in inches.

RIM DIAMETER

This is measured as the diameter of the wheel from just inside the rim, where the inner edge of the bead on the tyre sits.

STUD HOLES

You will need to know how many studs are used to secure the wheel (usually four or five), and their sizes, eg: '4 x M12'. The 'M' number is quite simply explained: the 'M' stands for 'Metric', and the number following it is the diameter of the stud in millimeters. You are most likely to have 12mm or 14mm wheel studs.

PCD

'PCD' stands for 'pitch circle diameter'. This refers to the diameter of the circle around which the studs are arranged, and is measured in millimeters.

OFFSET

This is the distance between the seating surface of the wheel/hub, and the vertical centre line of the wheel and tyre. 'Positive offset' is the sort shown in the diagram. This means that the vertical centre line is behind the seating surface of the hub when it's bolted up. If the vertical centre line of the wheel was stuck out in front of the hub/wheel union, then it would be called 'negative offset'.

CENTRE BORE

This is the diameter of the clearance hole left in the centre of the rim to make room for the bearing boss. This is measured in mm, if present.

Tyres

You will find the specification of your trailer's tyres embossed into the rubber on the sidewall. Look for a number combination which looks like this: 185/70 R13'

'185'. The first bit of the number refers to the section width of the tread. If the tyre is a radial, this measurement is made in mm. If the tyre is a cross-ply, the measurement will have been made in inches.

'70'. The second part of the number indicates the 'aspect ratio' of the tyre. This means the ratio between the height of the side wall and the width of the tread, and is a percentage figure. It is sometimes also referred to as the tyre's profile. In this case, the height of the side wall is 70% of the width of the tread.

'R'. The letter 'R' means that the tyre is a radial. If there is no letter there at all, or if a letter 'D' appears in place of the 'R', then the tyre is a cross-ply.

'13'. The final part of the tyre's code number refers to the diameter of the wheel that it is intended to fit. This figure is almost always measured in inches.

SPECIFYING YOUR OWN TYRES

If you are building your own trailer from scratch, you will need to know the outer diameter of the tyres as well, so you can plan your wheels' clearances. Here are some approximate overall diameters, measured in millimeters, and arranged according to the official sizes of the tyres.

TYRE SIZE	OUTER DIAMETER (MM)	TYRE SIZE	OUTER DIAMETER (MM)
4.00 x 8"	410	165 R13	596
145 R10	490	185/70 R13	600
5.00 x 10"	516	175 R13	608
155/70 R12	531	185 R13	617
145 R12	540	185 R14	650
155 R12	550	6.70 x 13"	660
145 R13	566	6.50 x 16"	742

The strength of a tyre is dictated by the number of 'plies', or layers of material, which make it up. In other words, the higher the ply rating of a tyre, the stronger it will be.

For example, a 145 R10 tyre with a four-ply wall can hold a pressure of 35psi, and can support a weight of 345 kg. Another tyre of exactly the same size - but with an eight-ply wall - will be able to hold 65psi of pressure, and could support a weight of 500 kg. The Tyre Pressures Fact File given with Job 11 of Chapter 6 tells you the ply ratings, maximum axle loads and recommended pressures for a wide sample range of different tyres.

When ordering tyres, you will probably find that the information embossed on the tyre walls does not relate to trailer use. In view of the potential legal, safety, and rapid-wear problems you could face if you do not buy the right tyres for your trailer, it is recommended that you always buy your tyres from a reputable trailer or tyre dealer who will be able to provide you with the information you'll need to choose the right ones.

APPENDIX 7
GLOSSARY OF TERMS

12N and 12S leads: The black and grey leads which run from the trailer to the car when on the move. Used to power the road lights and any extra equipment.

A-frame: The pointed section right at the front of the trailer's chassis, to which the hitch is attached.

AL-KO: A brand name for hitches and brakes.

Auto-reverse: A mechanism fitted to modern trailer brakes so that the brakes do not apply themselves as the trailer is reversed.

Bradley: A well-known make of hitch.

Breakaway cable: A steel cable which is attached to the rear of the car and to the trailer's braking system. It acts as a fail-safe device to actuate the brakes should the trailer break free from the tow ball.

Checker plate: The patterned aluminium plate used to make up trailer floors.

Compensator: The compensator is part of the brake system, and serves to ensure that all the brakes come on at the same time.

Cone: Part of the taper-roller bearing assembly. See 'Cup', below.

Coupling: See 'Hitch', below.

Cup: The bevelled ring in which the 'cone' (above) runs.

Drawbar: The single piece of tube or channel extending from the front of the trailer, to which the hitch is attached.

GRP: 'Glass Reinforced Plastic', also known as fibreglass. GRP is used to make certain moulded trailer bodies.

GVW: 'Gross Vehicle Weight'. The maximum weight which your trailer (or tow vehicle, where relevant, including the nose weight) is allowed to be when fully laden.

Hitch: The mechanism at the front of the trailer which you attach to the car's towball.

Hydraulic: A mechanism operated by the exertion of pressure on a closely contained body of liquid is a 'hydraulic' mechanism.

Jockey wheel: The wind-down wheel at the front of the trailer which is used to hold it steady when hitching up, and to help wheel the trailer about.

Kerb weight: The weight of the unladen car.

Knott: A well-known brand of trailer brakes. You pronounce the 'K'!

M.A.M: Maximum Authorised Weight. Latest jargon for GVW. See 'GVW'.

Nose weight: The amount of weight which is exerted downwards on a car's towball by the trailer's hitch. It can be measured using a nose weight gauge.

Outfit: The trailer and car when joined together.

Over-centre: The modern type of trailer handbrake operates on the over-centre principal rather than on a ratchet.

Over-run: Over-run is the phenomenon utilised to operate the trailer's braking system. When the car brakes, the trailer's momentum 'on the over-run' pushes on the hitch, which puts the brakes on.

Prop stands: The wind-down or flip-down legs which are lowered to hold the trailer steady when loading.

Snaking: The excessive side-to-side swaying motion of an unstable outfit.

Stabiliser: A sprung, or friction operated, device fitted to the trailer's A-frame to counteract snaking.

Torque wrench: A tool for tightening up nuts and bolts to a precisely measured degree of tightness.

Train weight: The weight of the towcar, plus the trailer, plus any load.